THE GREATEST BATMAN® STORIES EVER TOLD

INCLUDING THE BEST SELLING GRAPHIC NOVEL

SON OF THE DEMON™

Batman created by Bob Kane

HAMLYN

Cover illustration by Jerry Bingham

Published in 1989,
under licence from DC Comics Inc.,
by The Hamlyn Publishing Group Limited
a division of The Octopus Publishing Group,
Michelin House, 81 Fulham Road, London SW3 6RB

ISBN 0 600 56787 7

Printed in Italy

TO BOB KANE

AND BILL FINGER,

AND TO THE DOZENS

OF TALENTED MEN AND WOMEN

WHOSE CREATIVE CONTRIBUTIONS

OVER THE PAST FIFTY YEARS

HAVE MADE THE BATMAN

ONE OF THE MOST ENDURING

LITERARY LEGENDS

OF OUR TIME.

CONTENTS

Growing Up With The Greatest

Introduction By Dick Giordano

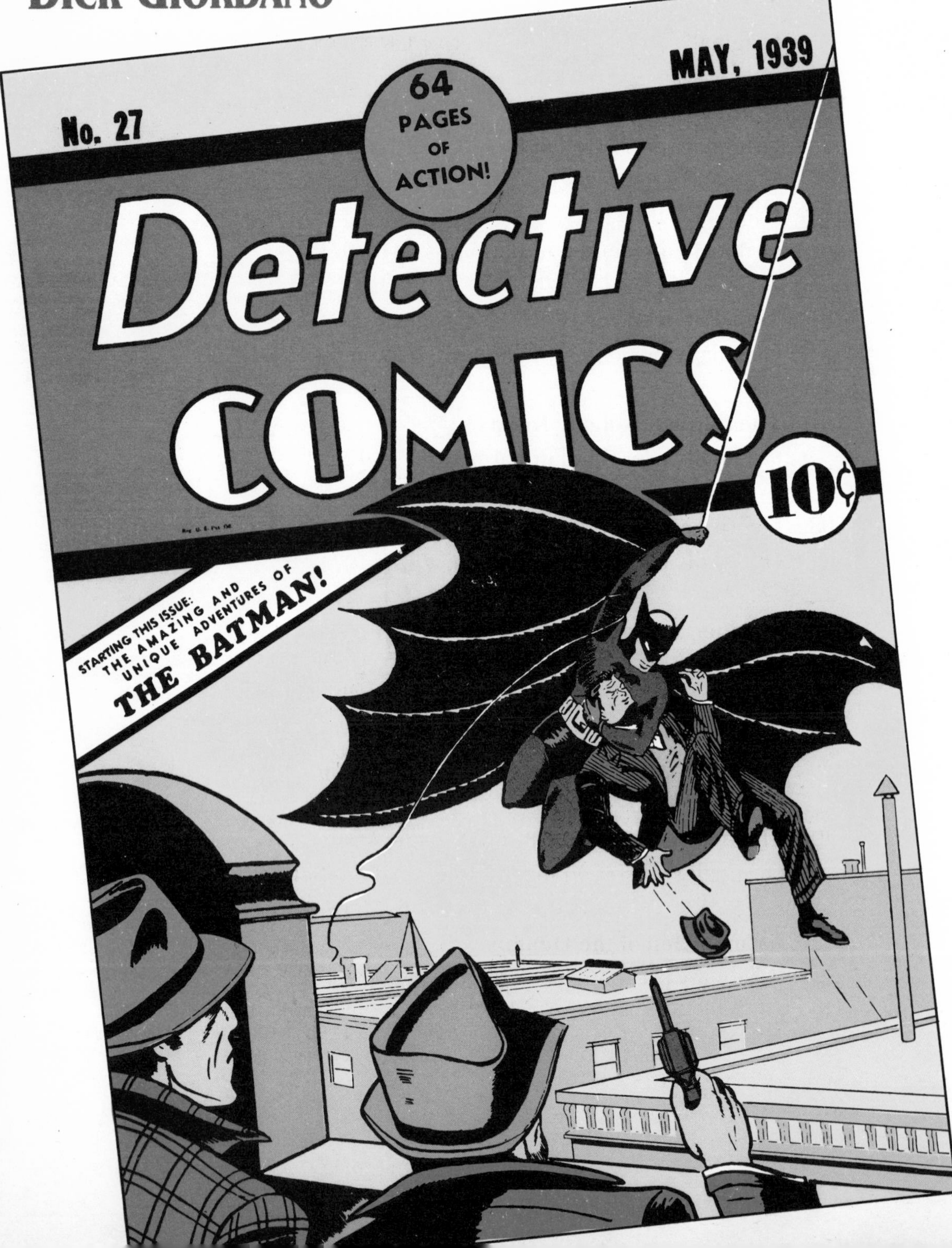

"Here. Dick, I picked up a couple of new comics for you." The paper bag containing the eagerly-awaited goodies plopped onto my bed. My father knew I loved to read comics. He'd been buying them for me regularly since *Famous Funnies* first hit the newsstands. Reading comics helped me while away the days and weeks spent in bed as a child, a victim of severe asthma attacks. They also were my passport to a fantasy wonderland where I could forget my unwelcome confinement and where the good guys always prevailed (some wearing nifty outfits and capes, even) over the bad guys.

Anyway, I flipped through the handful of comics in the bag, trying to decide which one to read first. One of them was DETECTIVE COMICS, a title I'd read before and enjoyed. DETECTIVE COMICS usually had several stories, all featuring the adventures and exploits of various crimefighter or detective types. Good reading as a rule, but nothing special.

Until now.

The comic book I held in my hand *was* special. It contained a story about a crimefighter I'd never seen before, one with a cape and a mask and a dark look to him, not at all like Superman or any of the other super-heroes I had read.

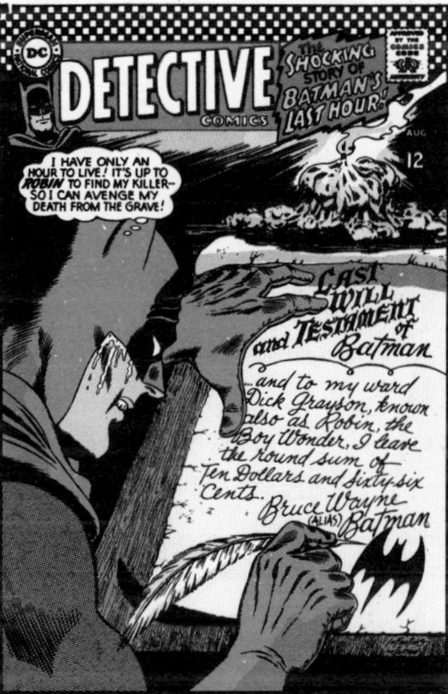

It was my very first exposure to The Batman. It was a special day in my life, although I surely didn't realize how special at the time. I don't remember the cover on that issue of DETECTIVE COMICS or the story that it contained. It *could* have been DETECTIVE #27, the first appearance of Batman ever, but I recall it was the first time *I'd* ever seen and read a Batman story. No matter—I was hooked... for life, as it turned out.

Time went by and I never missed an issue of DETECTIVE COMICS, featuring my favorite hero, The Batman. Later, I added BATMAN COMICS to my must-buy list and eventually WORLD'S FINEST COMICS, the first anthology book in which Superman and Batman both appeared regularly (in separate stories at first, though their adventures as a team started in the early 1950's, thereby creating the first regularly published crossover series in U.S. comics).

Young cartoonist Bob Kane, aided and abetted by writer Bill Finger and artist Jerry Robinson (one artist couldn't possibly produce all that work), knew the secrets of keeping a series fresh, exciting and creative: never rest on the oars, never let up, and never become predictable.

With those creative minds fired up, a long list of exciting villains, supporting players, environments, vehicles, and scientifically plausible contraptions were created, most of which still exist today. These characters and characteristics helped define The Batman *and* his series and made both unique in comics hero annals.

Over a period of only a few years, we were introduced to the Batcave, the Joker, Alfred the butler, Commissioner Gordon, the Batmobile, Wayne Mansion (with its secret places), Robin the Boy Wonder, the Penguin, the Batplane, Catwoman, the utility belt, Batwoman, two different Batgirls, the Batarang, Gotham City... and the best and most believable origin story ever created for a comic book hero.

An impressive list. Is it any wonder that I found the by-line "by Bob Kane" (I didn't know about Finger and Robinson at that time) a beacon for fun reading?

But, wait. Let's talk about Batman's origin and why I believe it is intrinsic to his believability, popularity, and longevity.

The Batman was born in a few, brief, violent moments in which a young Bruce Wayne was forced to

Opposite: DETECTIVE COMICS #27, May, 1939— The Batman's first appearance.

Left: Carmine Infantino and Murphy Anderson's classic cover from DETECTIVE #366 (1967).

watch the brutal murder of his parents at the hands of a street thief. At that moment of immense and intense grief, young Bruce commits himself to a life dedicated to making criminals pay for their deeds. His obsession guides and motivates him to accomplish feats that we are all, theoretically at least, capable of accomplishing... if only we were similarly motivated.

We all can understand Bruce's grief, we can all understand his frustration at having to watch helplessly as the lives of the most important people in his young life are taken uselessly, and we all can understand his need to do something to avenge the deaths of his parents. The origin of The Batman is grounded, therefore, in emotion. An emotion that is primal and timeless and dark.

The Batman does what he does for himself, for *his* needs. That society gains from his actions is incidental, an added value... but *not* the primary reason for his activities. And even when we're (perhaps ever so slightly) feeling unsettled by the dark side of the Batman's nature, we still understand. We're not sure we wouldn't try to do the same thing as The Batman does, if we watched our parents being murdered.

Of course, I didn't think of it exactly that way at the time. I was only six or seven years old and incapable of thought process at that level. To me, The Batman was a neat-looking crime fighter with acrobatic skills who was very strong and very smart, but with no superpowers. He was just an ordinary guy who learned how to do a lot of nifty things, like swinging from place to place on his bat-rope (that I never knew what the rope was attached to or how Batman attached it never really bothered me).

I knew that I could aspire to be Batman but I couldn't aspire to be Superman. No way could I get powers like Superman... I would have had to be born somewhere else for that... but I *could*, if I started young enough, train myself the way young Bruce Wayne did and maybe some day be just like Batman.

Well, I never started training and so remained ordinary, but I knew I *could* have, and that was a good portion of the character's appeal to the kids who read Batman.

Of course, there were many other elements that added to the basic appeal of the character—his alter ego Bruce Wayne being rich and pretending to be an ineffectual playboy was part of the fun. I felt like an "insider" when I saw Bruce acting silly at a party because *I* knew he was The Batman and before too long he would put aside his foppish ways, don cape and cowl and bring the bad guys to justice, returning to the role of useless playboy before the story ended. No one in the story knew, but I knew!

I also enjoyed the father/son relationship Bruce had with his ward, Dick Grayson (a.k.a. Robin the Boy Wonder); the faithfulness of Bruce's butler, Alfred; and the very special and unstated relationship between Commissioner Gordon and Batman—they both knew they were more effective working together but that it could never be official and that certain questions not pertaining to the case at hand could never be asked.

As I grew older, I continued to read and enjoy Batman stories. Many of the trappings of the series took on different meanings as I matured but they all remained valid nevertheless.

Sometime during those years I decided that I couldn't leave my childhood joys entirely behind and by the age of 13 I decided that I wanted to become a cartoonist. I had been drawing ever since I could remember and my experience in reading those early Batman stories convinced me that I wanted to use my meager talents to try to entertain people as I had been entertained.

Having made that decision, I then focused my energies on that goal and never thought of doing anything else with my life. So in a very real sense, that first contact with The Batman in my formative years played a very important role in my ultimate career choice and has been a factor in my remaining in this field for 36 years.

I became a working professional in the comics industry in March of 1952. I did a lot of "stuff" for 15 years. Then, my training period over, I came to work for DC Comics in 1967 (it was then called National Periodical Publications, a name that disguised its main activity of publishing comics). Although my "day job" of editing several of DC's popular titles was very satisfying, my real satisfaction came from spending my "spare" time at home at a drawing board inking stories for the other editors. Everyone seemed to like my work and after a spell, they gave me a Batman story to ink.

They gave *me* a Batman story to ink!

It was as if I had died and gone to heaven.

As I read the story I was given to ink and looked at the drawings, I was immediately transported back to that day many years before when, as a child, I removed a batch of comics from a paper bag and caught my first glimpse of the grim visage of The Batman. My reaction was: I'm back home again! I've gone full circle!

The rush was breathtaking. Words could not express how much pure joy I felt at being allowed to make a creative contribution to the continuing legend of a character that I loved and was widely acclaimed as one of the greatest fictional heroes of our time. I simply could not have been happier.

That was the start of my rekindled relationship with the Darknight Detective, but by no means the end. I've been fortunate enough to often be in the right place at the right time during the 20 or so years that have elapsed since that first Batman assignment and have benefited from being able to work with the most talented people in this business when opportunities to pencil and/or ink or edit the Batman presented themselves.

I've been lucky, too, in that I've gotten more than my fair share of important Batman stories to work on, several of which are presented again in this volume.

Which pretty much brings me to the reason for this lengthy (and sometimes windy) dissertation: Why did we cull these particular Batman stories out of the thousands that DC has published and call them THE GREATEST BATMAN STORIES EVER TOLD? Did we use completely objective criteria or did serendipity rule?

Well, maybe a bit of both, but we (Mike Gold, Bob Greenberger, Brian Augustyn and myself) tried

Opposite, above: Batman and Robin battle a misspelled Thunder Lizard courtesy Sheldon Moldoff (1958).

Opposite, below: Artists Ed Hannigan and Dick Giordano help Batman introduce his new partner—Jason (Robin) Todd (1984).

to put aside personal bias and choose important, pivotal stories in the Batman *mythos*: stories that introduced new characters or villains; origins of one kind or another; important events; or stories that in some way or another, illuminated some important aspect of the Batman mythos. We also tried to present a good cross-section of the creative people who have helped to shape the Batman's fortunes and guided him through the five decades that have elapsed since Bob Kane created him.

It is our fond hope that the stories we present here could, taken as a whole, be considered a definitive history of our Caped Crusader and provide the uninitiated reader (wherever he lurks) with all he needs to know to join the horde of those of us who worship at the shrine.

Failing that, we hoped that it would be a pretty good read. Incidentally, "we" were chosen to be "we" because between us we had probably read and/or owned and *could* read all of the hundreds (thousands?) of Batman stories published by DC Comics.

We met at Mike Gold's house and during the brainstorming session that followed, when one of us would mention a particular Batman story that might be appropriate, Bob Greenberger would appear to look heavenward for inspiration and then, trance-like, say something like "hmmm, that story appeared in BATMAN somewhere around issue number 235/240." We would then go through the bound volumes piled in front of us or Mike would jump up, dash to his bookcase and return with the appropriate volume. Bob was on the money most, if not all, of the time. His photographic memory made our day go faster and we finished with a great list. Alas, we had too much good material and had to trim enough to keep this book from being priced as high as a mint copy of BATMAN #1. Some pretty good stories didn't make the cut. Some went into our companion volume, THE GREATEST JOKER STORIES EVER TOLD. Others . . . well, maybe next time.

We are certain that you will agree that the stories in this edition are significant enough to have been included. We also know that many of you will feel that we were dumb not to include your personal favorite. Maybe you're right . . . or maybe The Batman is such a special hero that each of us has a highly personal view of who The Batman is and tend to favor those stories that reinforce our view.

I do know that various and radically different interpretations of The Batman can coexist. On occasion, we have published two or more Batman projects simultaneously that have presented different takes on the then-current Batman character or that might have slightly altered our continuity and have found that readers are *reasonably* comfortable with these personal and divergent views. How many fictional heroes, comic book or otherwise, could survive and even prosper with that kind of tinkering? That Batman can exist comfortably in such circumstances speaks volumes for the strength and lasting appeal of the character that although he celebrates his 50th birthday this year, seems as young as he did that day many years ago when he leaped out of the pages of DETECTIVE COMICS and caused young hearts to beat faster at that sight.

Happy Birthday, Batman!

Thank you, Bob Kane. . . . And good afternoon.

(One of the most respected artists and editors in the field, Dick Giordano presently is Vice-President/Executive Editor of DC Comics Inc.)

Opposite, above: A rare Bat-cover by Joe Kubert (1966).

Opposite, below: Neal Adams brings The Batman into a new decade with a classic look (1970).

Left: The Guardian of Gotham, once more courtesy of Neal Adams (1972).

Story by Gardner Fox/Art by Bob Kane/Coloring by Tom Ziuko

REMAIN UNTIL I GIVE YOU LEAVE TO GO!!
WHO... WHO ARE YOU?

THE BATMAN RECOGNIZES HIS FIANCEE, JULIE MADISON.
JULIE.. YOU!

WHA-WHAT AM I DOING HERE? WHO ARE YOU?

BUT...IF YOU ARE TAKING ME HOME...HOW DO YOU KNOW WHERE I LIVE? WHY WON'T YOU TALK? YOU WON'T TELL ME A THING!

BUT...WON'T YOU TELL ME WHO YOU ARE?
TELL YOUR FIANCE, BRUCE WAYNE, ALL THAT HAPPENED! G'NIGHT!

THE NEXT MORNING, BRUCE WAYNE IS CALLED TO HIS FIANCEE'S HOME!
BRUCE, THERE IS SOMETHING I MUST TELL YOU. A MAN DRESSED AS AN ENORMOUS BAT FOUND ME LAST NIGHT ON THE STREET ABOUT TO KILL A MAN!
GOOD LORD, JULIE - SUPPOSE YOU HAD! WE'D BETTER SEE DR. TRENT RIGHT AWAY!

AND SCARCELY TWO HOURS LATER.
YOUNG LADY, I'VE SEEN VICTIMS OF AN EXPERT HYPNOTIST EXHIBIT YOUR SYMPTOMS! DON'T YOU RECALL ANYTHING THAT WOULD SUGGEST SOMETHING LIKE THAT? I ADVISE AN OCEAN VOYAGE!

YET, AS DOCTOR TRENT TALKS, BRUCE WAYNE NOTICES HIS STARING EYES AND WONDERS...
YES, YES_AN OCEAN VOYAGE TO PARIS.. AND PERHAPS, LATER, TO HUNGARY_THE LAND OF HISTORY AND WEREWOLVES.

ONE TICKET TO PARIS, PLEASE. PORT CABIN.
LUNAR LINES

I DON'T LIKE THE CRACK THE DOCTOR MADE ABOUT WEREWOLVES, JULIE. AND HE SEEMED HYPNOTIZED HIMSELF, WHEN HE GAVE YOU THAT ADVICE. BUT MAYBE I'M IMAGINING THINGS.
OF COURSE YOU ARE! I'VE WORRIED YOU. BUT I'LL BE GOOD, I PROMISE.

BUT BACK AT THE WAYNE MANSION...
JULIE WOULD BE SUPRISED TO KNOW HER BATMAN IS HER FUTURE HUSBAND.

AND IN A SECRET HANGAR KNOWN ONLY TO HIMSELF...
TWO NEW WEAPONS. MY BATGYRO, IN WHICH TO FOLLOW JULIE, AND...

THE FLYING BATERANG - MODELED AFTER THE AUSTRALIAN BUSHMAN'S BOOMERANG!

LOOK!
A BAT!
THE END OF THE WORLD! WE ARE ATTACKED BY MARTIANS!

AND OUT TO SEA...

WHILE ON BOARD THE LUNAR LADY_
A MONSTER BAT! FLYING OVER THE OCEAN.

FIXING HIS AUTOMATIC CONTROLS, THE BATMAN PREPARES FOR A VISIT!

YOU... HERE!!

JULIE EXPLAINS HER PLIGHT TO THE BATMAN.
..AND SO THAT'S WHY I'M HERE. IF... LOOKOUT!

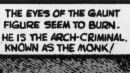

THE EYES OF THE GAUNT FIGURE SEEM TO BURN. HE IS THE ARCH-CRIMINAL, KNOWN AS THE MONK!

THAT MAN HAS UNCANNY POWERS. I SEEM TO BE HYPNOTIZED. IT IS HARDER AND HARDER TO MOVE.

BY A TREMENDOUS EFFORT OF WILL, THE BATMAN LEAPS INTO ACTION.

THE SPELL IS BROKEN! ... THE MONK EVADES THE BATERANG.
SWISH

THE BATMAN LEAPS FOR THE ROPE LADDER!

THE BATMAN, ANXIOUS TO GET TO THE BOTTOM OF THE MYSTERY, FOLLOWS THE SHIP, AND THE MONK - TO PARIS...

PARIS AT LAST!

THE SEARCH BEGINS . . .

THE TRAIL LEADS EVERYWHERE.

HELP! THE DEVIL HIMSELF.
CAB

THE WEIRD FIGURE IS SEEN ALL OVER PARIS, UNTIL, ONE NIGHT —
JULIE . . . AT LAST!

BUT A WARM RECEPTION HAS BEEN PREPARED FOR HIM!

THE BATMAN NIMBLY DODGES THE HUGE APE, ONLY TO FLY THROUGH A SLIDING DOOR . . .

. . . AND TUMBLES DOWN, DOWN, DOWN, INTO A GIGANTIC NET.

CAUGHT LIKE A RAT IN A TRAP, AS THE NET CLOSES ABOUT HIM...

THE BATMAN ONCE AGAIN FACES THE DIABOLICAL MASTER MONK!
RASH MORTAL... TO DARE FACE THE POWER OF THE MONK... LOOK BELOW YOU AT YOUR FATE! WHEN I PULL THIS LEVER-HEH! HEH!!

THE NET BEGINS TO DROP SLOWLY INTO THE DEN OF SNAKES.

IN A FLASH, THE BATMAN FLIPS HIS BATERANG.

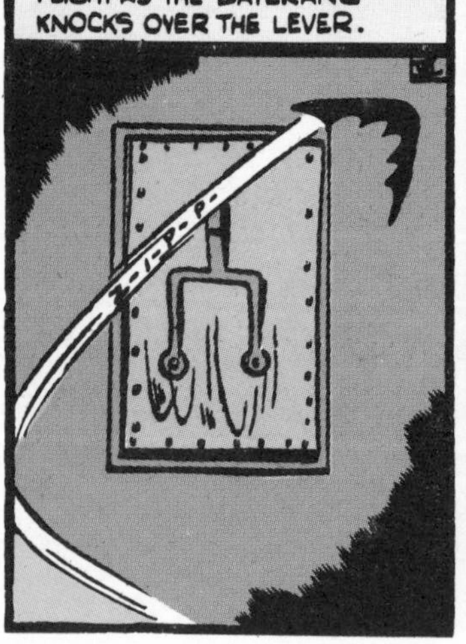
THE NET STOPS IN ITS DOWNWARD FLIGHT AS THE BATERANG KNOCKS OVER THE LEVER.

CONTINUING ON ITS UPWARD SWEEP, IT CRASHES INTO A GLASS CHANDELIER.
ZING

THE BATMAN GRASPS THE BATERANG AND THE BROKEN GLASS!
Z-I-N-G

A HEROIC GESTURE, BUT A FUTILE ONE. THE LEVER WILL REMAIN DOWN THIS TIME!

WORKING AGAINST TIME, THE BATMAN SEVERS STRAND AFTER STRAND.

FREEING HIMSELF NONE TOO SOON..

THE BATMAN, IN FULL PURSUIT OF THE FLEEING MONK...

SUDDENLY, A BARRED DOOR DROPS BETWEEN THE BATMAN AND THE MONK...
DIE HERE, YOU FOOL, WHILE I SEND THE GIRL, JULIE, ON TO MY CASTLE IN HUNGARY, TO FEED MY WEREWOLVES!

THE GIGANTIC GORILLA IS LOWERED, AS THE BATMAN IS CAGED BY BARS ALL ABOUT HIM.

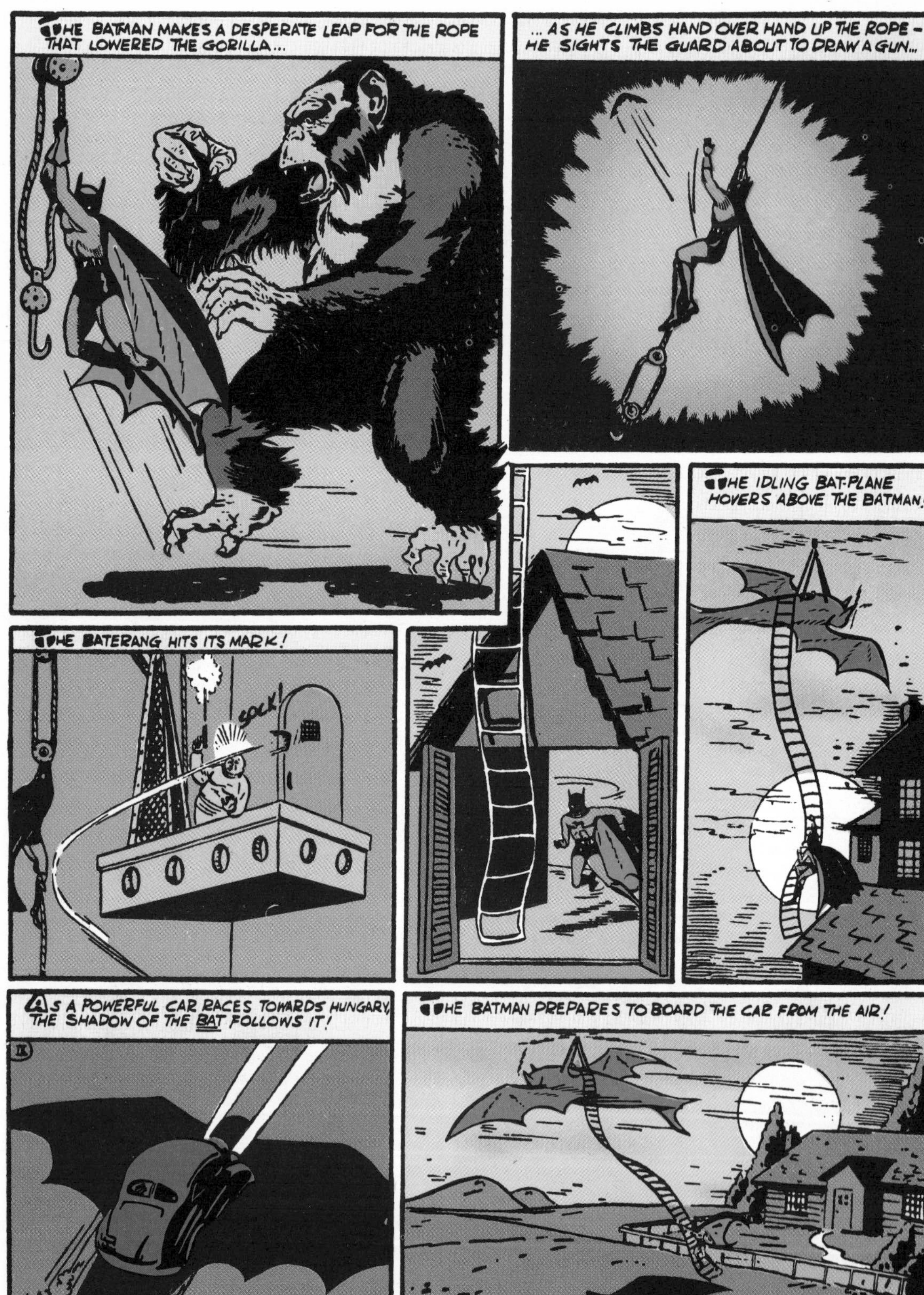
THE BATMAN MAKES A DESPERATE LEAP FOR THE ROPE THAT LOWERED THE GORILLA...
... AS HE CLIMBS HAND OVER HAND UP THE ROPE - HE SIGHTS THE GUARD ABOUT TO DRAW A GUN...
THE IDLING BAT-PLANE HOVERS ABOVE THE BATMAN!
THE BATERANG HITS ITS MARK!
SOCK!
AS A POWERFUL CAR RACES TOWARDS HUNGARY, THE SHADOW OF THE BAT FOLLOWS IT!
THE BATMAN PREPARES TO BOARD THE CAR FROM THE AIR!

A GLASS PELLET FILLED WITH GAS IS THROWN INTO THE CAR...

THE CAR SWERVES INTO A TREE...
THE MONK KNEW BETTER THAN TO COME - BUT I CAN SAVE JULIE!

THE BATMAN MAKES A VALIANT LEAP FOR THE LADDER OF HIS BAT-PLANE!

WITH JULIE SAFE, THE BATMAN PLANS ON VENGEANCE...
POOR KID!

... AND SETS HIS AUTOMATIC CONTROLS FOR HUNGARY - HOME OF THE VICIOUS MONK AND HIS WEREWOLVES!

Continue THE THRILLING ADVENTURES OF THE BATMAN AND HIS COMBAT AGAINST THE MYSTERIOUS MONK! WHAT PLANS HAS THE MONK IN MIND? WHY DOES HE WANT JULIE?
See THE NEXT EPISODE OF THE
BATMAN
BOB KANE

Story by Gardner Fox/Art by Bob Kane/Coloring by Tom Ziuko

HE WHIPS OUT A GLASS PELLET OF CHOKING GAS AND...

THE FUMES OVERCOME THE OCCUPANT OF THE CAB!

INSTEAD OF HIS QUARRY, THE MONK, THE BATMAN FINDS...
WHAT..?

THE EERIE FIGURE RETURNS TO HIS BATPLANE.
I DON'T KNOW WHO SHE IS, BUT I HAVE A FEELING I'LL SOON FIND OUT.

STRANGE FOR ANYONE TO BE TRAVELING ALONE WAY OUT HERE...AND YET THE MONK... I WONDER?

THE BATMAN ARRIVES AT HIS HOTEL, EMBEDDED DEEP IN THE CARLATHAN MOUNTAINS IN HUNGARY...
AH, SHE'S COMING TO! I HOPE JULIE IS SAFE.

AND FEARS FOR JULIE'S SAFETY.

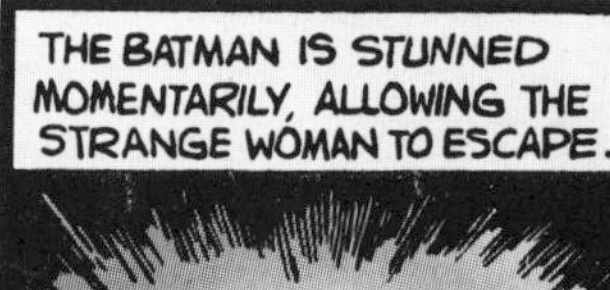

THE BATMAN RETURNS TO JULIE, WHOSE THROAT SHOWS TWO RED SPOTS... MARKS OF THE VAMPIRE!

I SHOULD HAVE KNOWN. NEVER SHOULD HAVE TRUSTED HER.

SHE WON'T GET FAR.

LIKE A PLUMMET, THE BATMAN OVER-TAKES HIS PREY.

YOU SHALL TALK NOW, DALA, YOU WITCH! I THOUGHT YOU AN ACCOMPLICE OF YOUR EVIL MASTER WHO CALLS HIMSELF THE MONK. SO YOU ARE VAMPIRES!!

YOU WANT TO KNOW WHERE THE MONK IS? YOU FEAR HIM - WELL, I DO, TOO. I'LL TELL YOU WHERE YOU MAY FIND HIM IF YOU PROMISE TO KILL HIM!

I'LL BE JUDGE OF THAT! WHERE DOES THE MONK HIDE?

IN THE LOST MOUNTAINS OF CATHALA BY THE TURBULENT RIVER DESS. I SHALL GUIDE YOU.

THIS MONEY WILL SAFE GUARD YOU. I AM GOING. YOU MUST FIGHT AGAINST THE POWER THAT CALLS YOU TO THIS MONK!

OH_ I WILL FIGHT. I WILL..., BUT I AM SO AFRAID WITHOUT YOU!!

AND SO THE BATMAN AND DALA DEPART ON THEIR WEIRD MISSION...

TOWARD THE STRONGHOLD OF THE 'MONK' WINGS THE EERIE BATPLANE...

SUDDENLY, THE BATMAN SEES...

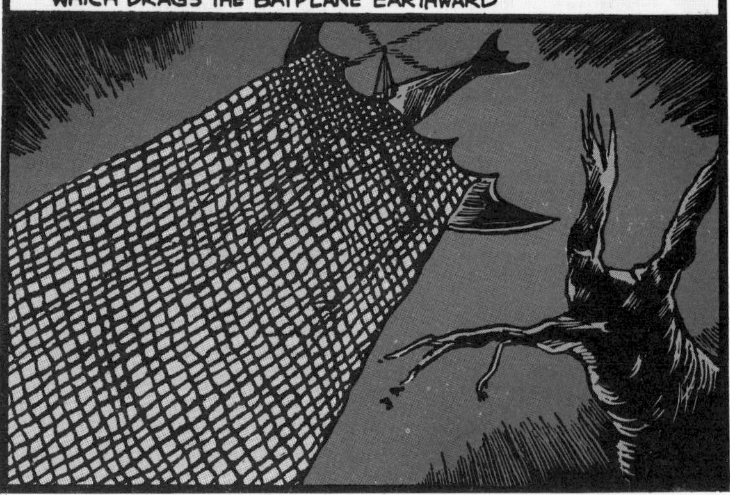
A GREAT SILVER NET THAT SEEMS TO OPERATE BY MAGIC, WHICH DRAGS THE BATPLANE EARTHWARD

FIRST YOU MUST BRING JULIE HERE! MAKE THE BATMAN SUFFER, KNOWING TO WHAT FATE THE GIRL IS DOOMED!

THE HELPLESS BATMAN SEES HIS FIANCEE DRAWN INTO THE MONK'S TRAP!
SOON YOUR JULIE WILL BE AS WE ARE - WEREWOLVES TO RAVISH ON ALL LIVING MEN - AND YOU SHALL BE DEAD - HELPLESS TO AVENGE HER!

THE BATMAN IS FORCED TO SUFFER IN SILENCE.
YOU HAVE DONE SOMETHING TO HIM. HIS EYES ARE SUFFERING, BUT HE CANNOT MOVE! OH_YOU FIEND!

INTO THAT DEN OF WOLVES WHICH I SHALL CALL FROM THE FOREST YOU SHALL BE CAST TO DIE BY THEIR THIRSTY FANGS!

BEFORE THE BATMAN'S HORRIFIED EYES, THE MONK BEGINS TO CHANGE...

THE MONK, AS A WOLF, HOWLS THE GATHERING CALL TO THE MOUNTAIN WOLVES...

- AND FROM THE SURROUNDING MOUNTAINS, THE WOLVES GATHER.

YOU SHALL BE THROWN INTO THE ARENA BELOW, TO DIE AT THEIR RENDING FANGS.. AS YOU ARE SCREAMING IN DEATH-REMEMBER THAT JULIE WILL BE A WEREWOLF HERSELF IN TIME! TO RUN WITH THE PACK ON MOONLIGHT NIGHTS!

AS HE IS PUSHED FORWARD, THE BATMAN'S SENSES SUDDENLY RETURN TO THEIR FULL POWER.

HE TWISTS IN MID-AIR AND TRIES A DESPERATE THROW WITH HIS SILKEN ROPE.

- HIS CAST FAILS!

-AND HE FALLS INTO THE WOLF DEN.

THE BATMAN SWIFTLY EXTRACTS A GLASS PELLET FROM HIS BELT!!

THE GAS IN THE EXPLODING PELLET OVERCOMES THE WOLVES..

I CAN HOLD THE WOLVES OFF ONLY AS LONG AS MY GAS PELLETS LAST- THEN IT'S OVER!

THE LIGHT BUT STRONG ROPE FAILS TO CARRY TO THE PIT'S EDGE.

TOWARD DAWN, THE WOLVES AWAKE..

FLASHING FANGS AGAIN MENACE THE BATMAN!

THE BATMAN'S FINGERS FIND HIS HIDDEN BATERANG!!

ONE STRONG CAST WILL WIN ME FREEDOM.

THE BATERANG SLIPS PAST A STONE POST AND THE ROPE HOLDS.

THE BATMAN CLIMBS TO SAFETY!

AND THEN SEEKS HIS VENGEANCE...

SAFE SO FAR- NOW FOR THE OTHERS!

A SILVER STATUE! WHILE THE VAMPIRES SLEEP, DURING THE DAYTIME, I SHALL MELT THIS STATUE AND MAKE TWO SILVER BULLETS- ONE FOR DALA AND ONE FOR THE MONK!

ONLY A SILVER BULLET MAY KILL A VAMPIRE!

NOW TO FIND THE OPEN TOMB IN WHICH THESE VAMPIRES SLEEP AND BRING THEM DEATH THAT WILL RELEASE JULIE!

THE BATMAN PAUSES BEFORE THE OPEN TOMBS OF THE VAMPIRES...

NEVER AGAIN WILL YOU HARM ANY MORTAL BEING!

THE SPELL IS BROKEN... AND LIFE RETURNS ONCE AGAIN TO JULIE!
I DON'T KNOW WHO YOU ARE, BUT YOU SAVED MY LIFE AND I SHALL BE FOREVER GRATEFUL!
BOB KANE

FINIS

A NEW INTRIGUING
BATMAN
STORY EVERY MONTH IN
DETECTIVE COMICS

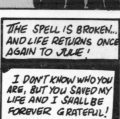

Story by Bill Finger/Art by Bob Kane/Coloring by Nansi Hoolahan

THAT NIGHT ... THE HOME OF BRUCE WAYNE
FLASH -- A GUARD IDENTIFIED PROFESSOR STRANGE AS THE LEADER OF THE MEN WHO FREED FIVE INSANE PATIENTS FROM THE CITY INSANE ASYLUM.
INSANE MEN?

CRIMINALS, MANIACS, AND STRANGE CAN ONLY ADD UP TO ONE THING ... SOMETHING NEW IN CRIME ... SOMETHING FANTASTIC AND TERRIBLE VERY TERRIBLE!!

A MONTH LATER ... A CROWDED STREET IN LOWER MANHATTAN

SUDDENLY A WOMAN STOPS AND SCREAMS IN FRIGHT!
AA-AA-AH! LOOK!
HELP!
WHAT IS IT? IT ISN'T HUMAN!

TOWERING UP A FULL FIFTEEN FEET, A GIGANTIC HULK LOOMS ABOVE THEM, HUGE AND TERRIBLE!!
BIJOU
HELP!
A MONSTER!
WE'LL ALL BE KILLED!

THE HORRIBLE CREATURE BEGINS ITS WAVE OF DESTRUCTION....
HELP!
W-WHAT IS IT?
YAA-A-A-A

BULLETS THUD INTO THE BEAST BUT THIS ONLY MADDENS HIM!
LOOK! BULLETS DON'T STOP HIM ... HE'S STILL LIVING!

THE ENRAGED BEAST SEEMS TO GO MAD!

THE PEOPLE ARE PANIC-STRICKEN!
HELP!!
RUN FOR YOUR LIVES!!
AS MORE POLICE RUN UP, THE MONSTER RIPS UP A LAMP POST...

THE MONSTER WIELDS THE WEAPON WITH TERRIBLE EFFECT!

SUDDENLY AS POLICE CARS APPEAR, THE MONSTER LUMBERS TOWARD A TRUCK IDLING NEARBY
THERE HE GOES TOWARDS THE TRUCK! STEP ON IT!!

THE POLICE CAR STARTS IN PURSUIT!

AS THE POLICE DRAW NEAR, THE MONSTER HURLS SOMETHING AT THE CAR ...

THERE IS A SHATTERING ROAR AS THE OBJECT HITS THE POLICE CAR!
BOOM!

THAT NIGHT...
AND THE MONSTER MADE GOOD HIS ESCAPE BY BOMBING THE POLICE CAR THE PEOPLE...
IT COULD BE THE WORK OF ONLY ONE MAN... STRANGE

IF I KNOW PROFESSOR STRANGE THERE WILL BE MORE OF THEM TO COME. I MUST STOP HIM... HMMM...

AGAIN THE NEXT DAY, THE MONSTER APPEARS!
HELP!! IT'S TEARING DOWN THE "EL" THEY'LL ALL BE KILLED!!
AS POLICE AGAIN PURSUE, THEY MEET THE SAME FATE AS THOSE THE DAY BEFORE!!
BOOM!

BUT HIGH ABOVE...
THAT TRUCK SHOULD LEAD ME STRAIGHT TO THE HIDEOUT OF HUGO STRANGE!

WELL, IT LOOKS LIKE THE END OF MY SEARCH!

A FEW MINUTES LATER...

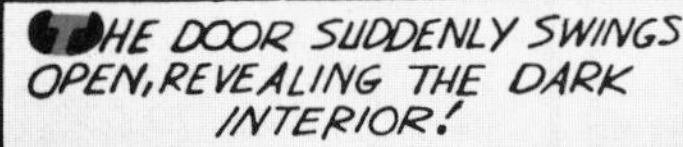
THE DOOR SUDDENLY SWINGS OPEN, REVEALING THE DARK INTERIOR!

WHAT TH', IT LOOKS LIKE A TRAP BUT I'VE GOT TO CHANCE IT!

THE BATMAN CAUTIOUSLY STEPS INSIDE. FAILING TO NOTICE HUGE HANDS....

SUDDENLY THE LIGHT FLASHES ON! THE BATMAN IS IN THE HANDS OF THE MONSTERS!!
ER.. GOOD EVENING, GENTLEMEN!

THEN... A VOICE!
CAUGHT! AND VERY NEATLY, TOO!
AH! I EXPECTED TO SEE YOUR UGLY FACE AROUND HERE--I HAD A HUNCH YOU WERE BEHIND THIS! WE MEET AGAIN. PROFESSOR STRANGE!

NOW THAT YOU'VE GOT ME, I DON'T SUPPOSE I'LL LIVE VERY LONG. GRANT ME A DYING MAN'S REQUEST AND TELL ME HOW YOU'VE CREATED THESE MONSTERS, AND WHY?
WITH THE GREATEST OF PLEASURE, MY DEAR BATMAN. IF YOU WILL LOOK CLOSELY YOU WILL RECOGNIZE THEIR PICTURES IN THE PAPERS. THEY ARE THE ESCAPED LUNATICS....

...AND THESE ARE MONSTERS. I MADE THEM, SO! I DISCOVERED AN EXTRACT THAT SPEEDS UP THE GROWTH GLANDS. I INJECT THIS FLUID INTO A NORMAL MAN. THE SUDDEN GROWTH NOT ONLY DISTORTS THE BODY BUT ALSO THE BRAIN--AND SOON HE IS A MONSTER!!

I HAVE SENT OUT A MONSTER IN CLOTHES OF BULLET PROOF MATERIAL SO THAT THE PUBLIC AND THE POLICE MAY BE--ER--ACQUAINTED WITH HIM TOMORROW I SHALL SEND OUT TWO MONSTERS AND WHILE THE POLICE ARE CONCERNED WITH THEM MY MEN WILL LOOT THE BANKS. CLEVER ISN'T IT? YOU KNOW, AT TIMES I AM AMAZED AT MY OWN GENIUS!

AN EVIL GENIUS, STRANGE!

REMOVE HIS BELT OF GAS CAPSULES... I WANT NO ESCAPE.. I AM GOING TO INJECT THIS FLUID INTO YOU! YOU, DEAR BATMAN, ARE TO BE A MONSTER! A MONSTER! HA-HA-HA

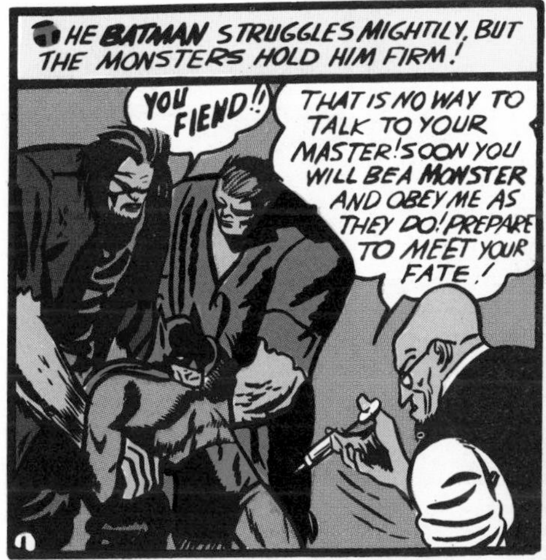
THE BATMAN STRUGGLES MIGHTILY, BUT THE MONSTERS HOLD HIM FIRM!
YOU FIEND!!
THAT IS NO WAY TO TALK TO YOUR MASTER! SOON YOU WILL BE A MONSTER AND OBEY ME AS THEY DO! PREPARE TO MEET YOUR FATE!

THE DEADLY NEEDLE PLUNGES DEEP INTO THE ARM OF THE BATMAN!
DONE!!

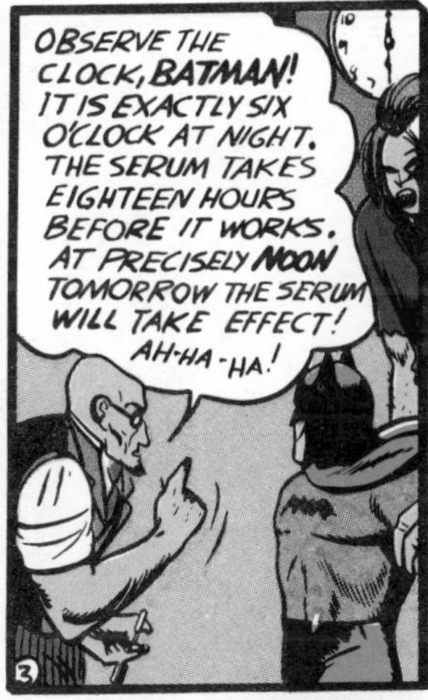
OBSERVE THE CLOCK, BATMAN! IT IS EXACTLY SIX O'CLOCK AT NIGHT. THE SERUM TAKES EIGHTEEN HOURS BEFORE IT WORKS. AT PRECISELY NOON TOMORROW THE SERUM WILL TAKE EFFECT! AH-HA-HA!

A MASSIVE FIST CRASHES AGAINST THE BATMAN'S JAW -- THEN BLACKNESS

HOURS LATER
WOW! WHAT HIT ME! THE CLOCK! IT SAYS ALMOST A QUARTER TO TWELVE I'VE BEEN UNCONSIOUS ALMOST EIGHTEEN HOURS... AND IT'S ALMOST TIME FOR THE SERUM TO WORK!!

THEN THE BATMAN SEES...
NOW REMEMBER! THREE MEN TAKE A MONSTER, ONE TRUCK WILL GO BY DALY AVENUE AND THE OTHER BY THE POST ROAD NOW, GET GOING.. AND NO SLIP UPS!
DON'T WORRY, STRANGE! THOSE BANKS ARE AS GOOD AS OPENED RIGHT NOW!

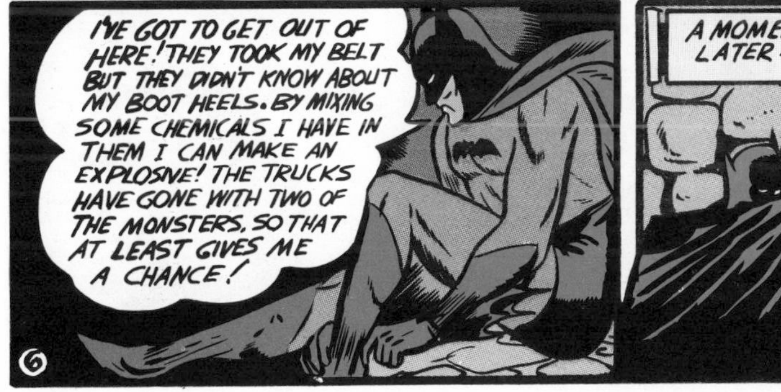
I'VE GOT TO GET OUT OF HERE! THEY TOOK MY BELT BUT THEY DIDN'T KNOW ABOUT MY BOOT HEELS. BY MIXING SOME CHEMICALS I HAVE IN THEM I CAN MAKE AN EXPLOSIVE! THE TRUCKS HAVE GONE WITH TWO OF THE MONSTERS, SO THAT AT LEAST GIVES ME A CHANCE!
A MOMENT LATER...
THAT DOES IT!
BOOM!

WHAT... YOU... OUT!!
YES...

AND SO ARE YOU!

THE POWERFUL BLOW SENDS STRANGE OUT-TO FALL TO MURKY WATERS BELOW...

I WONDER IF THIS REALLY IS THE END OF PROFESSOR HUGO STRANGE? ?? MEANWHILE, TIME IS FLYING - IT MUST BE ALMOST TIME FOR THE SERUM TO WORK! I'VE GOT TO STOP IT!

SUDDENLY A DOOR OPENS... AND THERE... THREE MONSTERS!!
THE REST OF THE MONSTERS!!

THE BATMAN SPIES THE LONG POLE USED TO OPEN THE SKYLIGHT!...
THERE'S STILL A CHANCE!

ALTHOUGH YOUR BULLET-PROOF CLOTHING PROTECTS YOU FROM BULLETS - IT DOESN'T FROM THIS!!

THE BATMAN TRIES FOR THE KNOB ON THE SKYLIGHT!
IF THIS DOESN'T CATCH, THEN I'LL CATCH IT FROM THE MONSTERS!
1.

THE HOOK CATCHES AND...
BIG BOY, HERE I COME!
2.

I BET YOU'RE SURPRISED!
?
3.

AS THE ENRAGED COLOSSUS LUMBERS FORWARD, THE BATMAN DEFTLY THRUSTS THE POLE BETWEEN HIS LEGS...
4.

...AND PULLS HARD!!
I HOPE THIS WORKS!
5

AS THE MONSTERS COLLIDE, THEY IMMEDIATELY BECOME ENRAGED AND STARE AT EACH OTHER WITH HATE IN THEIR EYES!
6

ALL THOUGHTS OF THE BATMAN ARE FORGOTTEN AS THE MADDENED BEASTS FIERCELY ENGAGE IN HEATED BATTLE!

IT WORKED! AND NOW I'VE GOT TO WORK FAST TO STOP THE SERUM ... I'VE JUST GOT FIVE MINUTES!

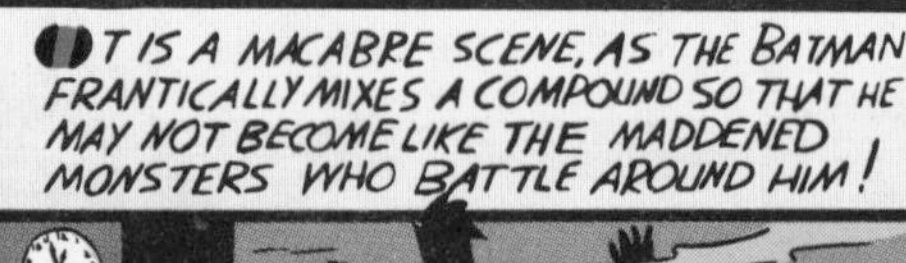
IT IS A MACABRE SCENE, AS THE BATMAN FRANTICALLY MIXES A COMPOUND SO THAT HE MAY NOT BECOME LIKE THE MADDENED MONSTERS WHO BATTLE AROUND HIM!

THIS COMPOUND WILL ACT AS AN ANTIDOTE AND STOP ANY EXCESS ACTION FROM THE GROWTH GLANDS ... THERE! IT'S IN! I'VE BEATEN HUGO STRANGE BY A SINGLE MINUTE!!

THEY'VE KILLED EACH OTHER AS I HOPED THEY WOULD! THEY ARE NOW DEAD! TWO STILL LIVE. THEY'RE IN THOSE TRUCKS. ONE IS ON DALY AVENUE AND THE OTHER ON POST ROAD I CAN STILL CATCH THEM..

A MOMENT LATER .. THE BATPLANE RISES INTO THE AIR!
THE POST ROAD FIRST!

ON THE POST ROAD ...
IT WON'T BE LONG NOW!
WHAT A CINCH! THE MONKEY IN THE BACK STARTS A RIOT, KILLS A FEW PEOPLE AND WE CRACK A BANK! A SWEET RACKET!

BUT OUT OF THE SKY, SPITTING DEATH AT THE BATMAN!
RAT.. TAT.. TAT.. TAT.. TAT..
SMOKE

MUCH AS I HATE TO TAKE HUMAN LIFE, I'M AFRAID THIS TIME IT'S NECESSARY!
RAT.. TAT.. TAT.. TAT.. TAT

THE BULLETS TAKE THEIR TOLL·· THE TRUCK CRASHES INTO A TREE!
AS THE MONSTER RISES, THE STEEL-LIKE ROPE OF THE BATMAN LOOPS ABOUT HIS NECK!
THE RISING BATPLANE JERKS THE MONSTER FROM THE GROUND
I'VE ROPED STEERS BEFORE, BUT YOU'RE MUCH MORE DEADLY!
THE GIANT TRIES TO BREAK THE EVER-TIGHTENING ROPE!
A FEW MOMENTS LATER...
HE'S PROBABLY BETTER OFF THIS WAY.
I'M IN TIME!! THERE'S THE TRUCK NOW!!
NOW I'LL CUT THIS FELLOW DOWN AND THEN GO TO DALY AVENUE ··· FOR THE LAST MONSTER!
TAT... TAT... TAT...

FROM THE BACK OF THE TRUCK!
HELP! THE MONSTER IS BACK!

AS THE MONSTER GAZES UP AT THE BATPLANE HE SEEMS TO REALIZE IT MEANT TO DO HIM HARM. HE MUST GET UP TO DO IT BATTLE

THE CRAZED BEAST, SEEING THE BUILDING REAR HIGH IN THE AIR, THINKS HE CAN REACH THE BATPLANE THAT WAY

THE INSANE MONSTER STARTS TO CLIMB THE TOWER
...AND FINALLY THE TOP!

UP... UP.. HE CLIMBS...

THE BULLET PROOF CLOTHES PROTECT THE MONSTER···
IF BULLETS DON'T STOP HIM - I KNOW WHAT WILL!
TAT...TAT... TAT...
RAT. TAT... TAT.

THIS TIME FROM THE BATPLANE GAS PELLETS!!

AS THE GAS TAKES EFFECT THE MONSTER ONCE MORE SEES THE BATPLANE··· SHAKES HIS HANDS DEFIANTLY---

...AND THEN TOPPLES OFF TO HIS DOOM!!

THERE GOES THE LAST OF THE MONSTERS··· YET I HAVE A FEELING THAT THE BIGGEST MONSTER OF THEM ALL, PROFESSOR HUGO STRANGE, STILL LIVES! PERHAPS WE SHALL MEET AGAIN··· PERHAPS!!
BOB KANE

THE
BATMAN
APPEARING EVERY MONTH
IN DETECTIVE COMICS

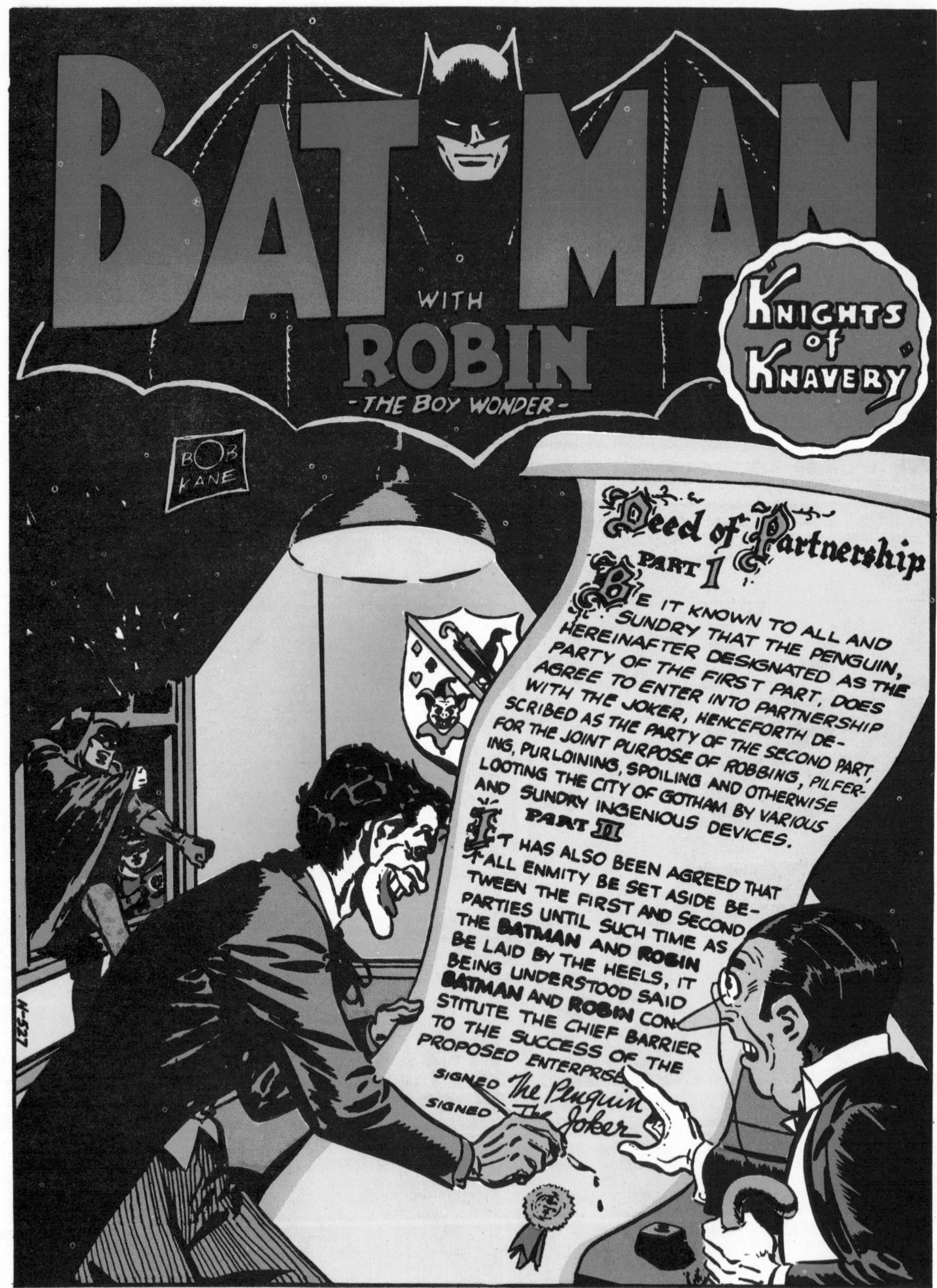

Art by Jerry Robinson & George Roussos/Coloring by Anthony Tollin

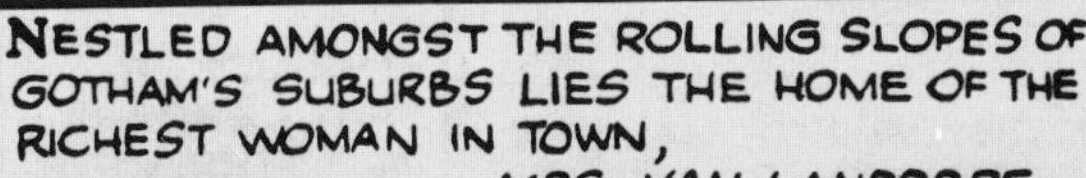
NESTLED AMONGST THE ROLLING SLOPES OF GOTHAM'S SUBURBS LIES THE HOME OF THE RICHEST WOMAN IN TOWN, MRS. VAN LANDORPF...

WHAT A SERENE AND TRANQUIL PICTURE ---

BUT WAIT--!
DEAR ME -- TO THINK THAT ONE OF MY INTELLECT SHOULD WALK INTO SUCH A TRAP. HASTE IS MY ONLY RESOURCE NOW!

NO-YOU ARE NOT DECEIVED. IT IS INDEED THE PENGUIN, THAT GROTESQUE BIRD OF ILL-OMEN!
THE BATMAN AND ROBIN! WILL THOSE TWO NEVER CEASE TO HAUNT MY WAKING MOMENTS?
HE CAN'T GET AWAY FROM US NOW, BATMAN!

QUICK AS A WINK, WE'LL HAVE YOU IN THE CLINK!
BUT I'LL BE OUT MUCH SOONER THAN YOU THINK!

A SHORT WHILE LATER, AT GOTHAM PENITENTIARY --
WELL, PENGUIN -- HOW DOES IT FEEL TO BE HOME AGAIN?
TERRIBLE! BUT WAIT AND SEE IF I DON'T BEGIN TO ROAM AGAIN.

.. TO BE DOGGED BY SUCH ILL-FORTUNE! HOW COULD I HAVE KNOWN THAT THEY WERE WAITING FOR ME TO STEAL THE VAN LANDORPF EMERALD? THAT THIS SHOULD HAPPEN TO ME -- THE SMARTEST CROOK IN TOWN!
2

HA-HA! HO-HO-HO! LOOK WHO CALLS HIMSELF THE SMARTEST CROOK IN TOWN!
HUH? WHY THIS RAUCOUS OUT-BURST OF MIRTH, MY LAUGHING HYENA?
THOSE SPINE-CHILLING CHUCKLES! THAT SATANIC VOICE! WHERE HAVE WE HEARD THEM BEFORE?
ALLOW ME TO INTRODUCE YOU TO THE SMART-EST CROOK IN TOWN -- MY CARD!
J
THE JOKER! THAT LEERING MONSTER OF MENACE! WHAT STRANGE TWIST OF FATE HAS PLACED HIM IN THE SAME CELL AS THE PENGUIN? WHAT IMPISH IRONY HAS BROUGHT THESE TWINS IN TRANSGRESSION FACE TO FACE? CAN PRISON WALLS CONTAIN THIS COMBINA-TION OF CRAFT AND CUNNING?

POOF--THE JOKER! I READ HOW **BATMAN** CAUGHT YOU TRYING TO LIFT THE VAN LAN-DORPF EMERALD LAST WEEK. YOU OUGHT TO HIDE YOUR SILLY, GRINN-ING FACE IN SHAME. ***I'M*** THE KING OF CRIME IN THESE PARTS.
IS THAT SO? LISTEN, YOU PUFFED CANARY-- IF YOU'RE SO GOOD, HOW IS IT ***YOU*** DIDN'T GET THE EMERALD?
ER- WE WON'T GO INTO THAT, YOU GIGGLING GHOUL. WHY, YOU COULDN'T PICK A BLIND MAN'S POCKET ON A FOGGY NIGHT!
NOW, LOOK HERE, YOU UMBRELLA-TOTING UNDERWORLD UPSTART- THIS TOWN ISN'T BIG ENOUGH FOR BOTH OF US TO OPER-ATE IN! WE'VE GOT TO SETTLE WHO GOES AND WHO STAYS!
THAT'S ALL RIGHT WITH ME. HOW ABOUT A LITTLE CON-TEST? WE'RE BOTH AFTER THE VAN LANDORPF EMERALD-- SHALL WE SAY THAT WHOEVER GETS IT FIRST WINS EXCLUSIVE CON-TROL OF THE GOTHAM CITY TERRITORY?
THAT SUITS ME FINE! NOW TO GET OUT OF THIS ESTABLISHMENT AND SHOW YOU UP!

LATER, THE TWO KNIGHTS OF KNAVERY BEGIN A FEARFUL CLAMOR IN THE CELL BLOCK...
WE DEMAND A CLEAN CELL! THIS PLACE IS A PIG-STY!
THE FLOOR HASN'T BEEN SWEPT IN A MONTH!
IF YOU NOISY STIR-NUTS WANT A CLEAN CELL, TRY CLEANING IT YOURSELVES!
THE SERVICE IN THIS JAIL IS WORSE THAN ALL THE OTHERS I'VE EVER BEEN IN!
3

BUT AS SOON AS THE GUARD LEAVES THEM WITH THE BROOM--
TAKING OFF THIS WIRE THAT BINDS THE BROOM'S STRAWS TOGETHER WAS QUITE A BRIGHT IDEA OF MINE!
NOT QUITE AS BRIGHT AS MY IDEA OF FASHIONING IT INTO A LONG HOOK!
HO-HUM--WHAT A DULL JOB THIS IS -- PLAYING NURSE TO A COLLECTION OF CROOKS. NOTHING EVER HAPPENS AROUND HERE...
GUESS I'LL GO SEE WHETHER THOSE TWO PUNKS HAVE SWEPT THEIR CELL YET-- OOGH!
THANKS FOR THE BROOM, DIM-WIT. HERE'S WHERE WE SWEEP YOU OFF YOUR FEET-- HA-HA!
CLUNK
AND BRIEF MINUTES LATER, TWO FLEEING FIENDS REGAIN THEIR FREEDOM--AS PRISON SIRENS BELATEDLY SOUND THE ALARM!
WELL, HERE'S WHERE WE SEPARATE. AND DON'T FORGET OUR AGREEMENT!
DON'T YOU FORGET IT! WHEN I GET THAT EMERALD, IT'S GOING TO BE GOOD-BYE, GOTHAM FOR YOU!
EEEEEEEEEEEE
THAT EVENING, AT THE HOME OF BRUCE WAYNE--
WITH THOSE TWO ON THE LOOSE, GOTHAM IS GOING TO BE TURNED UPSIDE-DOWN!
THE JOKER AND PENGUIN BOTH! IT WAS BAD ENOUGH WHEN WE HAD TO WORRY ABOUT ONE OF THEM AT A TIME. WE CAN'T AFFORD TO LOSE A MOMENT!
GOTHAM NEWS
JOKER AND PENGUIN MAKE SENSATIONAL ESCAPE FROM PENITENTIARY!
SCANT SECONDS ELAPSE BEFORE THE ANXIOUS PAIR IS TRANSFORMED INTO THAT DOUBLE-BARRELLED BLIGHT OF EVIL, THE BATMAN AND ROBIN--
WHAT'S OUR FIRST MOVE, BATMAN?
THE JOKER AND THE PENGUIN HAVE BOTH BEEN AFTER THE VAN LANDORPF EMERALD FOR A LONG TIME. THEY'RE SURE TO STRIKE AGAIN-- AND WHEN THEY DO, WE WANT TO BE THERE!
BUT THEY'RE NOT GOING TO WALK INTO A TRAP TWICE. THEY'RE TOO SMART FOR THAT.
NO--BUT I THINK WE MIGHT BE ABLE TO USE THEIR OWN SMARTNESS AGAINST THEM. I'LL NEED MRS. VAN LANDORPF'S COOPERATION...
4

SHORTLY AFTERWARD, AT THE VAN LANDORPF HOME...
-- AND SINCE YOU'RE GOING TO APPEAR AT THE RITZ FASHION SHOW TOMORROW NIGHT AS AMERICA'S BEST-TAILORED WOMAN, I'D APPRECIATE IT IF YOU'D GET THIS NOTICE INTO THE SOCIETY COLUMNS TOMORROW...
NATURALLY, I'LL DO EVERYTHING I CAN TO HELP YOU CAPTURE THOSE TWO AWFUL MEN, BATMAN!

--OH, YOU WANT ME TO SAY THAT I'LL BE WEARING THE EMERALD TOMORROW NIGHT! BUT I COULDN'T POSSIBLY!
I QUITE UNDERSTAND. I INSERTED THAT DELIBERATELY. YOU WON'T HAVE TO WEAR THE EMERALD. ROBIN AND I WILL TAKE CARE OF THAT!

YOU MAY BE SURE I'LL ARRANGE TO HAVE THE NOTICE INSERTED. AND I LEAVE THE EMERALD IN YOUR CARE. I DO HOPE IT WILL BE SAFE!
IT WILL BE.. NEVER FEAR!

I CAN'T IMAGINE ANYTHING DULLER THAN A FASHION SHOW, BUT I'M WILLING TO GO AS LONG AS YOU EXPECT TO LURE THE PENGUIN AND THE JOKER THERE!
YOU'RE WRONG, ROBIN-- WE'RE NOT GOING TO THE FASHION SHOW!

YOU SEE, THE JOKER AND THE PENGUIN ARE MUCH TOO CLEVER TO BE FOOLED BY THAT NOTICE. THEY'LL SMELL A TRAP IMMEDIATELY. THAT'S EXACTLY WHAT I WANT THEM TO DO. MY IDEA IS TO USE THEIR OWN CLEVERNESS AGAINST THEM!

LET'S PAY A VISIT TO THE HEADQUARTERS OF THE WILY PENGUIN AS HE SCANS THE PAPERS ON THE FOLLOWING AFTERNOON--
HMM-- HERE'S AN INTERESTING LITTLE PIECE IN THE SOCIETY COLUMN. JUST WHAT I'VE BEEN WAITING FOR!
LET'S SEE, BOSS. TEAR IT OUT!
GOTHAM NEWS

-- and Mrs. van Landorpf will appear at the fashion show wearing an elegant suit of grey tweed that should certainly justify her title of America's best-tailo woman. She also plans to wear her famous eme ald for the occasion.
DE EMERALD! I GUESS WE GO TO DE FASHION SHOW, BOSS!
5

SUCH STUPIDITY! DON'T YOU KNOW THAT ONE DOESN'T WEAR COURT EMERALDS WITH TAILORED CLOTHES? IT SIMPLY ISN'T DONE. MY GUESS IS THAT THE BATMAN HAD THIS NOTICE INSERTED--
BUT WHAT'S HIS ANGLE?
HE KNOWS I'M AFTER THE EMERALD, SO HE PLANS TO LURE ME TO THE FASHION SHOW, WHERE HE'LL BE WAITING FOR ME! BUT I'M A LITTLE TOO SMART FOR HIM...
SINCE EMERALDS AREN'T WORN WITH TAILORED THINGS, IT'LL BE IN THE SAFE AT THE LANDORPF HOME! AND WHILE BATMAN IS EXPECTING ME AT THE SHOW, WE'LL BE TAKING THE EMERALD OUT OF THE UN-GUARDED HOUSE!
GEE, PENGUIN-WHAT A BRAIN!

AND THAT NIGHT, AT THE VAN LANDORPF HOME...
I HEAR FOOT-STEPS OUTSIDE, ROBIN. WE'D BETTER HIDE!
THEY AREN'T EVEN TAKING THE TROUBLE TO SNEAK IN QUIETLY, THEY'RE SO SURE WE'RE EXPECT-ING THEM AT THE FASHION SHOW!
SEE- NOT A SOUL ABOUT. AND THEY DIDN'T EVEN BOTHER TO LOCK THE DOOR. BUT THE FUNNIEST PART OF ALL THIS IS THAT THE JOKER IS PROBABLY WALKING RIGHT INTO THE BAT-MAN'S TRAP! I ALMOST FEEL SORRY FOR HIM—
DERE'S DE SAFE!

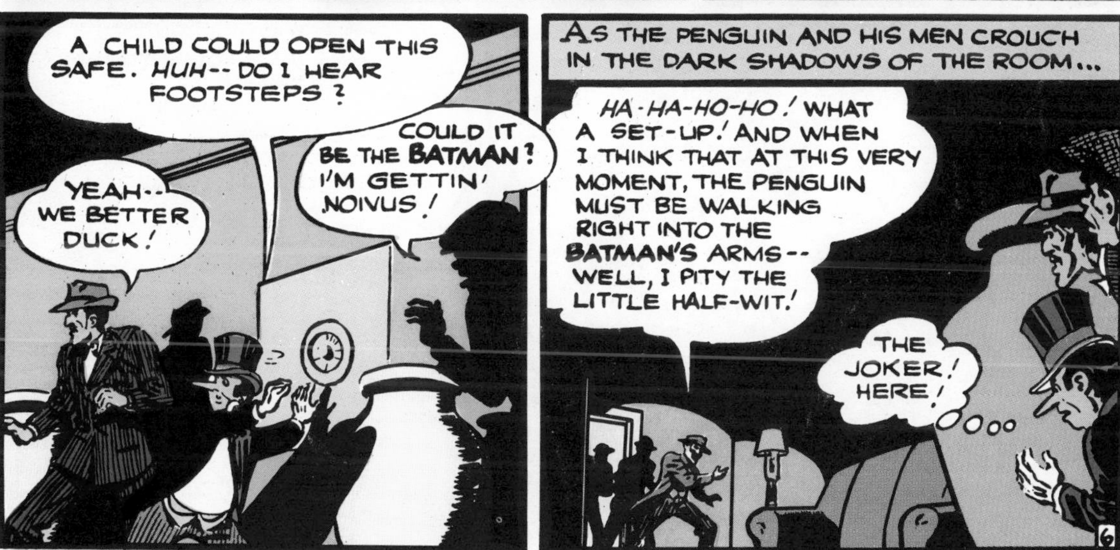
A CHILD COULD OPEN THIS SAFE. HUH-- DO I HEAR FOOTSTEPS?
YEAH-- WE BETTER DUCK!
COULD IT BE THE BATMAN? I'M GETTIN' NOIVUS!
AS THE PENGUIN AND HIS MEN CROUCH IN THE DARK SHADOWS OF THE ROOM...
HA-HA-HO-HO! WHAT A SET-UP! AND WHEN I THINK THAT AT THIS VERY MOMENT, THE PENGUIN MUST BE WALKING RIGHT INTO THE BATMAN'S ARMS-- WELL, I PITY THE LITTLE HALF-WIT!
THE JOKER! HERE!
6

THE JOKER'S SEARING REFERENCES ARE TOO MUCH FOR THE VAINGLO-RIOUS PENGUIN --
WHO'S A LITTLE HALF-WIT !?
WHAT? THE PENGUIN! BUT I THOUGHT--!
HOT INSULTS IGNITE GLOWING TEMPERS AND IN A MERE MATTER OF SECONDS --
I'LL TEACH YOU MANNERS, YOU BAB-BLING BUFFOON!
WHY, YOU WADDLING WIND-BAG -- TAKE THIS!
BUT WHEN THIEVES FALL OUT, TWO CAPED FIGURES SUDDENLY ENTER THE FRAY --
KEEP UP THE GOOD WORK, BOYS -- I'LL HELP YOU IN A SECOND!
WHA -- THE BATMAN!
ROBIN!
THIS TIME THE JOKE'S ON YOU, JOKER!
MY UMBRELLA'S ALWAYS READY TO MAKE BATMAN UNSTEADY!
THIS SMOKE BOMB SHOULD CLOUD THE ISSUE!
OH, NO, YOU DON'T, PENGUIN!
WHERE ARE YOU, BATMAN? I CAN'T SEE A THING!
RIGHT OVER HERE -- I'VE GOT ONE OF 'EM, BUT I CAN'T SEE WHO IT IS!
7

AND WHEN THE SMOKE LIFTS...
THE JOKER AND THE PENGUIN! THEY'RE GONE!
WE CAUGHT THE SMALL FRY WHILE THE BIG FISH GOT AWAY!
WHA--? NEEDLES-IT'S YOU!

IN THE MEAN-TIME --
WE DIDN'T GET THE EMERALD, BUT THEY DIDN'T GET US-- HA-HA!
WE MIGHT HAVE SUCCEEDED IN GETTING THE EMERALD IF WE HAD WORKED TOGETHER. AFTER ALL, BATMAN IS OUR REAL ENEMY!
YOU'RE RIGHT! FROM NOW ON, LET BYGONES BE BYGONES! WE'RE PARTNERS!
TOGETHER WE CAN PICK GOTHAM CITY CLEAN! HERE'S TO CRIME--MAY IT PROVIDE US WITH GOLD AND THE BATMAN WITH GLOOM!

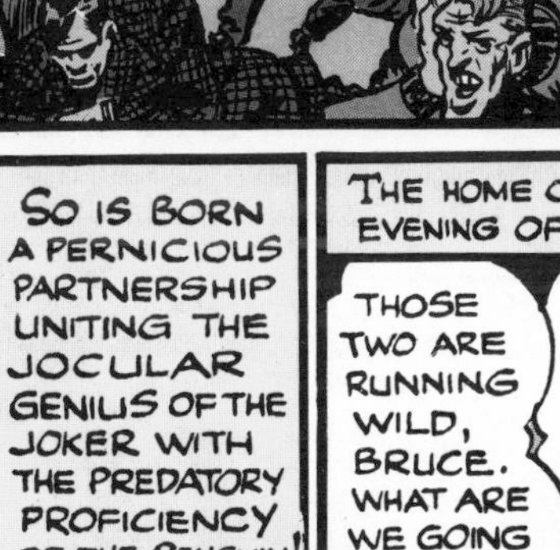
SO IS BORN A PERNICIOUS PARTNERSHIP UNITING THE JOCULAR GENIUS OF THE JOKER WITH THE PREDATORY PROFICIENCY OF THE PENGUIN! AND NOT MANY HOURS PASS BEFORE THIS UNHOLY UNION OF MASTER-MINDS STRIKES WITH SWIFT, EVIL EFFICIENCY!

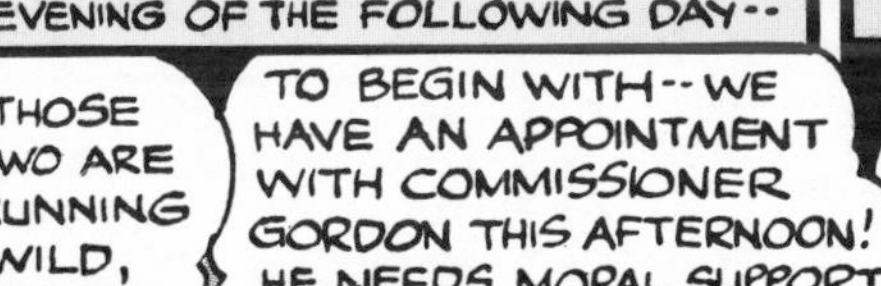
THE HOME OF BRUCE WAYNE ON THE EVENING OF THE FOLLOWING DAY--

THOSE TWO ARE RUNNING WILD, BRUCE. WHAT ARE WE GOING TO DO ABOUT IT?
TO BEGIN WITH--WE HAVE AN APPOINTMENT WITH COMMISSIONER GORDON THIS AFTERNOON! HE NEEDS MORAL SUPPORT -- ALTHOUGH I DON'T KNOW WHAT TO TELL HIM..
GOTHAM GAZETTE
DARING CRIME DUO SNATCH PAYROLL
PENGUIN PILFERS PEARLS AS JOKER JIMMIES JEWELRY FROM SAFE
GOTHAM NEWS
JOKER AND PENGUIN STEAL FORTUNE IN GEMS FROM HERRING HEIRESS!
SOME TIME LATER, AT THE POLICE COMMISSIONER'S OFFICE...
-- AND MY MEN ARE ABSOLUTELY STYMIED IN SPITE OF DOUBLE PATROLS EVERYWHERE.
THEY'RE TOO WISE TO FALL FOR ANOTHER TRAP. WE'LL HAVE TO GO OUT AND HUNT FOR THEM!

MEANWHILE, JUST ACROSS THE STREET, A VAGUELY FAMILIAR FIGURE HAWKS BALLOONS. WHY-- IT'S THE PENGUIN HIMSELF!
TOY BALLOONS! ONLY TEN CENTS!
AH-- HERE THEY COME!
WE'RE SUPPOSED TO DELIVER THIS AROUND THE COR-NER.. I DON'T KNOW WHY THEY NEED AN EXTRA GUARD.
YOU KNOW HOW IT IS-- A $50,000 PAY-ROLL--
BANK
A SUDDEN SNATCH --AND BEFORE THE STARTLED GUARDS CAN TURN, THE WILY PENGUIN UNHOOKS HIS BALLOONS--
THANK YOU, KIND SIR-AND FAREWELL!
THE JOKER HAD THIS ALL FIGURED OUT TO A T-I MUST ADMIT- BUT IT TOOK ME TO CARRY IT THROUGH!
WHA-?
8

AS THE BALLOONS STREAK SKYWARD, THE WIND CARRIES THE PENGUIN PAST COMMISSIONER GORDON'S WINDOW--
WHA--? BATMAN-- LOOK!
THE PENGUIN! I'D RECOGNIZE HIM ANYWHERE!
TWO CAPED FIGURES MAKE A DESPERATE PLUNGE ---
MAYBE OUR COMBINED WEIGHT'LL BRING HIM DOWN!
EITHER THAT--OR WE GO ALONG FOR THE RIDE!
ULP! STOWAWAYS!
YOU'VE SLOWED ME UP, BUT YOU HAVEN'T BROUGHT ME DOWN! AND WHEN WE DO LAND -- THERE'LL BE A NICE SURPRISE FOR YOU - IF THE WIND STAYS RIGHT!
I DON'T LIKE THE WAY HE SAYS THAT!
WELL, THERE'S NOTHING WE CAN DO ABOUT IT NOW! WE CAN'T LET GO!
ON A HIGHWAY SEVERAL MILES AWAY-- THE PENGUIN'S JOCUND PARTNER --
HERE HE COMES NOW! WHA--? HE HAS BATMAN AND ROBIN WITH HIM! GET THE NET READY, BOYS--AND PREPARE FOR ACTION!
WE'RE ALL SET!
THE BARK OF A SHOT-GUN FROM BELOW, AND--
AH-- MY PARTNER'S ON THE JOB!
WE'RE FALLING!
IF THE PENGUIN LANDS SAFELY-- SO WILL WE!
BANG BANG
WHOOMP! HERE I COME-- WITH THE BOODLE AND THE BATMAN!
THUMP!
HA-HA--SO THEY TRIED TO NAB YOU AND WE NABBED THEM! QUICK--LET'S GET THEM TO THE HIDEOUT!
THEY REALLY DID ME A FAVOR! THERE WAS TOO MUCH GAS IN THE BALLOONS AND WITHOUT THEIR HOLDING ON, I'D HAVE RISEN OUT OF SHOT-GUN RANGE!
9

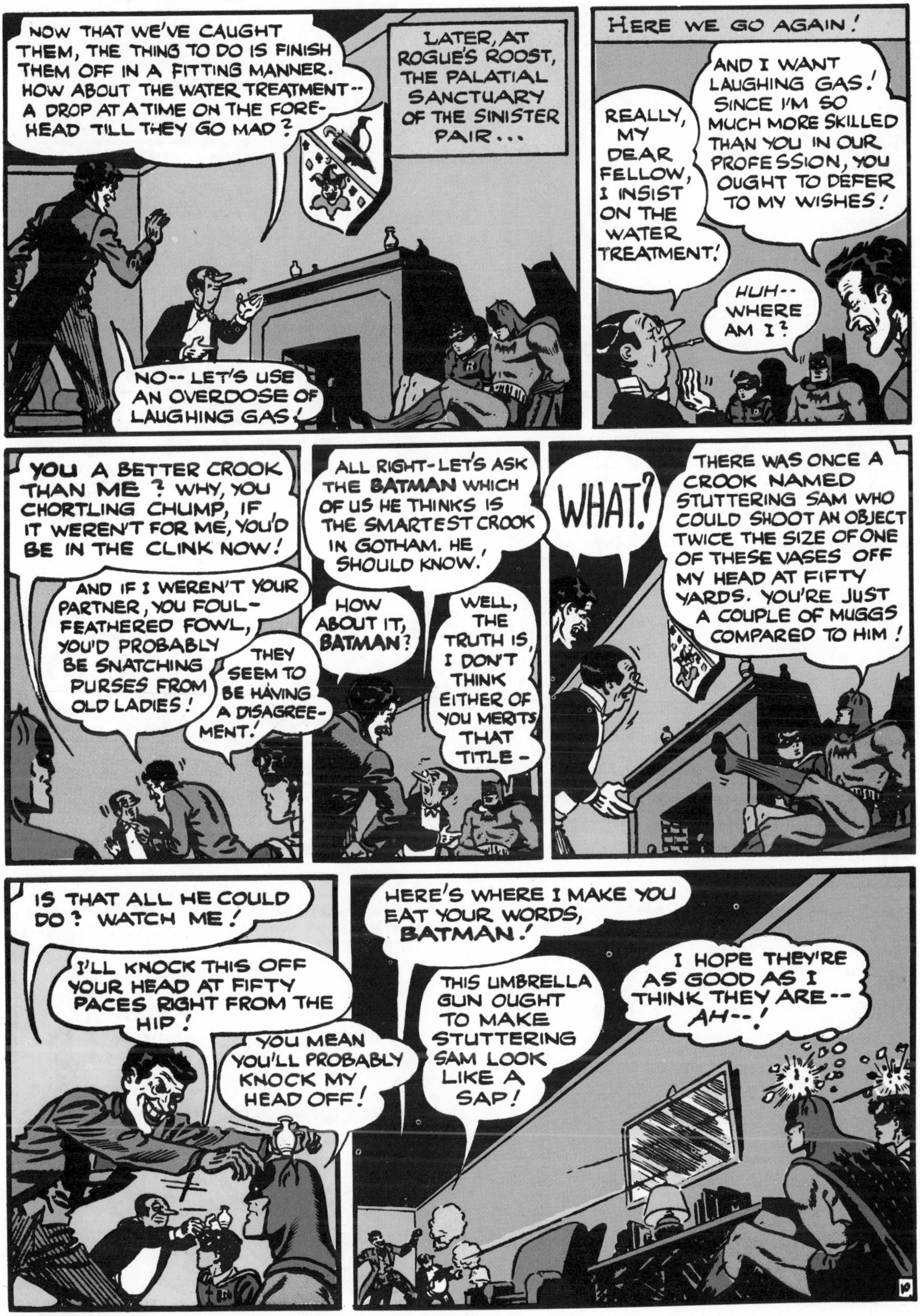

NOW THAT WE'VE CAUGHT THEM, THE THING TO DO IS FINISH THEM OFF IN A FITTING MANNER. HOW ABOUT THE WATER TREATMENT-- A DROP AT A TIME ON THE FORE-HEAD TILL THEY GO MAD?

LATER, AT ROGUE'S ROOST, THE PALATIAL SANCTUARY OF THE SINISTER PAIR...

NO-- LET'S USE AN OVERDOSE OF LAUGHING GAS!

HERE WE GO AGAIN!

AND I WANT LAUGHING GAS! SINCE I'M SO MUCH MORE SKILLED THAN YOU IN OUR PROFESSION, YOU OUGHT TO DEFER TO MY WISHES!

REALLY, MY DEAR FELLOW, I INSIST ON THE WATER TREATMENT!

HUH-- WHERE AM I?

YOU A BETTER CROOK THAN ME? WHY, YOU CHORTLING CHUMP, IF IT WEREN'T FOR ME, YOU'D BE IN THE CLINK NOW!

AND IF I WEREN'T YOUR PARTNER, YOU FOUL-FEATHERED FOWL, YOU'D PROBABLY BE SNATCHING PURSES FROM OLD LADIES!

THEY SEEM TO BE HAVING A DISAGREEMENT!

ALL RIGHT- LET'S ASK THE BATMAN WHICH OF US HE THINKS IS THE SMARTEST CROOK IN GOTHAM. HE SHOULD KNOW.

HOW ABOUT IT, BATMAN?

WELL, THE TRUTH IS, I DON'T THINK EITHER OF YOU MERITS THAT TITLE-

WHAT?

THERE WAS ONCE A CROOK NAMED STUTTERING SAM WHO COULD SHOOT AN OBJECT TWICE THE SIZE OF ONE OF THESE VASES OFF MY HEAD AT FIFTY YARDS. YOU'RE JUST A COUPLE OF MUGGS COMPARED TO HIM!

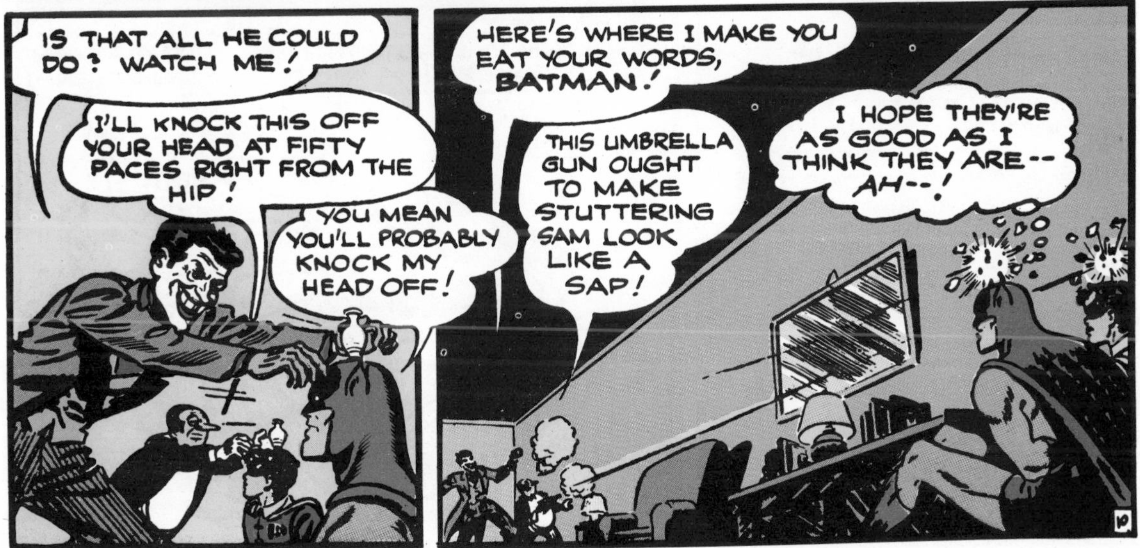

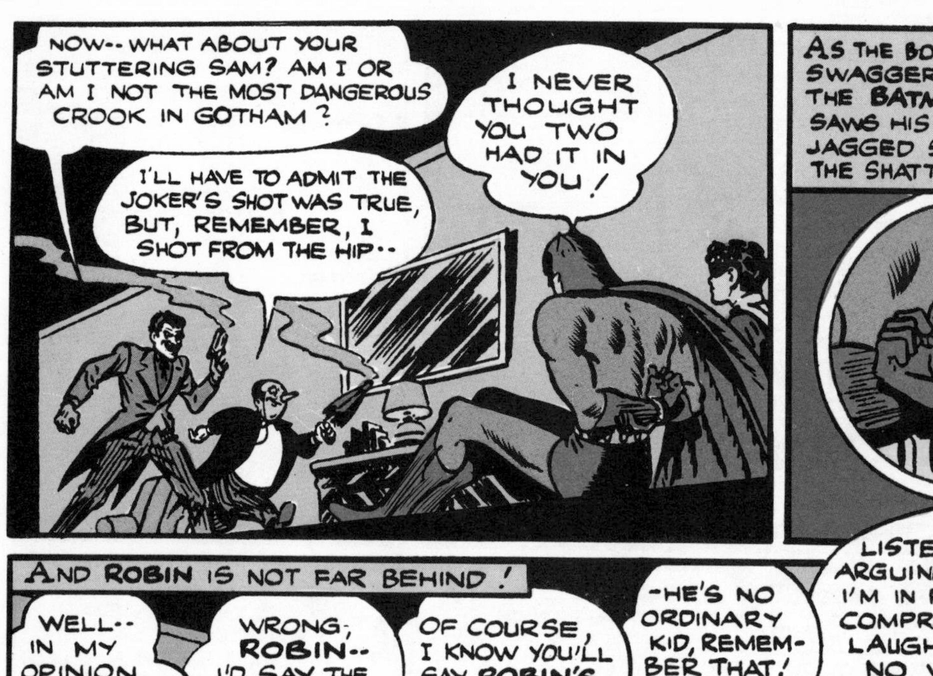
NOW-- WHAT ABOUT YOUR STUTTERING SAM? AM I OR AM I NOT THE MOST DANGEROUS CROOK IN GOTHAM?
I'LL HAVE TO ADMIT THE JOKER'S SHOT WAS TRUE, BUT, REMEMBER, I SHOT FROM THE HIP--
I NEVER THOUGHT YOU TWO HAD IT IN YOU!

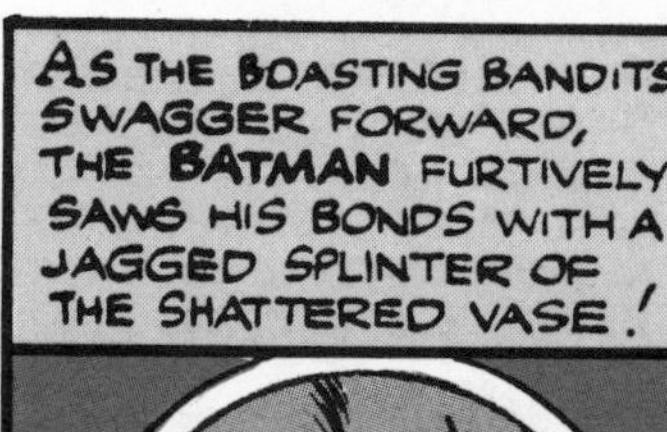
AS THE BOASTING BANDITS SWAGGER FORWARD, THE BATMAN FURTIVELY SAWS HIS BONDS WITH A JAGGED SPLINTER OF THE SHATTERED VASE!

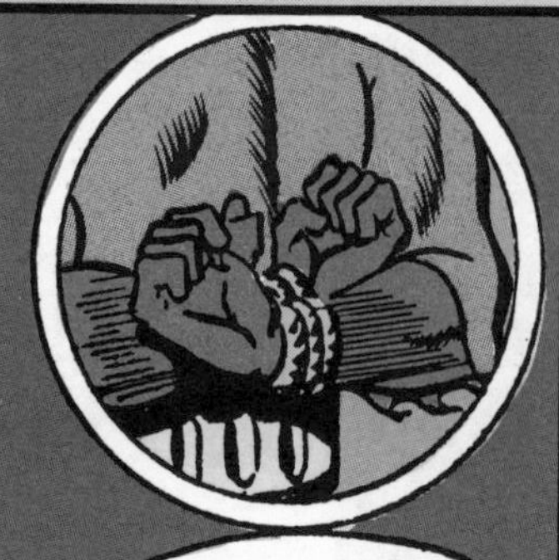

AND ROBIN IS NOT FAR BEHIND!
WELL-- IN MY OPINION, THE PENGUIN HAS IT ALL OVER THE JOKER!
WRONG, ROBIN-- I'D SAY THE JOKER WAS FAR SUPERIOR!
OF COURSE, I KNOW YOU'LL SAY ROBIN'S ONLY A KID, BUT--
-HE'S NO ORDINARY KID, REMEMBER THAT! HE'S AS GOOD AS BATMAN ANY TIME!
LISTEN--WE'LL BE ARGUING ALL DAY! I'M IN FAVOR OF A COMPROMISE. NO LAUGHING GAS-- NO WATER TREATMENT! LET'S FINISH THEM OFF RIGHT AWAY!

WELL, IF YOU PUT IT THAT WAY-ALL RIGHT! LET'S GET RID OF THEM NOW! WE'VE GOT IMPORTANT THINGS TO STEAL!
ANYWAY, I THINK BATMAN TRIED TO PROLONG THE ARGUMENT TO GAIN TIME. BUT NOW HIS TIME IS UP!

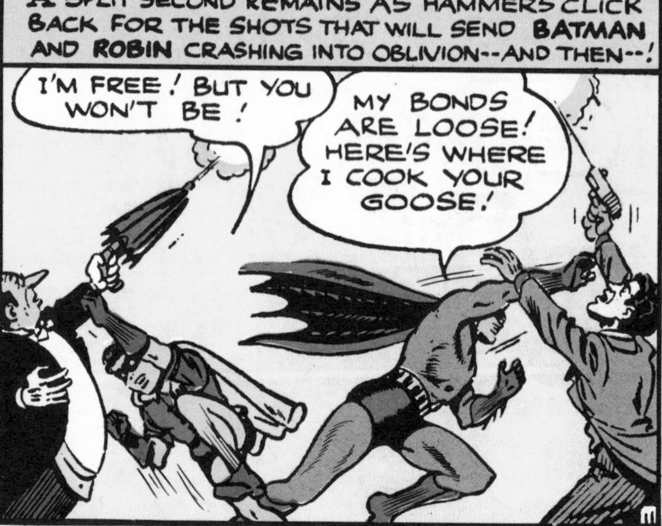
A SPLIT SECOND REMAINS AS HAMMERS CLICK BACK FOR THE SHOTS THAT WILL SEND BATMAN AND ROBIN CRASHING INTO OBLIVION--AND THEN--!
I'M FREE! BUT YOU WON'T BE!
MY BONDS ARE LOOSE! HERE'S WHERE I COOK YOUR GOOSE!

WE'VE BEEN TRICKED-- AGH!
I HATE TO UPSET YOU, BUT I PROMISED TO GET YOU!
I'M STARTING A VICTORY GARDEN... DO YOU MIND IF I PLANT MY FIST?
OOF-- MY UMBRELLAS!
CAREFUL, ROBIN! THE PENGUIN IS A DANGEROUS FOE WITH AN UMBRELLA IN HIS HAND--
SO YOU STILL WANT TO-- OOMP!
AN UMBRELLA IN THE WAY KEEPS ROBIN AT BAY!
I'LL SEE YOU SOON, I HOPE-- NOT!
HURRY-- WE'VE GOT TO STOP HIM!
AND HERE'S THE WAY WE'LL DROP HIM!
OOPS-- I CAN'T JUMP NOW!
WE'VE GOT HIM NOW. HE CAN'T JUMP DOWN TEN STORIES WITHOUT HIS UMBRELLA!
AND SO A UNIQUE PARTNERSHIP IS OFFICIALLY DISSOLVED WHILE ALL AWAIT THE ARRIVAL OF THE POLICE --
A FINE PARTNER YOU TURNED OUT TO BE! IF YOU HADN'T BEEN SO VAIN, WE'D NEVER HAVE BEEN CAUGHT!
AND I SUPPOSE YOU HAD NOTHING TO DO WITH IT! WELL, FROM NOW ON, I'M OPERATING ALONE!
RIGHT, PENGUIN--YOU'LL BOTH GET SEPARATE CELLS THIS TIME!
LATER--
-- AND FROM THE LIST FOUND IN THE HIDEOUT, THE POLICE MADE SHORT WORK OF ROUNDING UP THE REST OF THE GANG! WHICH MEANS THAT GOTHAM OUGHT TO BE QUIET FOR A WHILE!
HMM... NOT TOO QUIET, I HOPE!
THE END.
12

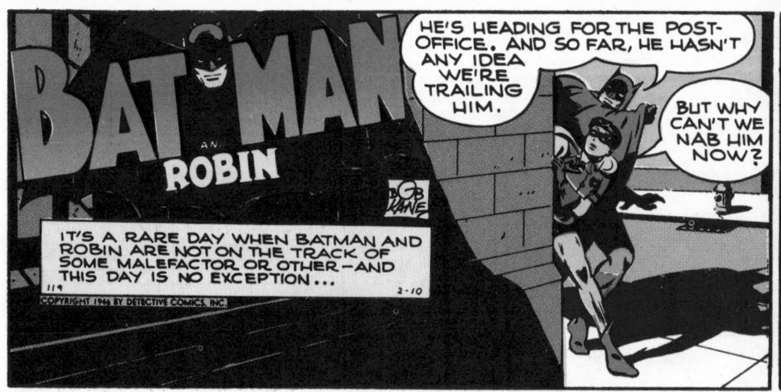

Art by Jack Burnley & Charles Paris/Coloring by Anthony Tollin

BATMAN
AND
ROBIN
by Bob Kane
BATMAN AND ROBIN HAVE JUST CAPTURED THEIR FAMED FOE, THE PENGUIN—"MAN OF A THOUSAND UMBRELLAS"—WHO HAS JUST FILCHED FROM THE LOCAL POST OFFICE A MYSTERIOUS CARD ADDRESSED TO...
COPYRIGHT 1946 BY DETECTIVE COMICS, INC.
OSWALD CHESTERFIELD COBBLEPOT! IS IT A NAME OR A PUBLICITY STUNT?
I'LL NEVER TELL YOU THAT, BATMAN. AND WHAT'S MORE-
POST OFFICE

—I'LL HAVE MY POST CARD BACK!
HUH! HE'S GOT MORE UMBRELLAS!

WAIT, PENGUIN! YOU FORGOT YOUR OTHER UMBRELLA!

NOW—LET'S SEE WHAT'S ON THIS POST CARD!
NO! NO!

Dear Oswald:
Congratulations again on your birthday. I'm happy to learn you're doing so well in the umbrella business. Your success only proves that honesty is always the best policy. And now for my surprise...

THE UMBRELLA BUSINESS, EH? WHY, PENGUIN-THEN YOU MUST BE—
YES! I AM OSWALD CHESTERFIELD COBBLEPOT! AND NO CRACKS!

OH—THIS IS AWFUL! DEAR AUNT MIRANDA! TO HAVE BROUGHT ME UP AND BELIEVED IN ME ALL THESE YEARS! THE DISGRACE WILL KILL HER!
WHAT'S WRONG?

HIS AUNT MIRANDA WHO HASN'T SEEN HIM IN TEN YEARS IS COMING TO VISIT HIM. HE'S SUPPOSED TO MEET HER ON THE AFTERNOON TRAIN!

BUT I WON'T BE THERE! I'LL BE IN JAIL! OH, BATMAN—I'M A HEEL, BUT YOU CAN'T BREAK THAT DEAR OLD LADY'S HEART! YOU'VE GOT TO DO SOMETHING!

ONE HOUR LATER AT THE RAILROAD TERMINAL...
ONE MOMENT, YOUNG MAN! IF YOU WERE NEVER TAUGHT THAT LADIES COME FIRST, I'LL TEACH YOU RIGHT NOW!

OSWALD!
AUNTIE—MEET MY VERY DEAR FRIENDS, BATMAN AND ROBIN!

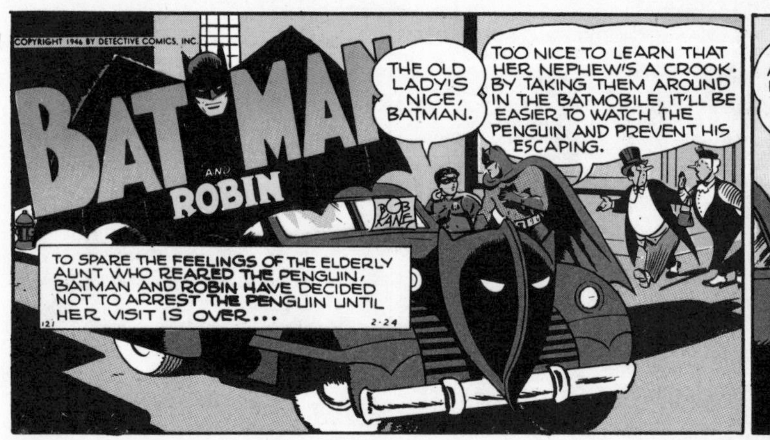
COPYRIGHT 1946 BY DETECTIVE COMICS, INC.
BATMAN AND ROBIN
THE OLD LADY'S NICE, BATMAN.
TOO NICE TO LEARN THAT HER NEPHEW'S A CROOK. BY TAKING THEM AROUND IN THE BATMOBILE, IT'LL BE EASIER TO WATCH THE PENGUIN AND PREVENT HIS ESCAPING.
BOB KANE
TO SPARE THE FEELINGS OF THE ELDERLY AUNT WHO REARED THE PENGUIN, BATMAN AND ROBIN HAVE DECIDED NOT TO ARREST THE PENGUIN UNTIL HER VISIT IS OVER...
121
2-24

SORRY-BUT AUNTIE ABSOLUTELY INSISTS ON SEEING THE TOWN FROM AN OPEN BUS.
WHAT A HEADACHE! WELL-ALL RIGHT! BUT LET ME WARN YOU! DON'T TRY TO ESCAPE, PENGUIN!

SHORTLY AFTER...
I DIDN'T KNOW YOU HAD SUCH DISTINGUISHED FRIENDS, OSWALD.
THE BATMAN? OH, YES. THIS IS A FINE UMBRELLA, AUNTIE. MAY I SEE IT?
KEEP YOUR EYE ON HIM, ROBIN.

BATMAN AND ROBIN! AND LOOK AT THE PENGUIN!
OSWALD! DID YOU HEAR THAT FRESH COUPLE? THEY CALLED ME A PENGUIN!
ER-AH-THEY'RE JUST IGNORANT, AUNTIE. PAY NO ATTENTION.
CO.

DID YOU HEAR THAT?
THAT'S REALLY FUNNY. SHE DOESN'T REALIZE HER NEPHEW IS KNOWN AS THE PENGUIN, THE MOST NOTORIOUS CROOK IN TOWN.

EXCUSE ME, AUNTIE, BUT I'LL SEE YOU LATER.
HE'S DONE IT!
457
OSWALD! COME RIGHT BACK HERE AND STOP SHOWING OFF!
5 FIFTH AVE

I'LL HAVE TO USE THE ROPE TRICK!
OOPS! I SHOULD HAVE LOOKED BEFORE I LEAPED!
5 FIFTH AVE

GOT HIM! AND SAVED HIS WORTHLESS LIFE AT THE SAME TIME.

PRESENTLY...
OSWALD! WON'T YOU EVER GROW UP? I'VE A GOOD MIND TO TAKE YOU ACROSS MY KNEE!
YOU LITTLE RAT! IF IT WEREN'T FOR YOUR AUNT-!

MEANWHILE, ELSEWHERE IN TOWN...
BOSS! BOSS! WE GOTTA DO SOMETHIN'! THE PENGUIN'S TURNED STOOL PIGEON! I JUST SEEN HIM PALLING AROUND WIT' THE BATMAN!!

BATMAN AND ROBIN
122
AFTER ALL YOUR LETTERS, OSWALD, ABOUT YOUR THRIVING UMBRELLA BUSINESS, I SIMPLY MUST SEE YOUR UMBRELLA SHOP!
GRACIOUS! HOW CAN I TAKE HER THERE WITHOUT BATMAN DISCOVERING MY HIDEOUT?
BUS STOP
BOB KANE
FOR THE SAKE OF THE PENGUIN'S VISITING AUNT WHO DOESN'T KNOW HE'S A CROOK, BATMAN HAS DEFERRED ARRESTING THE PENGUIN UNTIL AFTER HER VISIT. UNTIL THEN, HE MUST KEEP THE PENGUIN FROM ESCAPING... 3/3
COPYRIGHT 1946 BY DETECTIVE COMICS, INC.

AUNTIE-I-I MUST CONFESS. THE WHOLE PLACE JUST BURNED DOWN.
WHY, OSWALD, OLD PAL. YOU KNOW THAT'S NOT TRUE. YOU DON'T HAVE TO HIDE YOUR BUSINESS SECRETS FROM YOUR DEAR AUNT MIRANDA!

NOT FROM YOU, AUNTIE. BUT, WELL-FRIENDSHIP AND BUSINESS DON'T MIX. I DON'T THINK BATMAN SHOULD SEE IT.
I DECLARE! BATMAN JUST SAVED YOUR LIFE! WHAT INGRATITUDE! LEAD ON NOW, OSWALD, OR I'LL GIVE YOU SOMETHING TO REMEMBER!

SHORTLY AFTER...
IS THIS IT? BUT THAT SIGN DOESN'T MAKE SENSE. I THOUGHT YOU WERE IN THE UMBRELLA BUSINESS.
ER-MY UMBRELLAS ARE SO GOOD I HAVE TO CAMOUFLAGE THE PLACE TO KEEP THE MOBS AWAY!
ICE-COAL
CLOSED FOR WINTER

A FINELY EQUIPPED SHOP LIKE THIS AND I'LL BET YOU HAVEN'T HAD A CUSTOMER IN MONTHS! OSWALD, I ALWAYS SAID YOU HAD NO HEAD FOR BUSINESS!
BUT, AUNTIE-!

WELL-I'M DETERMINED TO HELP YOU! WE'LL START WITH A BIG ADVERTISED SALE AND GET RID OF ALL THIS OLD STOCK!
NO! DON'T TOUCH THAT UMBRELLA!

GOODNESS GRACIOUS! IT'S FULL OF BULLETS!
DON'T YOU KNOW IT'S BAD LUCK TO OPEN AN UMBRELLA INDOORS? CLOSE IT-QUICK!

OSWALD! WHAT KIND OF BUSINESS ARE YOU RUNNING HERE?
WHY-ER-AUNTIE-THAT UMBRELLA HAPPENS TO BE A NEW SECRET WEAPON I'M DEVELOPING FOR THE ARMY!

MEANWHILE, ELSEWHERE IN GOTHAM...
I TELL YOU, STONEHEAD, I'M POSITIVE! I SEEN THE PENGUIN GOING AROUND WITH BATMAN IN BROAD DAYLIGHT. HE MUSTA TURNED STOOL PIGEON!

IT'S HARD TO BELIEVE ME OLD PAL WOULD TURN STOOLIE. BUT-THIS AIN'T NO TIME FOR SENTIMENT!
To my dear cell-mate, Stonehead. The Penguin

ROUND UP THE BOYS! WE GOT BUSINESS AT THE PENGUIN'S UMBRELLA SHOP!

BATMAN AND ROBIN
123
BECAUSE BATMAN HAS DEFERRED ARRESTING THE PENGUIN UNTIL HIS AUNT MIRANDA'S VISIT ENDS, CERTAIN CROOKS SEEING THEM TOGETHER HAVE ASSUMED THAT THE PENGUIN HAS TURNED STOOL PIGEON!
3-10
COPYRIGHT 1946 BY DETECTIVE COMICS, INC.
DA PENGUIN A STOOL PIGEON! (SIGH) WHAT A SHAME!
YEAH! I WISH I WAS WRONG, STONEHEAD!

LOOK! HE'S ALREADY GAWN OUTA BUSINESS!
WHAT DID YOU CALL ME, YOUNG MAN?
COME OUTA THEM SKIRTS, PENGUIN! WE KNOW YA!
BIG SALE UMBRELL

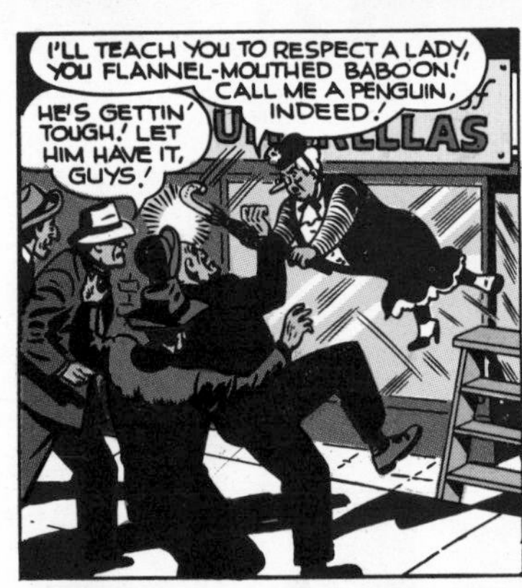
I'LL TEACH YOU TO RESPECT A LADY, YOU FLANNEL-MOUTHED BABOON! CALL ME A PENGUIN, INDEED!
HE'S GETTIN' TOUGH! LET HIM HAVE IT, GUYS!
UMBRELLAS

MY OWN BUDDIES PICKING ON MY AUNT MIRANDA! THIS IS TOO MUCH!
I'M SEEIN' DOUBLE! IT MUST BE A DOUBLE-CROSS!
THE BATMAN! I-I THINK I GOT AN IMPORTANT APPOINTMENT IN CHINA!
SALE
BRELLAS

NET PROFIT FOR THE DAY-ONE BULLY OF OLD LADIES!
OSWALD-DON'T YOU DARE CALL ME AN OLD LADY!
NOT BAD, THESE PENGUIN UMBRELLAS-WHEN THEY'RE ON OUR SIDE!

AFTER THE SMOKE OF BATTLE HAS CLEARED...
WELL-LOTS OF EXCITEMENT IN THE BIG CITY, BUT DEAR ME-I'VE BARELY TIME TO CATCH MY TRAIN FOR HOME! OSWALD-COME HERE!
ER-YES-AUNTIE!

GOOD-BYE, OSWALD. BEHAVE YOURSELF. REMEMBER TO EAT LOTS OF FRESH VEGETABLES. AND-OH, YES-HELP YOUR FRIEND BATMAN TAKE THESE HOODLUMS WHERE THEY BELONG.
DON'T WORRY, MISS COBBLEPOT. HE'S COMING ALONG.

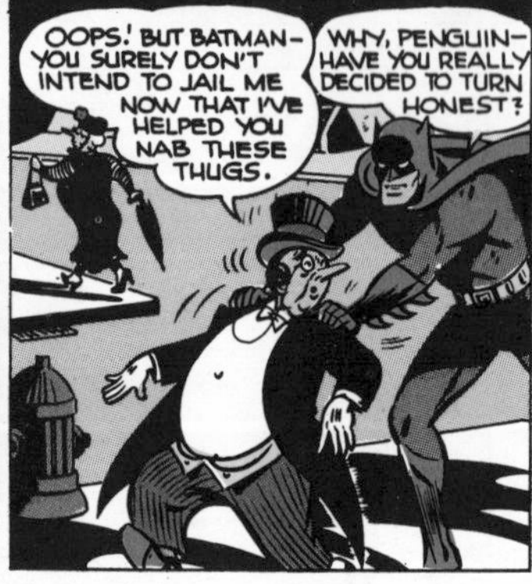
OOPS! BUT BATMAN-YOU SURELY DON'T INTEND TO JAIL ME NOW THAT I'VE HELPED YOU NAB THESE THUGS.
WHY, PENGUIN-HAVE YOU REALLY DECIDED TO TURN HONEST?

HONEST? ME? NOT A CHANCE! THERE ARE STILL 237 WAYS OF ESCAPING FROM JAIL I HAVEN'T TRIED OUT YET!
DON'T WORRY, OSWALD-ER-PARDON-PENGUIN! YOU'LL GET YOUR CHANCE TO TEST THEM!
THE END.

Art by Bob Kane & Lou Schwartz/Coloring by Adrienne Roy

BONG! BONG!
MIDNIGHT OUTSIDE GOTHAM CITY, AND AS A TRANSPORT TRUCK ROARS OVER THE HIGHWAY, A SUDDEN BLOWOUT SPELLS DOOM!
CRASH!!!

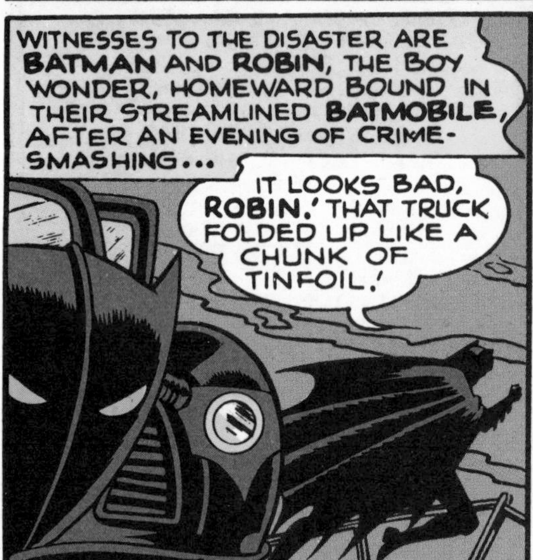
WITNESSES TO THE DISASTER ARE BATMAN AND ROBIN, THE BOY WONDER, HOMEWARD BOUND IN THEIR STREAMLINED BATMOBILE, AFTER AN EVENING OF CRIME-SMASHING...
IT LOOKS BAD, ROBIN! THAT TRUCK FOLDED UP LIKE A CHUNK OF TINFOIL!

THE DRIVER'S DEAD. HE WAS KILLED INSTANTLY!

BATMAN ... LOOK! A SECRET DOOR IN THE TRUCK'S SIDE... THERE'S A MAN COMING OUT!
OOHH... MY HEAD...

AS ROBIN ADVANCES TOWARD THE STUMBLING MAN TO HELP HIM...
YOU OKAY, MISTER...? UHHH!
ROBIN! YOU AIN'T TAKIN' ME IN!

YOU MUST HAVE A GOOD REASON FOR FLASHING THAT GUN! BETTER TELL IT—FAST!

BUT, ROBIN, DAZED, UNWITTINGLY TRIPS BATMAN, AND DEATH HOVERS OMINOUSLY OVER THE CAPED MANHUNTER...
I'M MEASURIN' YOU FOR A COFFIN, BATMAN-RIGHT NOW!

ABRUPTLY, A BULLET FROM NOWHERE CLIPS THE MURDEROUS THUG...
BLAM!
UH...

WE HEARD THE CRASH! I DIDN'T WANT TO KILL THAT TRIGGERMAN, BUT IT WAS HIM OR YOU!
THE RADIO PATROL!
P.D.

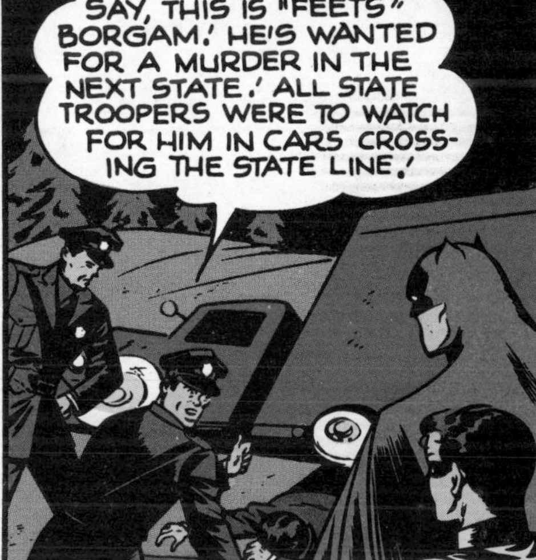
SAY, THIS IS "FEETS" BORGAM! HE'S WANTED FOR A MURDER IN THE NEXT STATE! ALL STATE TROOPERS WERE TO WATCH FOR HIM IN CARS CROSSING THE STATE LINE!

HMM.. CONTAINER OF MILK... SANDWICHES... CIGARETTES... ALL THE COMFORTS OF HOME IN THAT SECRET COMPARTMENT!
THAT PROVES THE DRIVER KNEW HE WAS CARRYING "FEETS"!
A NEW RACKET, EH? SMUGGLING HOT CROOKS ACROSS THE LINE INTO OTHER STATES!
IT'S OBVIOUS THE DRIVER WASN'T ALONE IN THIS SET-UP! I WONDER IF THE OWNER OF THE LAND-SEA-AIR TRANSPORT CO. IS TOP MAN?

AT POLICE HEADQUARTERS, COMMISSIONER GORDON SECURES QUICK INFORMATION..
THE REPORT SAYS THE NEW L.S.A. OWNER BOUGHT OUT THE OLD OWNER, FIRED THE OLD TRUCKERS AND HIRED A NEW STAFF! THE OWNER'S NAME IS JOE CHILL! HERE'S A RADIO-PHOTO OF HIM...
THAT FACE... AFTER ALL THESE YEARS... IT'S HE! THE FACE OF THE MAN WHO KILLED MY PARENTS!
AND BATMAN'S THOUGHTS WHIRL HIM BACK TO A VIVID NIGHT MANY YEARS BEFORE... TO A NIGHT WHEN HE WAS WALKING WITH HIS PARENTS, THOMAS AND MARTHA WAYNE...
THIS IS A STICKUP! I'LL TAKE THAT NECKLACE YOU'RE WEARIN', LADY!
OH... NOT MY NECKLACE...
YOU HOODLUM! DON'T YOU DARE PUT A HAND ON MY WIFE! UHHH...!
MAYBE YOU'LL KEEP QUIET... NOW!
THOMAS!
BLAM
THAT SINGLE BULLET REALLY KILLED TWO PEOPLE, FOR MARTHA WAYNE'S WEAK HEART STOPPED FROM THE SUDDEN SHOCK!
THEY'RE DEAD! YOU KILLED THEM... YOU KILLED MY MOTHER AND FATHER...
STOP LOOKIN' AT ME LIKE THAT!
SOMETHING ABOUT YOUNG BRUCE'S EYES MADE THE KILLER RETREAT... THEY WERE ACCUSING EYES THAT MEMORIZED HIS EVERY FEATURE... EYES THAT WOULD NEVER FORGET...

THE KILLER WAS NEVER FOUND, AND SOON AFTER, A YOUNG LAD MADE A GRIM PROMISE...
I SWEAR I'LL DEDICATE MY LIFE AND INHERITANCE TO BRINGING YOUR KILLER TO JUSTICE... AND TO FIGHTING ALL CRIMINALS! I SWEAR IT!
WAYNE
THOMAS MARTHA
THE YEARS PASSED AS BRUCE WAYNE PREPARED FOR HIS CHOSEN CAREER!
HE MASTERED SCIENTIFIC CRIMINAL INVESTIGATION!
HE TRAINED HIS BODY TO SUCH PHYSICAL AND ATHLETIC PERFECTION THAT HE COULD PERFORM ANY DAREDEVIL FEAT...
THEN, ONE DAY HE WAS READY FOR HIS NEW ROLE.
CRIMINALS ARE A SUPERSTITIOUS, COWARDLY LOT, SO I MUST WEAR A DISGUISE THAT WILL STRIKE TERROR INTO THEIR HEARTS! I MUST BE A CREATURE OF THE NIGHT, LIKE A... A...
AND, AS IF IN ANSWER, A WINGED CREATURE FLEW IN THROUGH THE OPEN WINDOW!
A BAT! THAT'S IT! IT'S LIKE AN OMEN! I SHALL BECOME A BAT!
THUS WAS BORN THIS WEIRD FIGURE OF THE SHADOWS...THIS AVENGER OF EVIL-THE BATMAN!
SOME DAY, I'LL FIND THE KILLER OF MY PARENTS ... SOME DAY...

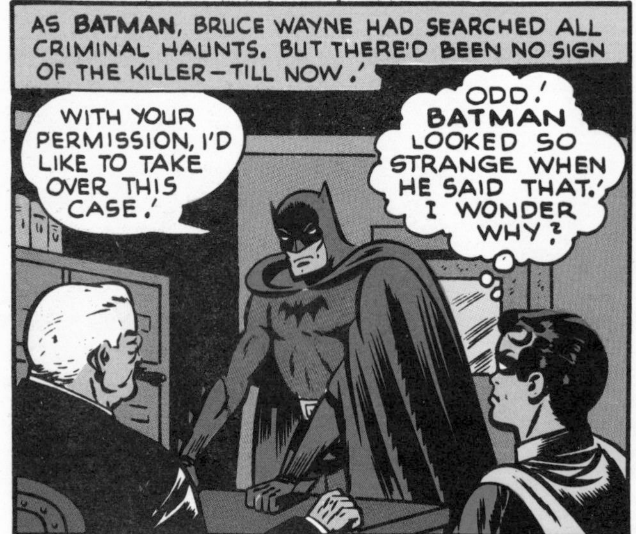
AS BATMAN, BRUCE WAYNE HAD SEARCHED ALL CRIMINAL HAUNTS. BUT THERE'D BEEN NO SIGN OF THE KILLER—TILL NOW.'
WITH YOUR PERMISSION, I'D LIKE TO TAKE OVER THIS CASE.'
ODD! BATMAN LOOKED SO STRANGE WHEN HE SAID THAT.' I WONDER WHY?

AT HOME, AFTER BATMAN EXPLAINS TO HIS YOUNG PARTNER...
THE KILLER OF YOUR PARENTS, EH? WELL... LET'S GO GET HIM.'
SORRY, ROBIN, THIS IS ONE JOB I'M DOING ALONE! I DON'T HAVE TO EXPLAIN—YOU CAN UNDERSTAND WHY.'

THE NEXT DAY, A DISGUISED BATMAN CALLS AT THE L.S.A. TERMINAL...
LSA
LAND, SEA, AIR TRANSPORT COMPANY
YOU WANT A JOB AS A TRUCKER? THAT'S UP TO THE BOSS, BUD!

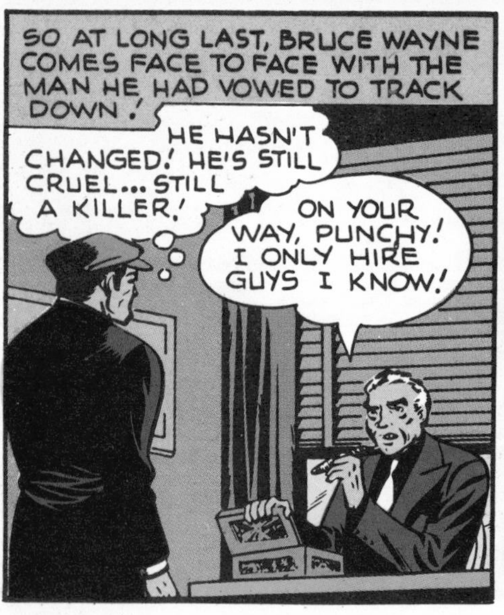
SO AT LONG LAST, BRUCE WAYNE COMES FACE TO FACE WITH THE MAN HE HAD VOWED TO TRACK DOWN!
HE HASN'T CHANGED! HE'S STILL CRUEL... STILL A KILLER!
ON YOUR WAY, PUNCHY! I ONLY HIRE GUYS I KNOW!

LATER...
HE'S CAGEY! ONLY WANTS DRIVERS HE'S SURE HE CAN TRUST! THAT KILLS MY CHANCES OF GETTING INSIDE HIS GANG! WHAT NOW?

I'VE GOT IT! I'M GOING TO BRING BUSINESS TO JOE CHILL!
SNAP!

THAT NIGHT, BATMAN RIDES WITH THE POLICE HARBOR PATROL...
SO THAT SHOWBOAT IS REALLY A GAMBLING SHIP, EH?
YES! RUN BY MONTY JULEP! HE HAS ALL HIS CREW COSTUMED LIKE OLDTIME MISSISSIPPI GAMBLERS! HIS SHOWBOAT PADDLES AROUND OUTSIDE THE LEGAL LIMIT SO WE CAN'T ARREST HIM!
POLICE 4

ONE HOUR LATER... ON THE GAMBLING SHIP, TWO SENTRIES IDLE AWAY THE TIME...

PETE, I THINK I'LL TRY SOME TARGET PRACTICE ON THAT SEA GULL!

YOU SAP! THE SHOTS WOULD PANIC THE CHUMPS AT JULEP'S TABLES! PUT YOUR GUN AWAY!

A GOOD THING, TOO... FOR THE "SEA GULL" IS IN REALITY A UNIQUE CAMOUFLAGE UNDER-WATER HELMET WORN BY BATMAN!

THEN, THE CHURNING STERNWHEEL CARRIES THE ACROBATMAN UNSEEN TO A TOP DECK!
TRICKY, BUT IT'S A SHORT-CUT TO THE WHEEL-ROOM!

JUST A LITTLE MUTINY, CAPTAIN!

SOON AFTER... A CYCLONIC FIGURE CHARGES INTO THE GAMBLING ROOM!
THROW IN YOUR CARDS, FOLKS! MONTY JULEP'S NOT DEALING ANOTHER HAND TONIGHT!
DON'T BE TOO SHORE, BATMAN! BOYS, COME A-RUNNIN'!

WHERE ARE YORE EYES? HIT HIM!
TELL HIM TO STAND STILL AND WE'LL DO IT!

CASHING IN YOUR CHIPS, JULEP?
THEN I'LL GET HIM MYSELF... YII-II!

WITH ONE MIGHTY HEAVE, BATMAN WRENCHES UP THE ROULETTE WHEEL... AND IT BECOMES A DISCUS!
WATCH THE SPINNING WHEEL, FOLKS.

SUDDENLY—THE GLOW OF A SEARCHLIGHT BRINGS EVERYONE TO THE DECK!
YOU CAIN'T ARREST ME! MY SHIP'S OUTSIDE THE LEGAL LIMITS!
SURRENDER IN THE NAME OF THE LAW!
POLICE 4

NOT ANYMORE! I LASHED YOUR WHEEL AND STAGED THIS FIGHT SO YOU'D BE TOO BUSY TO NOTICE YOUR BOAT WAS TURNING INSIDE THE LIMIT!

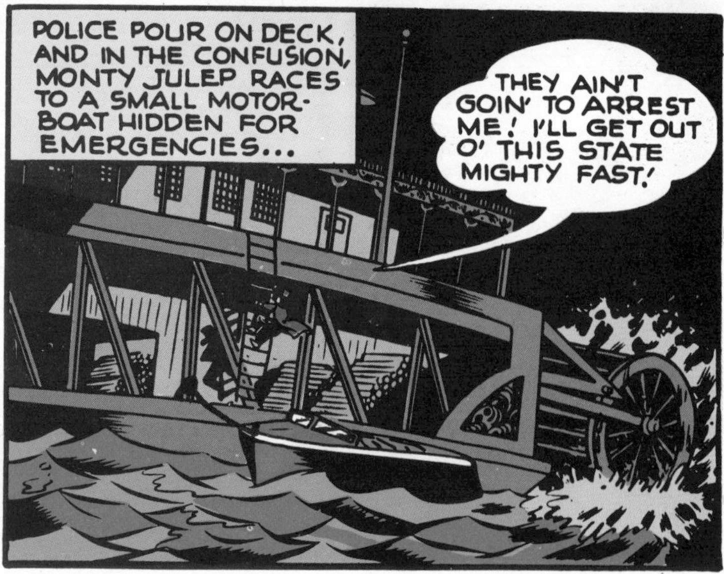
POLICE POUR ON DECK, AND IN THE CONFUSION, MONTY JULEP RACES TO A SMALL MOTOR-BOAT HIDDEN FOR EMERGENCIES...
THEY AIN'T GOIN' TO ARREST ME! I'LL GET OUT O' THIS STATE MIGHTY FAST!

THERE GOES JULEP.!
REMEMBER, BATMAN WANTS HIM TO ESCAPE! THOSE ARE ORDERS!
SOON AFTER...
CHILL, THE COPPERS ARE AFTER ME! BATMAN'S AFTER ME! YOU'VE GOT TO SMUGGLE ME OUT OF THE STATE!
WE-ELL... I'VE GOT A TRUCK TAKIN' A LOAD OF WOOLENS TO NEVADA! THE ONE-WAY TRIP WILL COST YOU $5,000!

ABRUPTLY, CHILL GETS UP AND SNAPS A SWITCH ON AN INSTRUMENT PANEL...
YOU'RE A-GOIN' TO LOOK AT TELEVISION... NOW?
NO! I'M JUST MAKIN' SURE YOU WEREN'T FOLLOWED! THIS IS REALLY A PERISCOPE THAT LOOKS OVER THE BACKYARD!

SUDDENLY, THE TELLTALE SCREEN REVEALS—
BATMAN! HE MUST'VE BEEN HIDDEN IN THE CABIN OF MY BOAT.
THIS IS A TRAP!

JULEP, YOU DIRTY DOUBLECROSSER, I'M SENDING YOU ON A ONE-WAY TRIP... AND I AIN'T CHARGIN' YOU A CENT!

HEARING THE SHOT, BATMAN BURSTS IN!
OH... BATMAN! THIS... THIS CRIMINAL WANTED ME TO SMUGGLE HIM OUT OF THE STATE IN ONE OF MY TRUCKS! I REFUSED... HE TRIED TO SHOOT ME... IT WAS SELF-DEFENSE...

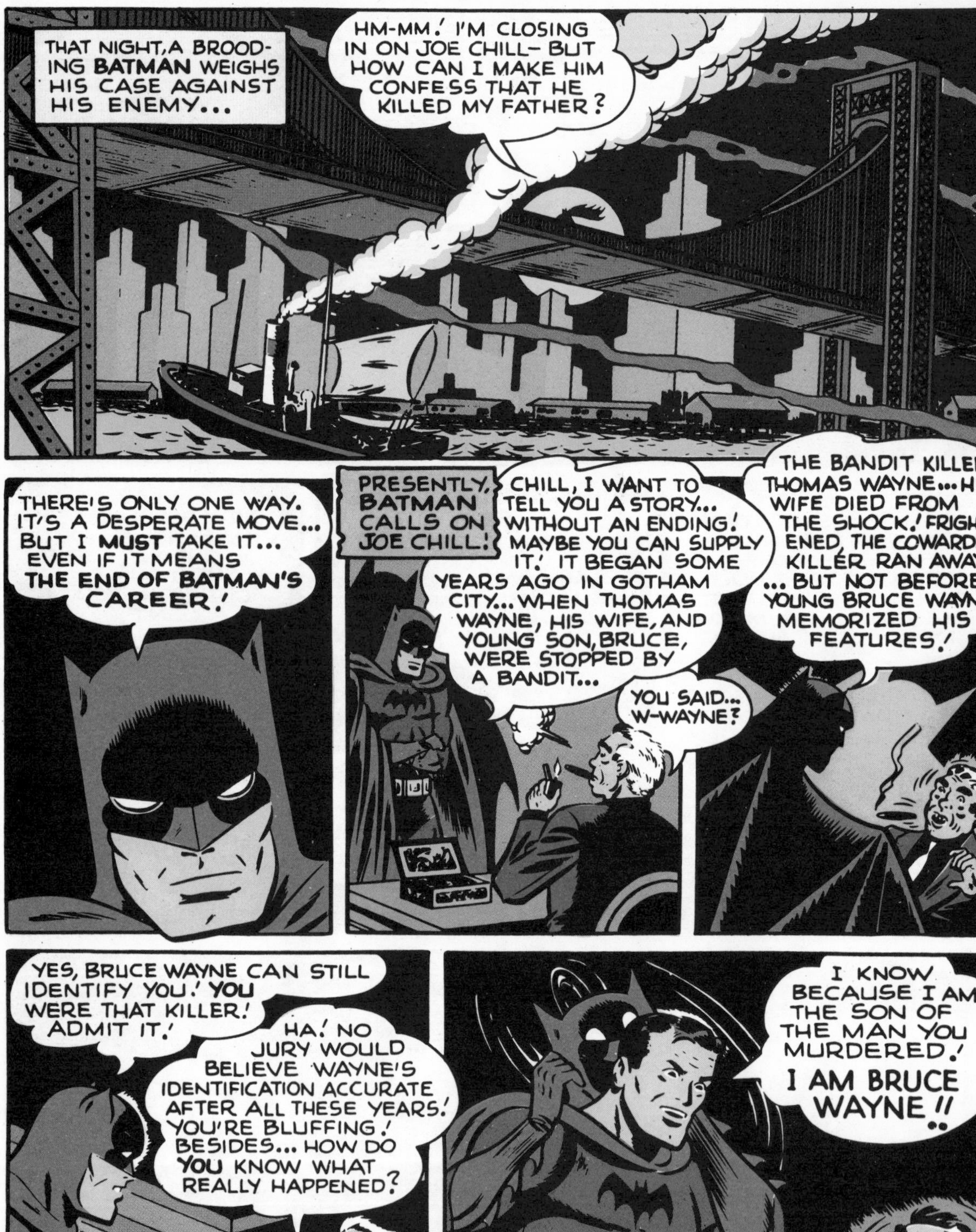

THAT NIGHT, A BROODING BATMAN WEIGHS HIS CASE AGAINST HIS ENEMY...

HM-MM! I'M CLOSING IN ON JOE CHILL- BUT HOW CAN I MAKE HIM CONFESS THAT HE KILLED MY FATHER?

THERE'S ONLY ONE WAY. IT'S A DESPERATE MOVE... BUT I MUST TAKE IT... EVEN IF IT MEANS THE END OF BATMAN'S CAREER!

PRESENTLY, BATMAN CALLS ON JOE CHILL!

CHILL, I WANT TO TELL YOU A STORY... WITHOUT AN ENDING! MAYBE YOU CAN SUPPLY IT! IT BEGAN SOME YEARS AGO IN GOTHAM CITY... WHEN THOMAS WAYNE, HIS WIFE, AND YOUNG SON, BRUCE, WERE STOPPED BY A BANDIT...

YOU SAID... W-WAYNE?

THE BANDIT KILLED THOMAS WAYNE... HIS WIFE DIED FROM THE SHOCK! FRIGHTENED, THE COWARDLY KILLER RAN AWAY ... BUT NOT BEFORE YOUNG BRUCE WAYNE MEMORIZED HIS FEATURES!

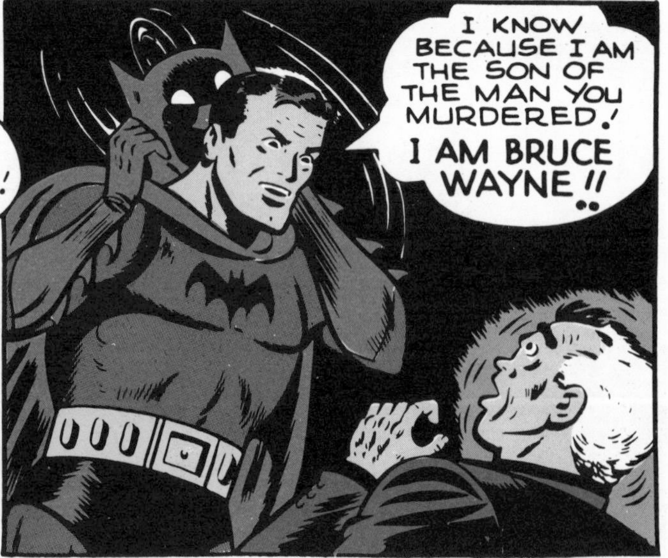

I BECAME BATMAN BECAUSE OF WHAT YOU DID AND I SWORE I'D ARREST YOU FOR IT SOME DAY! I CAN'T PROVE YOUR GUILT, BUT I'LL NEVER STOP HOUNDING YOU UNTIL I DO...

"WHATEVER YOU DO, I'LL BE WATCHING..."
Club Pelican

"WHEREVER YOU GO, I'LL BE WATCHING..."

I'LL ALWAYS BE WATCHING... AND SOMEDAY YOU'LL MAKE A MISTAKE... AND I'LL BE THERE... WAITING! REMEMBER THAT—AND THIS!

AND WHEN BATMAN LEAVES...
WHAT'LL I DO? BATMAN MEANS EVERYTHING HE SAID! HE PROVED IT BY REVEALING HIS IDENTITY! HE'LL GET ME... UNLESS I KILL HIM FIRST!

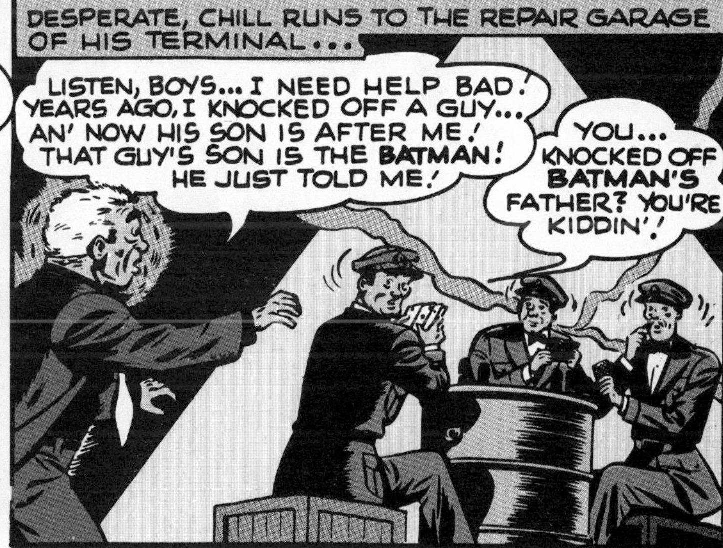
DESPERATE, CHILL RUNS TO THE REPAIR GARAGE OF HIS TERMINAL...
LISTEN, BOYS... I NEED HELP BAD! YEARS AGO, I KNOCKED OFF A GUY... AN' NOW HIS SON IS AFTER ME! THAT GUY'S SON IS THE BATMAN! HE JUST TOLD ME!
YOU... KNOCKED OFF BATMAN'S FATHER? YOU'RE KIDDIN'!

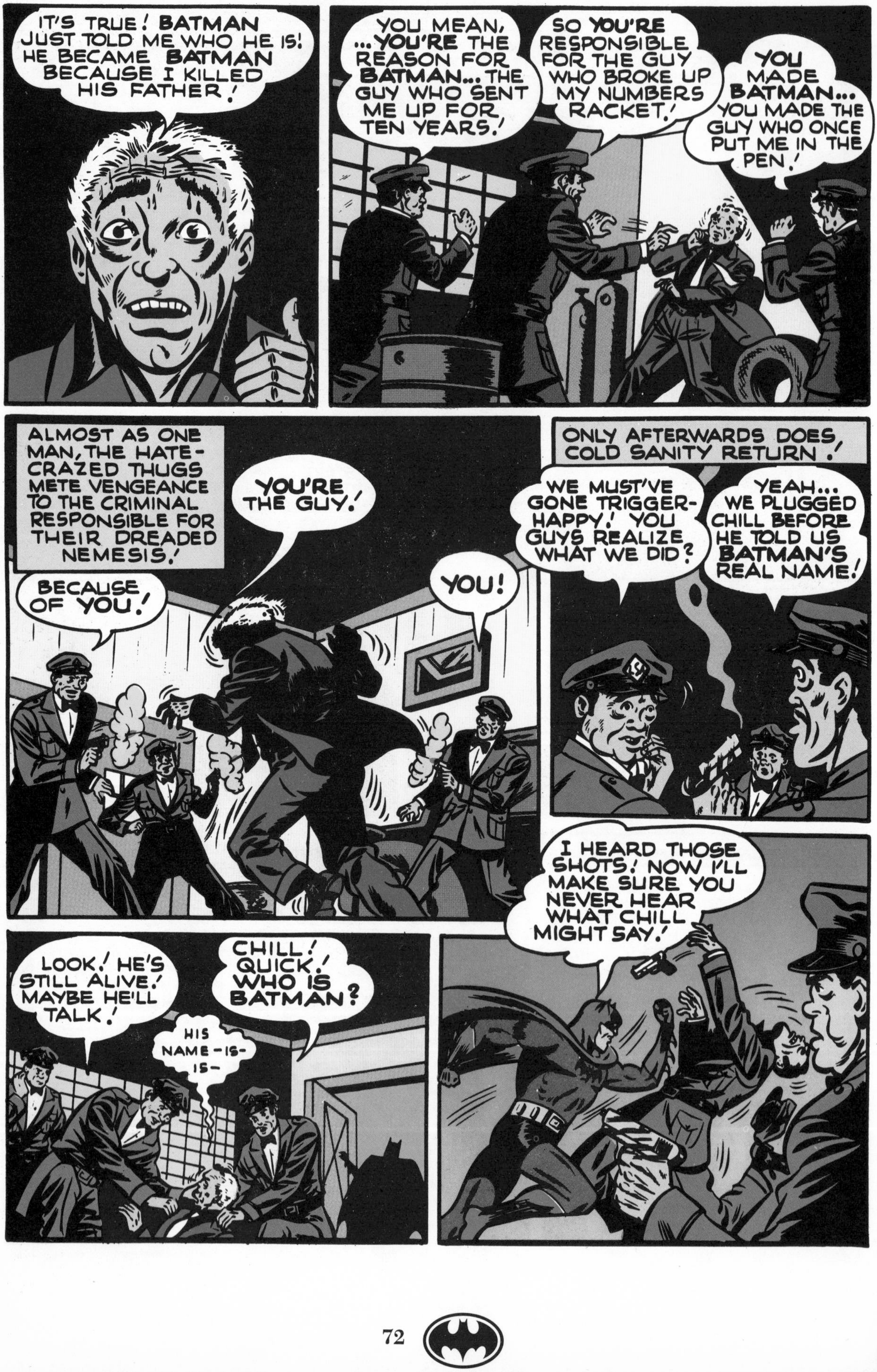

ALMOST AS ONE MAN, THE HATE-CRAZED THUGS METE VENGEANCE TO THE CRIMINAL RESPONSIBLE FOR THEIR DREADED NEMESIS!

YOU'RE THE GUY!

BECAUSE OF YOU!

YOU!

ONLY AFTERWARDS DOES COLD SANITY RETURN!

WE MUST'VE GONE TRIGGER-HAPPY! YOU GUYS REALIZE WHAT WE DID?

YEAH... WE PLUGGED CHILL BEFORE HE TOLD US BATMAN'S REAL NAME!

LOOK! HE'S STILL ALIVE! MAYBE HE'LL TALK!

CHILL! QUICK! WHO IS BATMAN?

HIS NAME-IS-IS-

I HEARD THOSE SHOTS! NOW I'LL MAKE SURE YOU NEVER HEAR WHAT CHILL MIGHT SAY!

WE GOTTA GET HIM BEFORE HE GETS US FOR THIS KILLING.'
THIS IS WHAT I WANT—THE LEVER THAT SENDS THE CAR HOIST TURNING.'
LSA
LAND, SEA, AIR, TRANSPORT COMPANY

THE HOIST SPINS... AND AT THAT INSTANT **BATMAN** SNATCHES UP A GREASE-GUN!
A GREASE SHAMPOO—NO EXTRA CHARGE.'
AGGGH!
OOF!

THE ONLY WAY I CAN KEEP YOU AWAY FROM CHILL... IS TO KNOCK YOU OUT.'

STILL WITH US, CHILL?
NOT... FOR LONG.' FUNNY ...BECAUSE I STARTED YOU OFF AS **BATMAN,** THE BOYS... PLUGGED ME.'

YEAH... I GUESS YOU GOT ME.... AFTER ALL! AHHHH...

AND SO, AT LAST, THE CASE IS CLOSED—THE CASE WITHOUT WHICH THERE WOULD NEVER HAVE BEEN A **BATMAN**.'
Murder of Thomas Wayne
Closed
THE END

Art by Dick Sprang & Charles Paris/Coloring by Glenn Whitmore

ONE DAY, IN THE OFFICES OF GOTHAM AIRLINES...
I'M SORRY, HAGGERTY... THE DOCTORS HAVE TURNED DOWN YOUR REQUEST TO PILOT ONE OF OUR PLANES!
WHAT? WITH MY WAR RECORD—AND FLYING EXPERIENCE?

DESPERATELY, "FLYING TIGER" HAGGERTY PRODUCES PHOTOGRAPHIC TESTIMONY OF HIS SKILL...
SEE? THAT WAS ME PILOTING THAT MUSTANG, MR. LANE! I WAS CREDITED WITH SHOOTING DOWN 22 JAP PLANES!

WHY, I'VE HANDLED ALL TYPES OF AIRCRAFT! LOOK AT THIS CARGO SHIP I FLEW OVER THE TREACHEROUS ALPS!

I KNOW—BUT, YOU'VE GOTTEN OLDER—YOUR REFLEXES ARE SLOWER! AND YOU KNOW, SAFETY IS OUR MAIN CONCERN! BUT REMEMBER—COME SEE ME ANY TIME YOU'RE READY TO TAKE A DESK JOB...
DESK JOB! WHY, I'D NEVER BE ABLE TO STAND IT!

LATER, AS "FLYING TIGER" HAGGERTY MAKES ONE LAST-DITCH EFFORT TO STAY IN THE GAME HE LOVES...
BUT, COLONEL WEBB—YOU CAN'T TURN ME DOWN! FLYING'S MY WHOLE LIFE!
SORRY, HAGGERTY.. REGULATIONS ARE REGULATIONS! I'D LOVE TO HAVE YOU--BUT I JUST CAN'T...
2

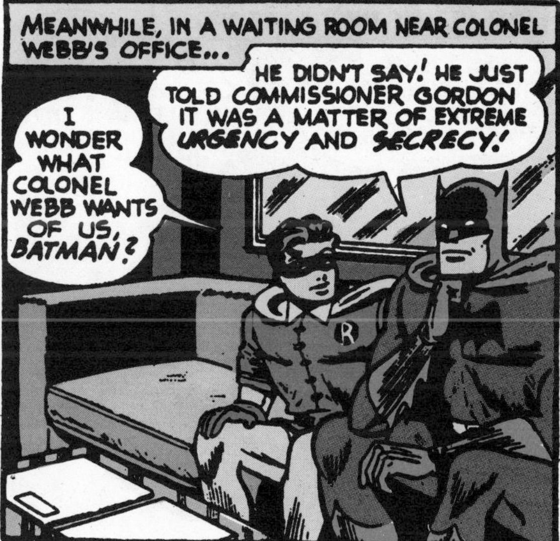
MEANWHILE, IN A WAITING ROOM NEAR COLONEL WEBB'S OFFICE...
I WONDER WHAT COLONEL WEBB WANTS OF US, BATMAN?
HE DIDN'T SAY! HE JUST TOLD COMMISSIONER GORDON IT WAS A MATTER OF EXTREME URGENCY AND SECRECY!

PRESENTLY, AS BATMAN AND ROBIN ARE SUMMONED FOR THEIR INTERVIEW...
THIS WAY, GENTLEMEN...
SAY- THERE'S "FLYING TIGER" HAGGERTY, BATMAN! REMEMBER?... WE MET HIM AT A BOND DRIVE, DURING THE WAR...
YES-BUT LET'S NOT BOTHER HIM, NOW! HE SEEMS VERY UPSET ABOUT SOMETHING!
AND WHEN THE DYNAMIC DUO IS ALONE WITH COLONEL WEBB...
SO YOU WANT US TO HELP YOU TEST AN IMPORTANT NEW WEAPON YOU'VE INVENTED, COLONEL!
YES, GENTLEMEN! IT'S NOT QUITE READY TO BE PRESENTED OFFICIALLY TO THE ARMY-- THAT'S WHY I PREFER NOT TO USE ARMY PLANES OR PERSONNEL IN THIS TEST...
WHAT I WOULD LIKE TO DO IS INSTALL THE WEAPON IN THE BATPLANE -AND USE MY PERSONAL PLANE AS THE TEST TARGET!
WHY, WE'LL BE GLAD TO ASSIST YOU, COLONEL!
NEXT DAY, AT AN ISOLATED AIRFIELD...
I CALL IT A "VACUUM BLANKET," BATMAN! WHEN TURNED ON DIRECTLY OVER ANOTHER PLANE, IT CREATES A VACUUM, WHICH CONKS OUT THAT PLANE'S ENGINE!
AND AS THEY TAKE TO THE AIR...
WHEN I GIVE THE SIGNAL, ROBIN, TURN ON THE "VACUUM BLANKET"!
RIGHT! AND IF IT WORKS, COLONEL WEBB SHOULD HAVE LITTLE TROUBLE GLIDING HIS PLANE TO A LANDING!
BUT AS ROBIN TURNS ON THE NEW WEAPON...
TURN IT OFF, ROBIN! SOMETHING'S GONE WRONG! THE BATPLANE'S CONTROLS HAVE FROZEN!
3

IT'S NO USE, ROBIN EVERYTHING'S JAMMED! WE'LL HAVE TO BAIL OUT!
AND HOW! IN A FEW MINUTES, WE'LL BE OVER THE OCEAN!

SECOND'S LATER...
WELL, THERE GOES THE BATPLANE! WE'VE LOST IT FOR GOOD, BATMAN!
YES—BUT WE CAN ALWAYS BUILD ANOTHER! LUCKY IT'S HEADED OUT TO SEA... WHEN IT RUNS OUT OF FUEL—AND CRASHES—NO ONE WILL BE HURT!

BUT LONG AFTER BATMAN AND ROBIN HAVE LANDED SAFELY, A PHENOMENON OF NATURE ALTERS THE BATPLANE'S COURSE...
...AS A FREAK CROSS-WIND SPINS IT AROUND AND HEADS IT BACK TO THE MAINLAND!

MEANWHILE, AT A SMALL AIRCRAFT FACTORY, NORTH OF GOTHAM CITY, RUN BY THE THREE BOLEY BROTHERS...
BULL, WE GOT A TIP THE COPS ARE ON TO US, FOR INCOME TAX EVASION!
AND WHEN THEY COME NOSIN' AROUND, THEY'RE SURE TO GET WISE THAT THIS FACTORY IS JUST A FRONT FOR OUR SMUGGLING RACKET!

AWRIGHT-AWRIGHT! SO WE'LL BLOW THIS JOINT BEFORE THEY COME. NOW, LEMME THINK... HOW'LL WE DO IT?
4

SUDDENLY...
HUH? THE BATPLANE! BATMAN AND ROBIN ARE HERE ALREADY! LET'S LAM!
NO, WAIT A MINUTE—THEY'RE IN TROUBLE! LISTEN TO THE MOTOR—IT'S CONKING OUT!

MOMENTS LATER...
LOOK! THE BATPLANE'S LANDED, LIGHT AS A FEATHER, IN THOSE PINE TREES! ARE THEY LUCKY!
MAYBE THEY'RE NOT SO LUCKY! HERE'S OUR CHANCE TO CATCH 'EM BY SURPRISE! SHOOT TO KILL!

BUT WHEN THE CROOKS CHARGE THE BATPLANE...
WHY- IT'S EMPTY! THEY AIN'T HERE! WHAT HAPPENED?
I DON'T KNOW, AND I DON'T CARE! WE JUST GOT OURSELVES A BATPLANE! WHAT AN IDEA THAT GIVES ME!

THINK OF THE JOBS WE CAN PULL WITH THE BATPLANE! ALL WE NEED IS A PILOT WHO CAN FIX THE MOTOR! THEN, WE'LL BUILD TWO MORE BAT-PLANES -ONE FOR EACH OF US! WHY, WE'LL RULE THE CRIME WORLD!

AT THAT MOMENT, IN THE BATCAVE, BATMAN AND ROBIN, IN THEIR EVERYDAY DISGUISES AS BRUCE WAYNE AND HIS YOUNG WARD, DICK GRAYSON, COMPLETE PLANS FOR A NEW BATPLANE...
COLONEL WEBB HAS CO-OPERATED IN KEEPING THE ACCIDENT OUT OF THE PAPERS, DICK!
HELICOPTER ASSEMBLY FOLDS INTO FUSELAGE
MAGNESIUM FIRED BATBEAM
THREE-WAY INTERCHANGING LANDING GEAR- WHEELS, PONTOONS, SKIS
"VACUUM BLANKET" ACTIVATOR
COMPLETE CRIME LAB WITHIN BATPLANE CABIN
SUPER RAM-JET POWER PLANT
HUMAN EJECTOR TUBES
TELEVISION, RADAR, RADIO ANTENNAE ALL CONTAINED IN THE WING STRUCTURES
GOOD, BRUCE! THERE'S NO SENSE IN LETTING CROOKS KNOW WE HAVEN'T GOT A BATPLANE!' WILL THE BE SUR-PRISED WHEN THEY SEE THIS NEW ONE! BOY-IT'S A CORKER!

AND AS THE DAYS PASS...
A MINIATURE BUT COMPLETE CRIME LAB WILL FIT IN HERE! BEHIND IT WILL BE OUR STORAGE SPACE!
HMMM... THAT'S WHERE WE CAN KEEP PROVISIONS, EXTRA UNIFORMS, DUMMIES OF OURSELVES, SPARE EQUIPMENT- AND ALL THE OTHER THINGS THIS TERRIFIC PLANE WILL NEED!

MEANWHILE, AS THINGS GO BADLY FOR "FLYING TIGER" HAGGERTY...
THAT MUST BE THE FLYER THEY TOLD US ABOUT IN THAT FLEA-BAG OF A HOTEL...
YEAH! AN OLD ARMY PILOT WHO'D DO ANY-THING TO FLY AGAIN! AND DON'T FORGET HIS OLD FOLKS, DOWN IN MISSISSIPPI--THAT'S OUR ACE IN THE HOLE!
5

WHEN THE CROOKS INVITE HAGGERTY FOR A RIDE..
YES, I COULD USE THE JOB! BUT ARE YOU SURE THIS FLYING DEAL YOU'RE OFFERING IS LEGITIMATE?
SURE, PAL! WE DID SOME REPAIRS ON THE BATPLANE FOR BATMAN AND ROBIN. NOW, ALL WE NEED IS A FERRY PILOT TO DELIVER THE PLANE!
SOON, AT THE BOLEY FACTORY...
ALL WE HAVE TO DO IS DELIVER IT TO THE MUNICIPAL AIRPORT... LET'S GO!
GOSH--THE BATPLANE! WHAT A SWEET JOB TO FLY!
HA-HA! HE'S FALLING FOR THE GAG!
WHILE AT GOTHAM CITY MUNICIPAL AIRPORT...
HERE COMES THAT DIAMOND SHIPMENT NOW, SIR...
RIGHT! WE'LL USE SECURITY PLAN "Y"! CLEAR THE FIELD-KEEP ALL INCOMING PLANES IN THE AIR-POSTPONE ALL TAKE-OFFS!
BUT AS THE TRANSPORT PLANE LANDS...
LOOK! THERE COME BATMAN AND ROBIN... PROBABLY TO LEND ADDITIONAL SECURITY! TELL THEM TO LAND AT ONCE!
SUDDENLY...
WHAT IS THIS!? WHERE'S BATMAN?
QUICK, SLATS-GRAB THE DIAMONDS!
ONE FALSE MOVE, HAGGERTY-AND I'LL DRILL YOU!
AND AS THE BRASH THIEVES MAKE THEIR GETAWAY...
OKAY, HAGGERTY-TAKE OFF! AND DON'T TRY TO BE A HERO! WE KNOW ALL ABOUT YOUR OLD FOLKS DOWN IN MISSISSIPPI...
YEAH-WE GOT FRIENDS DOWN THERE! YOU PLAY BALL OR YOU'LL NEVER SEE YOUR FAMILY AGAIN!
YOU RATS!

MINUTES LATER...
BUT HOW DID CROOKS EVER LAY HANDS ON THE BATPLANE, BATMAN?
PROBABLY BY SOME FREAK OF NATURE! THIS IS SERIOUS ROBIN! WE'VE GOT A REAL FIGHT ON OUR HANDS!

NO - I DIDN'T RECOGNIZE ANY OF THE CROOKS! BUT I COULDN'T MISTAKE THEIR PILOT - HE WAS "FLYING TIGER" HAGGERTY!
HAGGERTY! WE KNEW HE WAS DOWN AND OUT, BUT WE NEVER FIGURED HE'D TAKE UP WITH CRIMINALS! ROBIN, YOU KNOW WHAT THAT MEANS... WE MUST FINISH OUR NEW PLANE AHEAD OF SCHEDULE!

AND SO, THE BAT-CAVE SOON STARTS TO HUM WITH CONSTRUCTION ACTIVITY...
THE NEW BATPLANE CAN ALSO CONVERT INTO A HELICOPTER OR A SUBMARINE! SEE, DICK? THE WINGS AND RUDDER ASSEMBLY FOLD INTO THE FUSELAGE!
WOW! A BATMARINE!

THESE "HUMAN EJECTOR" TUBES ARE THE ESCAPE HATCHES WE CAN USE, IF WE GET INTO TROUBLE!
YES - AND THEY'LL ALSO GET US OUT OF THE BATMARINE, IF, BY CHANCE, IT SHOULD SINK TO THE BOTTOM!

BUT ELSEWHERE, OTHER BATPLANES ARE ALSO TAKING SHAPE...
IN ANOTHER WEEK, THEY'LL BE FINISHED, BULL!
GOOD. I HEAR BATMAN IS BUILDING A NEW PLANE! BUT WAIT TILL WE MEET HIM. THREE BATPLANES AGAINST ONE!

BY THE WAY, HAGGERTY, I GOT A LETTER, HERE, FROM MY FRIEND IN MISSISSIPPI. HE'S KEEPIN' A SHARP EYE ON YOUR FOLKS-- WANNA READ IT?
DON'T RUB IT IN, BULL! I'M WORKING FOR YOU... ISN'T THAT ENOUGH?
7

DAYS LATER:...
THERE IT IS, DICK - THE NEW BATPLANE! COMPLETE WITH JET-PROPULSION, TELEVISION, RADAR, CRIME LAB...
..."VACUUM BLANKET," BATMARINE, EJECTORS, THE BAT-BEAM - GOSH, BRUCE - WE COULD GO ON AND ON!
ABRUPTLY...
FLASH! A BATPLANE, BELIEVED TO BE THE ONE IN POSSESSION OF CRIMINALS HAS BEEN SIGHTED IN THE AIR, NORTH OF GOTHAM CITY...
WHAT? WE DIDN'T FINISH A MOMENT TOO SOON!
DICK! IT'S TIME FOR BATMAN AND ROBIN TO TRY OUT THEIR NEW PLANE!
SOON, IN THE SKIES OVER GOTHAM CITY...
HERE COMES BATMAN, BULL! THIS COULD MEAN OUR FINISH!
HA-HA! NOT WITH DAVE AND SLATS HIDING IN THE CLOUDS ABOVE! REMEMBER- BATMAN DOESN'T USE GUNS -AND WE DO!
SUDDENLY, AS THE COLORFUL CRIME-BUSTERS APPROACH BULL'S PLANE...
LOOK! THREE BATPLANES! AND THEY'RE FIRING HEAVY CANNON!
TOO MUCH FIRE-POWER EVEN FOR THIS PLANE, ROBIN!
WITHIN SECONDS, SMOKE POURS FROM THE NEW BATPLANE, AND...
NICE AIM, BOYS! YOU SET 'EM AFIRE AND THEY'RE BAILING OUT! WHAT A TARGET THEY'LL MAKE, FLOATING DOWN TO EARTH!
8
SO WHAT! HA-HA! THE NEW BATPLANE DIDN'T LAST LONG, DID IT? AND BATMAN AND ROBIN ARE SHOT FULL OF HOLES!
IT'S MURDER, BULL! PLAIN COLD-BLOODED MURDER!

BUT AS THE NEW BATPLANE HITS THE WATER AND CHANGES INTO THE BATMARINE...
THOSE DUMMIES AND THE SMOKE BOMB WE RELEASED FOOLED THEM! I STILL HEAR THEM ON THE RADIO...THEY THINK WE'RE DEAD!
IT'S NO FUN TO RUN FROM A FIGHT, BUT IT'S OUR BEST STRATEGY! WE'LL DO BETTER TAKING THEM ONE AT A TIME!

THINKING US OUT OF THE WAY, THEY'LL PROBABLY FEEL THERE'S NO NEED TO COME OUT IN FORCE! THEY'LL STRIKE WITH ONE PLANE AT A TIME!
...AND THAT'S WHEN THEY'LL FALL INTO OUR TRAP!

NEXT DAY, AS THE LUXURY YACHT "TROY" CRUISES OFF-SHORE, WITH A GALA PARTY ABOARD..
LOOK--A BATPLANE! WHAT'S IT DOING?
HAVEN'T YOU READ THE PAPERS? A CROOK CONTROLS THAT PLANE NOW!

A MESSAGE FROM THAT PLANE, SIR! HE ORDERS US TO CHANGE COURSE--TO PUT IN AT BLACK HOOK COVE--OR HE'LL SINK US WITH BOMBS OR CANNON!
WHY--THE PIRATE! THERE'S A FORTUNE ABOARD THIS VESSEL! HE CAN'T GET AWAY WITH IT... RADIO FOR HELP!

BUT BEFORE A MESSAGE CAN BE SENT THROUGH..
HE'S TUNED TO OUR RADIO CHANNEL, SIR! HE SAYS IF HE HEARS ONE PEEP OF AN SOS, HE'LL SINK US ON THE SPOT!
GOOD GRIEF! HE MEANS BUSINESS, ALL RIGHT... AND I CAN'T RISK THE LIVES OF MY PASSENGERS! WE'LL HAVE TO OBEY!

MEANWHILE, AS BRUCE AND DICK MAINTAIN A CONSTANT VIGIL BEFORE A HUGE RADAR SCREEN IN THE BATCAVE...
THERE IT IS...THE OUTLINE OF A BATPLANE!
ACCORDING TO THE CO-ORDINATES, HE'S OUT AT SEA! COME ON--TIME TO GET STARTED AS BATMAN AND ROBIN!
9

IMMEDIATELY, OUT AT SEA...
THERE HE IS, ROBIN! THIS LOOKS LIKE A GREAT OPPORTUNITY TO USE THE NOW-PERFECTED "VACUUM BLANKET"!
BOY— WILL HE BE SURPRISED!

AND, AS THE "VACUUM BLANKET" GOES TO WORK...
HE'LL HAVE TO BAIL OUT, ROBIN! RADIO THAT YACHT, DOWN THERE, TO PICK HIM UP AND HOLD HIM!
HUH? THE BATPLANE... WITH BATMAN AND ROBIN ALIVE! AND MY MOTOR... IT'S CONKING OUT! MY RADIO'S DEAD!

HE'D ORDERED THE CAPTAIN TO PUT IN AT BLACK HOOK COVE, BATMAN...
THEN HE MUST HAVE A HENCHMAN WAITING THERE TO HELP LOOT THE SHIP! LET'S TAKE A LOOK-SEE!

PRESENTLY, AT BLACK HOOK COVE...
THERE HE IS! WE'VE CAUGHT ANOTHER FISH!
I'VE GOT AN IDEA, ROBIN— TURN ON THE BATBEAM!

INSTANTLY, A POWERFUL FLASH OF LIGHT, AND...
UGH! A BAT! I CAN'T SEE!
WE'VE BLINDED HIM, ROBIN—AND STALLED HIS TAKE-OFF! NOW, QUICKLY... SHIFT TO HELICOPTER AND TURN ON THE "VACUUM BLANKET"! THEN, GET THE GRAPPLING HOOKS READY!
10

AS ROBIN CARRIES OUT HIS INSTRUCTIONS...
IT WORKED, ROBIN! WE'VE HOOKED HIM FORE AND AFT! NOW, WE'LL TOTE HIM TO POLICE HEADQUARTERS!
I GET IT... CARRY HIM JUST HIGH ENOUGH SO THAT HE CAN'T LEAP OUT WITHOUT A CHUTE—AND TOO LOW TO LEAP OUT WITH A CHUTE!
STILL CAN'T SEE... WH-WHAT'S HAPPENING?

THAT NIGHT, ON THE ROOF OF POLICE HEADQUARTERS
A T-MAN IDENTIFIED THE TWO MEN YOU CAPTURED AS SLATS AND DAVE BOLEY! THEY'VE GOT A BROTHER, BULL, AT AN AIRCRAFT FACTORY NORTH OF HERE...
THAT'S, OUR MAN ... AND HAGGERTY'S UNDOUBTEDLY WITH HIM! THANKS, COMMISSIONER--LET'S GO, ROBIN!

MEANWHILE, AT THE BOLEY FACTORY...
THEY GOT MY BROTHERS--BUT THEY AIN'T GETTIN' ME! C'MON, HAGGERTY-- YOU'RE FLYIN' ME TO MEXICO!

ABRUPTLY...
YOU FORGOT SOMETHING, BULL! WITH YOUR BROTHERS IN JAIL, WHO'S GOING TO TIP OFF YOUR FRIENDS IN MISSISSIPPI, NOW THAT I'M NOT PLAYING BALL ANYMORE?

SECONDS LATER...
WHAT A PLEASURE IT'LL BE TO TURN YOU OVER TO BATMAN, YOU RAT!
BOLEY A

BUT IN THE SKIES OVER GOTHAM CITY, AS THE TWO BATPLANES MEET...
WE'VE GOT THEM BOTH, ROBIN-- BOLEY AND HAGGERTY! LET'S JUST RUN THEM RAGGED, UNTIL WE CAN FORCE THEM DOWN ON AN OPEN FIELD!
BATMAN! BATMAN! DON'T--I'M A FRIEND... A FRIEND!

I CAN'T SET THIS PLANE DOWN HERE--AND I CAN'T BAIL OUT WITH BULL TIED UP BESIDE ME... THAT WOULD BE MURDER!
BOY-WATCH BATMAN FLY RINGS AROUND THOSE CROOKS! AND REMEMBER-- BATMAN USES NO LETHAL WEAPONS!
11

HAGGERTY SEEMS TO BE WAVING AT US!
MOST LIKELY SHOUTING HIS DEFIANCE! I CAN'T UNDER STAND WHAT GOT INTO THE MAN--BUT I'M GOING TO SHOW HIM SOME FLYING EVEN HE NEVER SAW BEFORE!

SUDDENLY, BEFORE THE STUNNED EYES OF THE ONLOOKING CROUD...
LOOK! THE CROOKS' PLANE IS IN A TAILSPIN! THEY'LL BE KILLED!
BATMAN'S WON! BUT I THOUGHT HE NEVER USED LETHAL WEAPONS! HE CERTAINLY DID UP THERE!

THEY'RE OUT OF CONTROL-SPINNING INTO A CRASH!
I DON'T UNDERSTAND! I KNOW I BUZZED THEM PRETTY CLOSELY, BUT I DON'T THINK I SHEARED OFF ANY OF THAT PLANE!

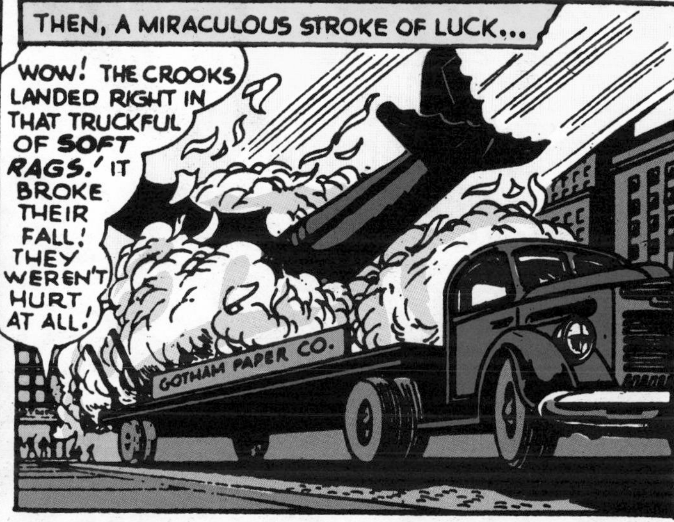
THEN, A MIRACULOUS STROKE OF LUCK...
WOW! THE CROOKS LANDED RIGHT IN THAT TRUCKFUL OF SOFT RAGS! IT BROKE THEIR FALL! THEY WEREN'T HURT AT ALL!
GOTHAM PAPER CO.

LATER...
WE'RE SURE GLAD YOU'RE OKAY, HAGGERTY! BOLEY JUST CONFESSED! IT LOOKS LIKE WE HAD YOU PEGGED ALL WRONG!
BUT THERE'S ONE THING I DON'T UNDERSTAND... HOW COME YOU CRACKED UP? DID WE DISABLE YOUR PLANE?
12

OH, NO... I SIMPLY BLACKED OUT! THE DOCS WERE RIGHT, BATMAN... MY FLYING DAYS ARE OVER! I JUST HAD TO LEARN IT THE HARD WAY!
YOUR FLYING DAYS MAY BE OVER, HAGGERTY-BUT THERE ARE STILL PLENTY OF JOBS IN AVIATION FOR YOU! ROBIN AND I ARE GOING TO SEE THAT YOU GET ONE!
THE END

Art by Dick Sprang & Charles Paris/Coloring by Helen Vesik

A PLANE MAKES A ROUTINE LANDING AT A SMALL GOTHAM CITY AIRPORT ---
--- AND ITS PILOT GETS A FEARFUL WELCOME!
WHAT-- A BLACK PANTHER-- HELP!
BUT BEHIND THE PANTHER APPEARS AN EVEN MORE SINISTER FORM!
CATWOMAN! SAVE ME FROM THAT PANTHER!
I WILL-- BUT ONLY IF YOU GIVE ME THAT CASE OF DIAMONDS YOU WERE HIRED TO DELIVER TO THE GOTHAM JEWELERS COMPANY!
AND SECONDS LATER, A POWERFUL CRAFT ROARS AWAY INTO THE NIGHT!
AND NOW TO FLY TO MY SECRET HIDEOUT, WHERE NOT EVEN BATMAN CAN FIND US!
CATWOMAN STOLE THE DIAMOND SHIPMENT--- CALL THE POLICE!
SOON, AS THE ALARM GOES OUT, AN EERIE SIGNAL PIERCES THE NIGHT-SKY!
--- ESCAPED IN FAST PLANE!
LISTEN TO THAT POLICE FLASH-- IT'S CATWOMAN AGAIN!
AND THERE'S THE BAT-SIGNAL! WE'RE WANTED AS BATMAN AND ROBIN!
A SWIFT CHANGE, AND PLAYBOY BRUCE WAYNE AND HIS WARD, DICK GRAYSON, BECOME BATMAN AND ROBIN, THE BOY WONDER!
WE'LL GET THE BATPLANE OUT AND GO STRAIGHT TO THAT AIRFIELD!
SHE'LL BE GONE-- SHE STRIKES AS FAST AS THE CATS SHE LOVES!
AT THE AIRFIELD, BATMAN AND ROBIN HEAR AN INCREDIBLE STORY!
YOU SAY SHE USES A HUGE BLACK PANTHER IN HER ROBBERY? HOW COULD EVEN CATWOMAN CONTROL SUCH A BEAST?
IT'S UNCANNY! HMM --- IF WE HAD SOME CLUE TO WHERE SHE WENT, THE BATPLANE MIGHT STILL OVERTAKE HER!
2

THE TRAINED EYES OF THE WORLD'S GREATEST SLEUTHS DISCOVER WHAT OTHERS MIGHT HAVE MISSED!

THIS IS WHERE HER PLANE TOOK OFF-- YOU CAN SEE ITS WHEEL-MARKS!
THE DRIED MUD THAT FELL OUT OF HER TIRE-TREADS--- IT'S VOLCANIC CLAY OF A TYPE FOUND ONLY ON CERTAIN TROPICAL ISLANDS! COME ON, ROBIN!

PRESENTLY, THE MIGHTY BAT-PLANE'S JETS ROAR LOUDLY AS IT SCREAMS UP SKYWARD ON A TENUOUS TRAIL!

CATWOMAN HAS A START, BUT MAYBE WE CAN OVER-TAKE HER BEFORE SHE REACHES THOSE ISLANDS, ROBIN!
HMM... I KNOW SHE'S ALWAYS LIKED CATS, BUT I NEVER DREAMED SHE'D USE KILLER-CATS LIKE THAT PANTHER!

AS DAWN FLARES, THE BATPLANE HAS STREAKED FAR SOUTHWARD IN ITS GRIM PURSUIT!

HANG ON-- I'M GOING TO FORCE HER DOWN!
THAT'S HER PLANE-- HEADING TO-WARD A LARGE ISLAND!

SO BATMAN TRAILED ME! WELL, HE'LL LEARN THAT THOSE WHO BOTHER CATS CAN GET SCRATCHED!
CLAW RETRACTOR

FROM THE CATWOMAN'S PLANE, GREAT RETRACTABLE STEEL CLAWS MECHANICALLY REACH FORTH!

NOW TO SUDDENLY THROTTLE DOWN AND LET THE BATPLANE ZOOM PAST CLOSE BENEATH ME, AND---

--THEY'LL LEARN I STILL HAVE CLAWS!
SHE'S RIPPED OUR WINGS TO FORCE US DOWN! I'LL HAVE TO LAND AT ONCE!
3

WE'LL LAND HERE AND REPAIR OUR WINGS LATER, BUT FIRST, WE'LL GET AFTER THE CATWOMAN!
BATMAN, I SAW WHAT LOOKS LIKE A MINE HERE!
PRESENTLY, THE CAPED CRIME-FIGHTERS ENTER THE HEART OF THE TROPICAL JUNGLE ISLE!
WE'LL FIND OUT WHAT THOSE MINERS KNOW OF CATWOMAN. SHE MUST HAVE A LAIR HERE SOMEWHERE!
LOOK! NOT ONLY PANTHER TRACKS, BUT LION, LEOPARD AND TIGER TRACKS, TOO! THEY MUST HAVE BEEN MADE BY HER PETS -- BUT HOW CAN SHE HANDLE SUCH FIERCE BEASTS?
WELCOME, BATMAN AND ROBIN! I'M JOHN JARROW AND THIS IS MY SMALL DIAMOND-MINE --- AND I'M SURE GLAD TO SEE YOU TWO!
THEN YOU KNOW THAT CATWOMAN'S HERE?
WITH HER TERRIBLE FELINES, SHE'S USED THIS ISLE AS A CRIME-BASE AND WE'RE TOO AFRAID OF HER BEASTS TO STOP HER!
WE'RE AFRAID SHE'S AFTER THE DIAMONDS WE MINE! IF YOU COULD ONLY SET A TRAP TO PROTECT US AGAINST HER JUNGLE CATS...
WE CAN!
PRESENTLY...
IF ANY OF HER BEASTS COME HERE, THIS NOOSE-TRAP WILL CATCH THEM!
YES, CUTTING THIS TRIGGER-ROPE THAT HOLDS THE TREE DOWN WOULD TRAP ANYTHING---
WHRRHIP!
--EVEN BATMAN AND ROBIN!
HA, HA-- NICE OF THEM TO SET A TRAP FOR THEMSELVES! NOW WE'VE GOT THEM!
4

BATMAN THESE MEN ARE CROOKS-- PROBABLY WORKING WITH CATWOMAN. WE STEPPED RIGHT INTO IT!
HERE'S OUR CHANCE TO GET RID OF OUR BIGGEST ENEMY! ALL TOGETHER-- WE'LL FIRE IN A VOLLEY!
STOP!
BUT WHY STOP US, CATWOMAN? THEY'RE YOUR ENEMIES, TOO!
I'VE A BETTER IDEA! CUT THEM DOWN!
SO THEY ARE IN LEAGUE WITH CATWOMAN!
WHY NOT KNOCK THEM OFF AT ONCE?
I WANT THE PLEASURE OF HUNTING THEM DOWN, AS THEY HUNTED ME! TAKE AWAY THEIR UTILITY BELTS AND COSTUMES AND GIVE THEM JUNGLE CLOTHING SO THEY'LL HAVE NO TRICKS LEFT!
SOON, ANIMAL SKINS TRANSFORM THE DETECTIVE DUO INTO PRIMITIVE MEN OF THE JUNGLE!
I'LL GIVE YOU BOTH TEN MINUTES' START BEFORE I BEGIN TRAILING YOU WITH MY CATS! AND TAKING OFF YOUR MASKS WILL BE THE CLIMAX OF MY CHASE!
WHY, YOU FEMALE FELINE...
DON'T WASTE TIME, ROBIN-- LET'S GET GOING!
MY LITTLE PETS WILL ENJOY THIS HUNT!
A SWELL IDEA, CATWOMAN! I WISH I COULD SEE IT WHEN THOSE BEASTS OF YOURS TRACK THEM DOWN!
PRESENTLY, BATMAN AND ROBIN TRY TO LOSE THEMSELVES IN THE GREEN MAZE OF THE JUNGLE...
I STILL DON'T UNDERSTAND--IF THOSE CROOKS REALLY HAVE A DIAMOND MINE, WHY WOULD THEY BE IN WITH CATWOMAN?
THEY'RE AFRAID OF HER FELINES AND SHE DOMINATES THEM THAT WAY-- BUT QUICK, ROBIN, FOLLOW ME!
5

WHEW-- THAT'S A RELIEF! I WAS AFRAID SHE'D SEE US IN THAT SHALLOW WATER, BUT SHE DIDN'T!

DIDN'T SHE, ROBIN? I WONDER! ANYWAY, WE'VE GOT WORK TO DO--- COME ON!

THEN, AS NIGHT BLANKETS THE JUNGLE, TWO EERIE FIGURES FOLLOW ON THE TRACK OF THE GREAT CATS!

WE CAN SOLVE THE MYSTERY OF THE DIAMOND MINE LATER -- AND TAKE CARE OF THOSE CROOKS! BUT RIGHT NOW I WANT TO FIND CATWOMAN'S SECRET LAIR-- AND THESE TRACKS SHOULD LEAD US THERE!

I STILL DON'T GET IT! WILD LIONS, TIGERS, AND LEOPARDS-- HOW DOES SHE CONTROL THEM, ANYWAY?

AS SILENT AS TWO SHADOWS IN THE NIGHT, BATMAN AND ROBIN STEAL INTO THE SINISTER CAT-TEMPLE!
LIONS--- TIGERS--- LEOPARDS, THEY COULDN'T BE ALL NATIVE TO THIS ISLAND!
THEY'RE ANIMALS RAISED IN CAPTIVITY, ROBIN--- WILD LIONS NEVER HAVE BUSHY MANES LIKE THOSE IN ZOOS! THAT EXPLAINS WHY SHE'S ABLE TO HANDLE THEM! COME ON--- I WANT TO LOOK FOR SOMETHING!
PRESENTLY, SCOUTING AROUND THE AWESOME RUIN, BATMAN FINDS WHAT HE EXPECTED!
THESE ARE CIRCUS ANIMALS--- BROUGHT HERE BY CATWOMAN! AND THAT GIVES ME AN IDEA! LISTEN, ROBIN---
I'LL BE READY-- BUT BE CAREFUL, BATMAN! IF IT DOESN'T WORK---
I'M RELYING ON THE FACT THEY WERE CIRCUS ANIMALS, TO MAKE IT WORK!
A MOMENT LATER, A DRAMATIC FIGURE STRIDES INTO THE CATWOMAN'S NEW CATACOMB!
A CIRCUS TRAINER ALWAYS DISMISSES HIS ANIMALS WITH A VOLLEY OF FAST WHIP-CRACKS AND IT OUGHT TO WORK ON THESE BEASTS!
CRACK!
BATMAN. ARE YOU MAD, TO COME HERE---
AT THE CRACK OF THE LASH, THE STARTLED FELINES REVERT TO OLD TRAINING...
THEY MADE FOR THEIR CAGES AS BATMAN FIGURED---AND I CAN SHUT THEM IN!
CRACK
BUT A MORE DANGEROUS HUMAN FELINE REMAINS TO BE DEALT WITH!
YES, BATMAN! I BROUGHT TAME CIRCUS CATS HERE! YOU WERE CLEVER TO GUESS IT AND TRICK THEM, BUT NOT CLEVER ENOUGH!
JARROW AND HIS "MINERS" ARE YOUR CONFEDER-ATES, AND I THINK I KNOW WHAT YOU'VE BEEN UP TO!
7

UNKNOWN TO BATMAN, THE VERY CRIMINAL OF WHOM HE SPEAKS IS CLOSE AT HAND!
CATWOMAN FAILED TO GET HIM -- AND HE'S GOT HER! IF I SHOOT ONE OF THE DUO, THE OTHER MIGHT GET ME --- I'LL USE SOMETHING THAT WILL GET THEM BOTH!
RUTHLESS IN STRATEGY, THE EVIL JARROW UNLEASHES A THING OF TERROR...
THIS GORILLA MAY DESTROY CATWOMAN, TOO, BUT I DON'T CARE AS LONG AS IT GETS BATMAN AND ROBIN!
THEN, A CRY OF WARNING FROM BATMAN, BUT TOO LATE!
ROBIN, LOOK OUT!
YOU CAN'T SAVE ROBIN-- THAT GORILLA IS A KILLER!
ALL ANIMALS FEAR FIRE-- MY ONLY CHANCE---
ROBIN'S UNCONSCIOUS, BUT IT'S DROPPED HIM-- NOW IT'S AFTER ME--
WHIRLING THE BURNING BRAND IN CIRCLES, BATMAN DRIVES BACK THE RAGING MONSTER!
IT'S RECOILING INTO ITS CAGE-- NOW TO SLAM THE DOOR QUICK!
8

BUT AS THE CAGE DOOR CLICKS SHUT UPON THE MIGHTY APE...
NICE WORK, BATMAN-- BUT I'LL TAKE OVER NOW!

A GOOD THING I CAME TO MAKE SURE YOU'D GOT BATMAN! I'M TAKING HIM DOWN TO THE MINE AND WE'LL MAKE CERTAIN HE'S DONE FOR THIS TIME!
I MUST RELEASE MY PETS AGAIN!

LEAVE THOSE CRITTERS HERE-- WE DON'T LIKE THEM! GOOD THING THE GORILLA GOT THE BRAT!
HE DOESN'T KNOW ROBIN'S ONLY STUNNED! I WON'T SAY ANYTHING-- ROBIN IS NEAR THE FIRE AND THE BEASTS WON'T BOTHER HIM!

ONE SURE WAY TO GET RID OF HIM SO HE'LL NEVER BE FOUND--- TOSS HIM IN THE RIVER, TIED HAND AND FOOT!
WE'LL DO IT!

PUT HIS COSTUME BACK ON HIM SO *IT* WILL NEVER BE FOUND EITHER! I TOOK EVERYTHING OUT OF THE UTILITY BELT!

THAT'S A CLEVER IDEA, CATWOMAN! DO IT, BOYS! WE MUST DESTROY ALL THE EVIDENCE THAT COULD PROVE WE MURDERED HIM!

PRESENTLY, BOUND HAND AND FOOT, BATMAN IS TOSSED TO HIS DOOM!

HAW, HAW, THAT BIG FALL WON'T LEAVE ANY-THING OF HIM!
9

MEANWHILE, ROBIN HAS AWAKENED TO A REALITY WORSE THAN A NIGHTMARE!

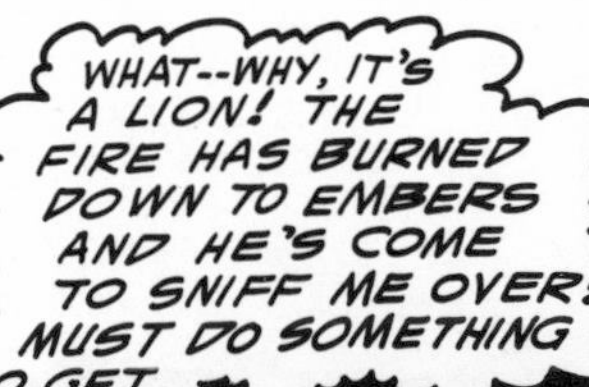
WHAT--WHY, IT'S A LION! THE FIRE HAS BURNED DOWN TO EMBERS AND HE'S COME TO SNIFF ME OVER! MUST DO SOMETHING TO GET RID OF HIM!

LACKING EVEN HIS UTILITY BELT THE BOY WONDER MOVES HIS HAND SLOWLY AND SOFTLY!

BY SLOWLY PRESSING THIS PLANT DOWN SO ITS GREEN TOP-LEAVES ARE IN THE HOT FIRE-EMBERS --

SNORT!
--AS I'D HOPED. HE DIDN'T LIKE THE SMOKE, AND IS LEAVING! WHAT A RELIEF!

THE BOY WONDER'S KEEN EYES SOON DEDUCE WHAT HAS HAPPENED WHILE HE WAS SENSELESS!
JARROW'S AND CATWOMAN'S FOOTPRINTS OVER BATMAN'S HEADING TOWARD THAT MINE! THAT MEANS THEY FORCED HIM AHEAD OF THEM! I'VE GOT TO GO TO HIS AID---
I CAN USE THIS SMOKE-GAG ON A BIG SCALE AND DRIVE THE BEASTS TOWARD THE MINE! IF THEY STAMPEDE INTO ITS STREET, IT'LL CREATE SUCH A CONFUSION, I CAN SLIP IN AND FIND BATMAN!

MEANWHILE, HURLED INTO THE RAGING TORRENT WITH HANDS AND FEET BOUND, BATMAN HAS NOT SURRENDERED TO DESPAIR!

CATWOMAN SAID SHE TOOK EVERYTHING OUT OF MY UTILITY-BELT, BUT SHE SLIPPED UP! I CAN FEEL MY SILKEN CORD AND MY EMERGENCY KNIFE-BLADE STILL IN IT! GOT TO GET THE KNIFE OUT FAST AND CUT MY WRISTS FREE!
10

AS THE CURRENT SWEEPS HIM TOWARD THE WATERFALL OF DOOM, **BATMAN** WORKS SWIFTLY!

GOT MY HANDS FREE--BUT I CAN'T SWIM OUT OF THIS TERRIFIC CURRENT IN TIME TO ESCAPE THE FALLS! ONLY ONE CHANCE--THE SILKEN ROPE IN MY UTILITY BELT!

IF I CAN GET A NOOSE OF MY ROPE OVER A PROJECTING ROCK IN THE BOTTOM -- GOT IT! AND JUST IN TIME, FOR I'M RIGHT AT THE FALLS!

SECONDS LATER, CRIMINALS SEE THEIR GREATEST ENEMY APPARENTLY PLUNGE TO HIS DOOM!

THERE HE GOES, AND THAT FINISHES HIM! NO HUMAN BEING COULD SURVIVE THAT PLUNGE!
BATMAN GONE? IT--IT SEEMS IMPOSSIBLE!

BUT THE SUPER-STRONG SILKEN ROPE HAS HELD, AND, UNSEEN BY WATCHING EYES, HAS CHECKED **BATMAN'S** FALL IN TIME...

THE ROPE HELD! NOW IF I SWING IN AND CUT LOOSE AT THE RIGHT MOMENT, I CAN LIGHT ON THOSE ROCKS AND GET UP TO SQUARE ACCOUNTS WITH THOSE THUGS!

BATMAN... GONE. AND I THOUGHT HE'D SAVE HIMSELF-- HE ALWAYS HAS IN THE PAST---

AND HE DID THIS TIME! I'LL JUST TIE YOU UP SAFELY WHILE I BREAK UP YOUR ACCOMPLICES' RACKET FOR GOOD!

WHAT WAS LEFT OF MY ROPE CAME IN HANDY! NOW FOR THESE "DIAMOND MINERS"!

11

SOON, IN ONE OF THE "MINE" BUILDINGS, BATMAN CONFIRMS HIS SUSPICIONS!
I THOUGHT SO! THEY GET STOLEN DIAMONDS FROM ALL OVER AND RE-CUT THEM-- THEN PRETEND THEY MINED AND CUT THE GEMS THEMSELVES!
YOUR NUMBER'S UP, BATMAN! OUTSIDE!

YOU'RE HARD TO KILL, BUT THIS TIME WE'LL MAKE SURE WITH BULLETS!
JARROW, LOOK OUT-- CATWOMAN'S BEASTS ARE STAMPEDING THIS WAY!

AND AS THE PANICKY CROOKS RECOIL FROM A JUNGLE STAMPEDE...
LOOKS LIKE I SENT MY "FRIENDS" HERE JUST IN TIME!
AND YOU'RE WELCOME! WE'LL JUST CAGE THESE HUMAN SPECIMENS NOW!

BUT MEANWHILE, A GREAT CAT HAS GONE LOYALLY TO ITS MISTRESS...

MY FAITHFUL PET-- YOUR SHARP CLAWS ARE HELPFUL NOW, THOUGH YOU DON'T KNOW IT!

12

AND WHEN THE DYNAMIC DUO FINISHES SECURING THE CROOKS, THEY GET AN AMAZING SURPRISE!

CATWOMAN! SHE'S GETTING AWAY, TO HER HIDDEN PLANE!

AND WE CAN'T FOLLOW TILL THE BATPLANE IS REPAIRED! I GUESS SHE ESCAPES US FOR NOW, THOUGH WE'VE BROKEN UP HER CRIME-SCHEME!

FUNNY, THAT SHE ACCIDENTALLY LEFT THAT KNIFE-BLADE AND SILKEN CORD IN YOUR UTILITY BELT.. OR WAS IT AN ACCIDENT? SHE'S ALWAYS BEEN SOFT ON YOU!

THAT WAS NO ACCIDENT, ROBIN. MURDER ISN'T IN THE CATWOMAN'S HEART. SENTIMENT IS HER WEAKNESS-- AND THAT'S WHY WE'LL CATCH HER THE NEXT TIME!

THE END.

Art by Sheldon Moldoff /Coloring by Michele Wolfman

ONE DAY, AS BRUCE WAYNE AND HIS YOUNG WARD, DICK GRAYSON, CLEAN OUT THEIR ATTIC...
BRUCE! LOOK! I MUST HAVE TOUCHED A HIDDEN SPRING IN YOUR FATHER'S OLD DESK!
A SECRET DRAWER! AND THERE'S SOMETHING INSIDE IT!
TO HIS SURPRISE, BRUCE WITHDRAWS A FANTASTIC GARMENT...
IT'S... A KIND OF BATMAN COSTUME!
DICK, I THINK I'VE SEEN THIS COSTUME BEFORE--ON MY FATHER--LONG, LONG AGO!
THEN THAT MEANS YOUR FATHER WAS A "BATMAN" BEFORE YOU!
BUT THAT'S IMPOSSIBLE! I WAS THE FIRST "BATMAN"! I ADOPTED THE FIRST BATMAN COSTUME YEARS AFTER I SAW MY PARENTS KILLED BY A ROBBER!
BRUCE'S THOUGHTS WHIRL BACK TO WHEN HE WAS A BOY AND MADE A PROMISE TO THE MEMORY OF HIS PARENTS...
I VOW THAT I'LL DEDICATE MY LIFE TO BRING YOUR KILLER TO JUSTICE... AND TO FIGHT ALL CRIME!
AS YEARS PASSED, BRUCE MASTERED SCIENTIFIC CRIMINAL INVESTIGATION... TRAINED HIS BODY TO ATHLETIC PERFECTION...
ONE NIGHT, HE WAS AT LAST READY FOR HIS CHOSEN CAREER, BUT HE NEEDED A DISGUISE THAT WOULD STRIKE TERROR INTO CRIMINAL HEARTS...
A BAT-- IT'S FLOWN IN THE WINDOW! IT'S LIKE AN OMEN! I SHALL BECOME A BAT-- A BATMAN!
YEARS PASSED, AND BATMAN NEVER GAVE UP HIS SEARCH FOR THE KILLER! THEN ONE DAY, WHILE INVESTIGATING A CRIMINAL NAMED JOEY CHILL...
IT'S THE MAN WHO KILLED MY PARENTS! HE'S OLDER NOW-- BUT I COULD NEVER FORGET THAT FACE!
2

BUT, IRONICALLY, JOEY CHILL WAS SHOT DOWN BY OTHER MOBSTERS WHO HAD A GRUDGE AGAINST HIM...
BANG!
HE'S DEAD! HIS OWN CRIMES FINALLY CAUGHT UP WITH HIM!
THIS THEN, WAS THE ORIGIN OF BATMAN! THEN HOW COULD HIS FATHER HAVE BEEN A BATMAN BEFORE HIM?
LOOK! HERE'S SOMETHING ELSE IN THE DRAWER! A CAN OF MOVIE FILM AND A DIARY!
LET'S LOOK AT THE FILM FIRST! I'LL SET UP THE PROJECTOR!
SOON, THE TWO VIEW AN EPISODE FROM THE PAST...
LADIES AND GENTLEMEN, AS YOU ALL KNOW, THE THEME OF THIS YEAR'S MASQUERADE BALL IS "FLYING CREATURES"!
AND OUR FIRST PRIZE FOR THE BEST "FLYING CREATURE" COSTUME GOES TO DR. THOMAS WAYNE FOR HIS BAT-MAN COSTUME!
MY FATHER!
SUDDENLY...
WE FIGURED THERE'D BE A DOC IN THIS CROWD! COME ON, DOC-- WE NEED YOU! MAKE IT SNAPPY!
YOU CAN'T THREATEN ME!
ATTABOY, DAD!
3

BETTER COME ALONG, DOC--OR SOMEBODY SURE IS GONNA GET HURT!
I--I HAVE NO CHOICE--NOW!

HERE THE MOVIE ABRUPTLY ENDS!
AT LEAST THE MOVIE TOLD US WHY YOUR FATHER WORE A BAT-MAN COSTUME!
LISTEN TO WHAT HIS DIARY SAYS...

"TONIGHT, MARTHA AND I ARE GOING TO THE ANNUAL MASQUERADE BALL! OUR LITTLE BOY SEEMS FASCINATED BY MY COSTUME..."
GEE, DADDY, I WISH I COULD WEAR A SUIT LIKE THAT!
I'LL SAVE IT FOR YOU, BRUCE--TO WEAR WHEN YOU GROW UP!

DICK, WHEN THAT BAT FLEW INTO MY ROOM, IT MUST HAVE PRODDED MY SUBCONSCIOUS MEMORY OF MY FATHER'S COSTUME! NOW I REALIZE I ADOPTED A **BATMAN** COSTUME BECAUSE I REMEMBERED MY FATHER WEARING ONE!

READING ON, BRUCE LEARNS WHAT HAPPENED AFTER THE HOODLUMS TOOK HIS FATHER FROM THE BALL...

"THE GUNMEN TOOK ME TO AN OLD WAREHOUSE WHERE THEIR BOSS WAS IN HIDING..."
YOU'RE LEW MOXON, THE BANK ROBBER THE POLICE ARE AFTER!
YEAH--ONE OF THEM WINGED ME! I WANT YOU TO REMOVE THE SLUG!

"I KNEW THAT ONCE I REMOVED THE BULLET, MOXON WOULD NEVER LET ME LIVE TO REVEAL HIS WHEREABOUTS TO THE POLICE..."
I'VE GOT TO DO SOMETHING--BUT WHAT?
4

"I SUDDENLY HOOKED ONE FOOT AROUND MOXON'S CHAIR AND..."
WHAT...?!
"THAT LEFT ONLY THE HOODLUMS TO DEAL WITH!"
I'LL LET THE POLICE TAKE OVER FROM HERE!
WOW! EVEN THOUGH HE DIDN'T HAVE ANY TRAINING IN FIGHTING CROOKS, YOUR FATHER PULLED A TYPICAL BATMAN STUNT!
MY FATHER WAS QUITE A GUY!
THE DIARY CONTINUES--"AT HIS TRIAL, MOXON WAS SENTENCED TO TEN YEARS FOR ARMED ROBBERY..."
YOU DID THIS TO ME! I'LL GET YOU FOR THIS, WAYNE-- I'LL GET YOU!
"TEN YEARS ROLLED BY! I'D INVESTED MY SAVINGS WISELY AND BECAME WEALTHY! I'D ALMOST FORGOTTEN MOXON UNTIL TODAY..."
MOXON-- FREE!
YEAH-- I SERVED MY TEN YEARS IN JAIL-- WHERE YOU PUT ME! I SWORE I'D GET YOU, AND I WILL!
BUT I'M TOO SMART TO DO IT MYSELF! THE POLICE WOULD ARREST ME ON SUSPICION FAST! I'LL GET SOMEONE ELSE TO DO IT FOR ME!
HERE THE DIARY ENDS!
THIS MEANS JOEY CHILL ONLY PRETENDED TO BE A HOLDUP MAN-- ACTUALLY HE WAS MOXON'S HIRED KILLER! MOXON MUST HAVE ORDERED CHILL NOT TO KILL ME, TOO-- SO I'D BE ALIVE TO TESTIFY THAT MY PARENTS WERE KILLED BY A ROBBER!
5

GOSH, BRUCE-- MOXON USED YOU AS HIS ALIBI!
HE USED ME AS A COVERUP FOR HIS DELIBERATE MURDER OF MY PARENTS! PUT ON YOUR COSTUME, DICK-- WE'VE JUST REOPENED THE WAYNE MURDER CASE!
LATER, IN THE OFFICE OF POLICE COMMISSIONER GORDON...
COMMISSIONER, I'D LIKE TO KNOW THE WHEREABOUTS OF LEW MOXON!
I'LL HAVE THIS TELE-PHOTOED TO EVERY POLICE DEPART-MENT IN THE COUNTRY!
AND WHEN THE INFORMATION COMES...
MOXON IS NOW IN THE BILLBOARD BLIMP BUSINESS OUT WEST-- IN COASTAL CITY!
SOON AFTER, THE SLEEK BATPLANE RACES THROUGH THE SKIES...
WHY DID YOU HAVE ME BRING ALONG YOUR FATHER'S COSTUME, BATMAN?
IT GIVES ME THE FEELING THAT MY FATHER IS WITH ME ON THIS CASE!
HOURS LATER, AT THEIR DESTINATION, TWO FIGURES MOVE LIKE SHADOWS TOWARDS A BLIMP HANGAR...
MOXON SKY-HI ADVERTISING CO.
BUT, IN THE DARKNESS, ROBIN'S FOOT KICKS A MISPLACED GASOLINE CAN...
CLANK
BATMAN AND ROBIN! GET 'EM!
6

AS ROBIN DARTS FORWARD, A SWINGING SANDBAG TREACHEROUSLY FELLS HIM!
UH-H!
WE GOT THE BRAT! BATMAN WILL BE EASIER TO TAKE NOW!
BOP!
UNDER THE IMPACT OF FOUR THUGS, BATMAN IS BROUGHT DOWN...
...BUT NOT FOR LONG!
THIS'LL TAKE THE FIGHT OUT OF ALL OF YOU!
LATER... LEW MOXON, I'M CHARGING YOU WITH THE MURDER OF DR. THOMAS WAYNE!
IS THAT WHAT YOU'RE AFTER ME FOR?
INCREDIBLY, A SMILE OF RELIEF PASSES OVER THE ACCUSED'S FACE...
I NEVER HEARD OF ANY DR. WAYNE! I'M EVEN WILLING TO TAKE THE LIE DETECTOR TEST TO PROVE IT!
ALL RIGHT, WE'LL SOON SEE IF YOU ARE LYING!
7

SOON...
DIDN'T YOU HIRE JOEY CHILL TO MURDER DR. WAYNE?
NO! I NEVER EVEN HEARD OF JOEY CHILL!
YOU KNOW YOU HATED DR. WAYNE, THAT YOU SWORE YOU'D GET HIM!
I DON'T KNOW ANY DR. WAYNE-- AND I DON'T KNOW WHAT YOU'RE TALKIN' ABOUT!
BATMAN CONTINUES TO HAMMER QUESTIONS AT THE PRISONER, AND WHEN THE INTERROGATION IS OVER...
SEE FOR YOURSELF, BATMAN-- THE NEEDLE DIDN'T JUMP ONCE. NOBODY CAN BEAT THE MACHINE-- SO HE MUST BE TELLING THE TRUTH!
HELPLESSLY, BATMAN SEES MOXON RELEASED ON BAIL FOR ASSAULT AND BATTERY...
HOW COULD MOXON BE TELLING THE TRUTH WHEN WE KNOW HE WAS INVOLVED IN YOUR FATHER'S MURDER? THAT'S SOMETHING NOBODY CAN FORGET!
FORGET? HMM-MM! I THINK I'LL PLACE A LONG DISTANCE PHONE CALL TO POLICE COMMISSIONER GORDON!
LATER...
YOU SAY MOXON WAS IN AN AUTOMOBILE ACCIDENT RIGHT AFTER DR. WAYNE WAS MURDERED?
YES! HE HAD A HEAD INJURY! ONE DAY HE WANDERED AWAY FROM THE HOSPITAL AND NOBODY EVER SAW HIM AFTER THAT!
ROBIN, THAT HEAD INJURY GAVE MOXON AMNESIA, LOSS OF MEMORY! HE DOESN'T REMEMBER MY FATHER OR ANYTHING THAT HAPPENED BEFORE THE AUTO ACCIDENT!
GOLLY! WHAT'LL WE DO NOW?
KEEP AFTER MOXON! HE MUST BE INVOLVED IN SOMETHING SHADY--OTHERWISE HIS MEN WOULDN'T HAVE JUMPED US! TONIGHT WE'RE GOING TO TRAIL HIS BLIMP!
8

THAT NIGHT, A FLOATING BILLBOARD FLASHES ITS SKY-HIGH ELECTRIC SIGN...
NOTHING SUSPICIOUS HAPPENING SO FAR, BATMAN!
SUDDENLY, THE ELECTRIC LIGHTS WINK OUT, LEAVING THE DARK BLIMP ALMOST UNSEEN AGAINST THE NIGHT SKY...
LOOK! A MAN IS BEING LOWERED TO THAT PENTHOUSE! SO THAT'S MOXON'S ANGLE-- USING HIS BLIMP TO PULL SKY-HIGH BURGLARY JOBS!
AFTER SETTING THE VERSATILE BATPLANE ON ROBOT STABILIZER CONTROLS...
ROBIN, YOU GO AFTER THE MAN ON THE ROOF-- I'LL TAKE THE GONDOLA!
LIKE A HAWK, ROBIN PLUMMETS DOWN ON HIS QUARRY!
LOOKS LIKE I'VE GOT THE DROP ON YOU!
MEANWHILE, THE ACROBATMAN TRAPEZES THROUGH SPACE...
...AND SWIFTLY SCALING THE BLIMP'S ROPE LADDER, BURSTS INTO ITS GONDOLA!
BATMAN!
THIS BLIMP'S NEXT STOP WILL BE POLICE HEADQUARTERS!
LATER, AFTER THE PRISONERS ARE JAILED...
NOW LET'S PICK UP MOXON! BUT FIRST YOU'D BETTER CHANGE TO YOUR SPARE BATMAN COSTUME-- THAT LAST SCRAP REALLY SHREDDED THIS ONE!
OH, OH! I FORGOT TO PACK A SPARE IN THE BATPLANE!
9

SAY--HOW ABOUT WEARING YOUR FATHER'S COSTUME?
YES--IT WOULD BE APPROPRIATE! IT'D BE ALMOST AS IF DAD WERE ARRESTING MOXON!
LATER, ALONE IN HIS OFFICE, MOXON LOOKS UP TO SEE A GRIM FIGURE FRAMED IN THE DOORWAY!
WHO--?!
THAT COSTUME--I'VE SEEN IT BEFORE--LONG AGO! I'M BEGINNING TO REMEMBER--A DOCTOR--DOC WAYNE--HE WORE THAT COSTUME!
GREAT SCOTT! I DIDN'T REALIZE THE SHOCK OF SEEING THIS COSTUME WOULD JAR MOXON'S MEMORY!
GO AWAY! YOU'RE DEAD! I HAD JOEY CHILL KILL YOU! LEAVE ME ALONE!
FEAR-RIDDEN, MOXON WRENCHES OPEN A SIDE-DOOR AND RUSHES OUT INTO THE NIGHT...
HE'S COME BACK TO HAUNT ME! I'VE GOT TO GET AWAY--GET AWAY!...
MOXON! LOOK OUT! THAT TRUCK!
A SCREECH OF BRAKES--A CRY--AND MOXON'S CAREER OF VIOLENCE ENDS IN VIOLENCE...
I WANTED TO TAKE HIM ALIVE... TO STAND TRIAL FOR HIS CRIMES... BUT HIS OWN GUILT CONVICTED HIM!
10
SOON AFTER, A COSTUME OCCUPIES AN HONORED SPACE IN THE BAT-CAVE'S TROPHY ROOM!
FROM THE WAYNE MURDER CASE
CASE FINALLY SOLVED BY THIS COSTUME ONCE WORN BY THE FIRST BAT-MAN
THE END.

Art by Dick Sprang & Stan Kaye/Coloring by Daniel Vozzo

ONE NIGHT, IN THE GOTHAM CITY MANSION OF SOCIALITE BRUCE WAYNE AND HIS WARD, DICK GRAYSON...
AND HERE'S A BULLETIN FROM METROPOLIS! LUTHOR, THE SCIENTIFIC GENIUS OF CRIME, HAS ESCAPED FROM PRISON!
OH, OH-- THAT MEANS TROUBLE AHEAD!
LUTHOR ALWAYS BOASTED THAT SOME DAY HE'D HAVE HIS REVENGE ON BOTH SUPERMAN AND METROPOLIS!
LET'S NOT WASTE TIME, DICK-- WE'RE GOING TO METROPOLIS!
AND IN THE BAT-CAVE UNDER THE MANSION, THE TWO SWIFTLY CHANGE TO-- BATMAN AND ROBIN, THE BOY WONDER...
SUPERMAN MAY NEED OUR HELP IF LUTHOR USES KRYPTONITE FOR HIS VENGEANCE!
YES---KRYPTONITE WEAKENS SUPERMAN, BUT IT DOESN'T AFFECT ORDINARY PEOPLE LIKE US!
A SWIFT RIDE BY BATMOBILE BRINGS THEM WITHIN A FEW HOURS TO THE OUTSKIRTS OF METROPOLIS...
SUPERMAN WILL SEE OUR IMPROVISED BAT-SIGNAL AND COME HERE-- THEN WE'LL PLAN HOW TO DEAL WITH LUTHOR!
THERE HE COMES NOW-- BUT SOMEONE'S WITH HIM!
HELLO, SUPERMAN! WE FIGURED YOU MIGHT NEED HELP IF LUTHOR USED KRYPTONITE!
THANKS, BATMAN-- BUT MY NEW PARTNER, POWERMAN, WILL HELP ME, IF NECESSARY--
-- WHICH RELIEVES YOU! AND---ER--- POWERMAN DOESN'T WANT ANY MORE PEOPLE ON OUR TEAM!
SUPERMAN AND I CAN HANDLE THIS JOB BY OURSELVES!
2

WE CAN'T WASTE ANY MORE TIME HERE! WE MUST FIND LUTHOR!
YOU'RE RIGHT, POWERMAN! SORRY, BATMAN--!

WHOEVER POWERMAN IS, HE HASN'T SUPER-POWERS-- SUPERMAN IS CARRYING HIM!
AFTER ALL OUR CASES TOGETHER, HOW COULD SUPERMAN REJECT US LIKE THAT?

IT HURTS TO HAVE AN OLD FRIEND CAST YOU OFF!
IT JUST ISN'T LIKE SUPERMAN! MAYBE THIS POWERMAN MADE HIM DO IT-- HE MAY HAVE SOME HOLD ON SUPERMAN!

THAT MIGHT BE IT! POWERMAN DID SPEAK TO SUPERMAN DOMINEERINGLY! WE'LL GO ON TO METROPOLIS AND SECRETLY WATCH THEM, TO FIND OUT!

LATER, AS THE MAN OF STEEL AND HIS MYSTERIOUS NEW PARTNER SEARCH THE CITY...
AS LONG AS WE STAY BEHIND LEAD, LIKE THIS ORNAMENTAL CORNICE, SUPERMAN CAN'T SPOT US!
HE'S USING HIS X-RAY VISION FROM ABOVE WHILE POWERMAN SEARCHES ON FOOT!
PRODUCTS

IT WASN'T LIKE THIS THE FIRST TIME WE MET SUPERMAN, WHEN HE WAS MENACED BY KRYPTONITE, TOO!
YES, I REMEMBER!
3

"WE'D READ OF HIS FEATS WITH ADMIRATION, BUT HAD NEVER MET HIM---"
WOW, THAT SUPERMAN CAN DO ANYTHING! HE'S TERRIFIC!
I AGREE-- BUT WE'D BETTER GET ALONG WITH OUR SEARCH!
GOTHAM DAILY NEWS
SUPERMAN AVERTS METEOR DANGER
"WE'D BEEN LOOKING FOR THE LEADERS OF A SMUGGLING RING, AND THAT NIGHT OUR HUNT CAME TO AN END..."
HERE'S YOUR SHARE, BOYS!
SMUGGLING IN THAT KRYPTONITE WAS THE BEST-PAYING JOB YET!
GOTHAM IMPORT CO.
YOU'RE OUT OF BUSINESS--
CRACK
--BUT YOU'LL LEARN A NEW TRADE IN JAIL!
"OUR PRISONERS WOULDN'T ANSWER QUESTIONS"...
THEY MENTIONED KRYPTONITE! IT'S THE ONE ELEMENT THAT WEAKENS SUPERMAN!
IT MUST BE FOR SOMEONE TO USE IT AGAINST HIM! WE'RE GOING TO METROPOLIS TO WARN HIM! LET'S GET THE BATPLANE...
GEE, BATMAN, WE'RE GOING TO MEET SUPERMAN HIMSELF!
"WHEN WE REACHED METROPOLIS..."
BATMAN, LOOK-- A HELICOPTER SNATCHING UP AN ARMORED CAR!
4

THEY'RE GETTING AWAY, BATMAN!
WE DAREN'T RISK FORCING IT TO CRASH IN THE STREETS-- WE'LL HAVE TO FOLLOW!
"SUDDENLY, ACROSS THE SKY STREAKED AN INCREDIBLE FIGURE!"
BATMAN LOOK--IT'S HIM-- SUPERMAN!
"FOR THE FIRST TIME, WE SAW SUPERMAN IN ACTION!"
THERE HE COMES-- GET THE GUN READY!
YOU KNOW THAT GUNS DON'T STOP ME!
BUT THIS GUN WILL! IT SHOOTS LIQUID KRYPTONITE!
"TO OUR ASTONISHMENT, WE SAW SUPERMAN FALL HELPLESSLY!"
BATMAN, WHAT'LL WE DO?
WE'VE GOT TO PREVENT HIM FROM FALLING INTO THE CROWDED STREETS--
"I SENT THE BAT-PLANE INTO A SCREAMING POWER-DIVE..."
5

GOT HIM!
AND JUST IN TIME -- HE'S INVULNERABLE, BUT IF HE FELL INTO THE CROWD BELOW, HE'D INJURE MANY PEOPLE!
THOSE THIEVES ESCAPED WHILE WE DIVED TO CATCH SUPERMAN!
BATMAN, I CAN'T ROUSE HIM! PUT ON THE AUTOMATIC PILOT, AND HELP ME!
HE'S SPATTERED WITH THAT KRYPTONITE SOLUTION! WE'VE GOT TO GET IT OFF HIM FAST, AND I THINK I KNOW HOW!
"WE RIGGED A ROPE SLING AND THEN, ZOOMING TOWARD A NEARBY WATERFALL..."
THIS SHOULD WASH EVERY PARTICLE OF KRYPTONITE OFF HIM!
HE'S STIRRING, BATMAN!
"PRESENTLY..."
BATMAN! I'VE HEARD OF ALL YOUR GREAT FEATS! YOU CAME IN THE NICK OF TIME!
BUT WE WERE TOO LATE TO WARN YOU OF THE KRYPTONITE DANGER!
WE'RE IMMUNE TO KRYPTONITE, SO WE CAN HELP YOU AGAINST THOSE CROOKS, IF YOU WISH!
IF I WISH? IT WOULD BE AN HONOR TO WORK WITH BATMAN AND ROBIN!
6

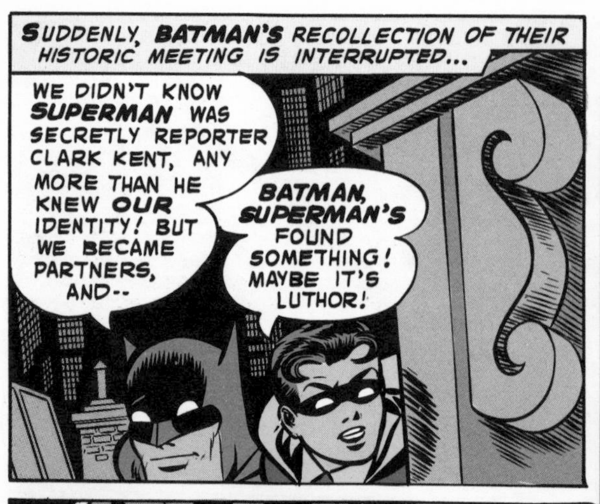
SUDDENLY, BATMAN'S RECOLLECTION OF THEIR HISTORIC MEETING IS INTERRUPTED...
WE DIDN'T KNOW SUPERMAN WAS SECRETLY REPORTER CLARK KENT, ANY MORE THAN HE KNEW OUR IDENTITY! BUT WE BECAME PARTNERS, AND--
BATMAN, SUPERMAN'S FOUND SOMETHING! MAYBE IT'S LUTHOR!

THERE'S GAS LEAKING FROM A LOOSE MAIN UNDER THE BUILDING! IT'LL EXPLODE AT THE FIRST SPARK--

THERE'S NO ONE IN THE BUILDING. I'LL LIFT IT AND LET THE GAS DISSIPATE! POWERMAN CAN TIGHTEN THE LOOSE PIPE!

POWERMAN IS MAKING THE REPAIR! HE MAY NOT HAVE SUPERPOWERS, BUT HE'S STRONG!
MAYBE HE'S A PROFESSIONAL STRONG-MAN--- BUT WHY WOULD SUPERMAN CHOOSE HIM?

IT'S SAFE NOW! WE'VE GOT TO GO ON LOOKING FOR LUTHOR!
I'M RIGHT WITH YOU!

I STILL DON'T UNDERSTAND WHY SUPERMAN WOULDN'T LET US HELP HIM SEARCH FOR LUTHOR, TOO.
IT WAS POWERMAN WHO OBJECTED TO US! IF WE FIND OUT WHO HE IS, WE MAY LEARN THE REASON!
7

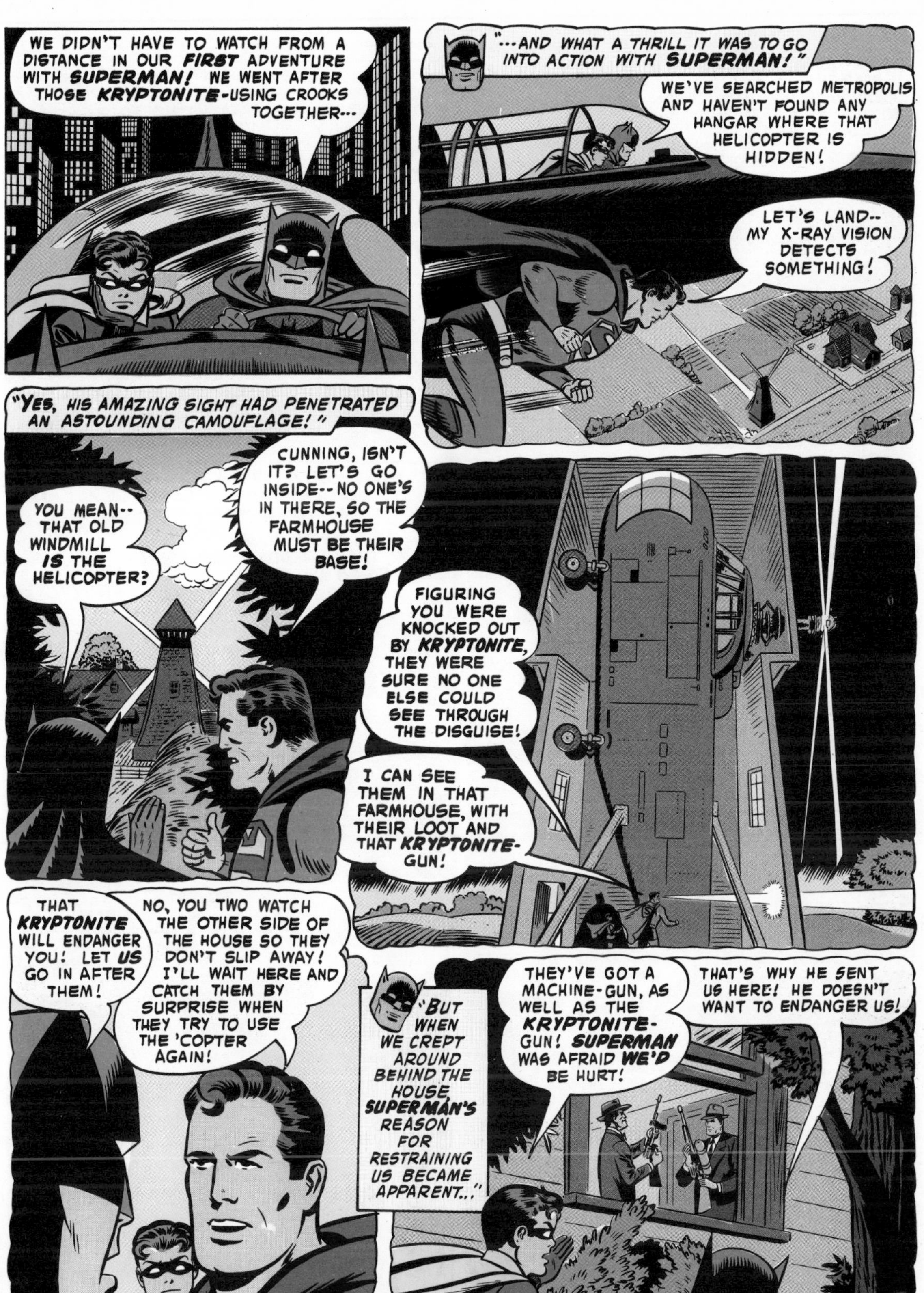
WE DIDN'T HAVE TO WATCH FROM A DISTANCE IN OUR FIRST ADVENTURE WITH SUPERMAN! WE WENT AFTER THOSE KRYPTONITE-USING CROOKS TOGETHER...
"...AND WHAT A THRILL IT WAS TO GO INTO ACTION WITH SUPERMAN!"
WE'VE SEARCHED METROPOLIS AND HAVEN'T FOUND ANY HANGAR WHERE THAT HELICOPTER IS HIDDEN!
LET'S LAND-- MY X-RAY VISION DETECTS SOMETHING!
"YES, HIS AMAZING SIGHT HAD PENETRATED AN ASTOUNDING CAMOUFLAGE!"
YOU MEAN-- THAT OLD WINDMILL IS THE HELICOPTER?
CUNNING, ISN'T IT? LET'S GO INSIDE-- NO ONE'S IN THERE, SO THE FARMHOUSE MUST BE THEIR BASE!
FIGURING YOU WERE KNOCKED OUT BY KRYPTONITE, THEY WERE SURE NO ONE ELSE COULD SEE THROUGH THE DISGUISE!
I CAN SEE THEM IN THAT FARMHOUSE, WITH THEIR LOOT AND THAT KRYPTONITE-GUN!
THAT KRYPTONITE WILL ENDANGER YOU! LET US GO IN AFTER THEM!
NO, YOU TWO WATCH THE OTHER SIDE OF THE HOUSE SO THEY DON'T SLIP AWAY! I'LL WAIT HERE AND CATCH THEM BY SURPRISE WHEN THEY TRY TO USE THE 'COPTER AGAIN!
"BUT WHEN WE CREPT AROUND BEHIND THE HOUSE SUPERMAN'S REASON FOR RESTRAINING US BECAME APPARENT..."
THEY'VE GOT A MACHINE-GUN, AS WELL AS THE KRYPTONITE-GUN! SUPERMAN WAS AFRAID WE'D BE HURT!
THAT'S WHY HE SENT US HERE! HE DOESN'T WANT TO ENDANGER US!
8

WE CAN'T LET SUPERMAN FACE THAT KRYPTONITE GUN TO PROTECT US!
I'VE AN IDEA-- LET'S SLIP BACK TO THE BAT-PLANE!

"AND INSIDE THE PLANE..."
MY DISGUISE WILL BE FINISHED IN A MINUTE!
AND SO WILL THE MAKESHIFT COSTUME--LUCKY FOR US WE USE COLORED PARACHUTES FOR IDENTIFICATION!

"MINUTES LATER, MY DISGUISE WAS COMPLETE..."
YOU'RE A DEAD RINGER FOR SUPERMAN NOW, BATMAN!
I ONLY HOPE MY PLAN WORKS!

BUT AGAIN, BATMAN'S MEMORIES OF THEIR FIRST GREAT CASE WITH SUPERMAN ARE INTERRUPTED...
BATMAN, WE'VE LOST THEIR TRAIL! I DON'T SEE SUPERMAN AND POWERMAN ANYWHERE AHEAD!
WE'RE HERE, ROBIN!

YOU COULDN'T KEEP THE BATMOBILE SHIELDED. I GLIMPSED YOU FOLLOWING ME!
AND NOW WE'VE REACHED THE AREA WHERE LUTHOR MUST BE HIDING, WE DON'T WANT YOU AROUND!

LET US GO WITH YOU, SUPERMAN! IF LUTHOR USES KRYPTONITE, YOU'LL NEED OUR HELP!
I'M ALL THE HELP SUPERMAN NEEDS!
9

I AGREE WITH POWERMAN-- YOU MUST LEAVE!
YOU'RE REJECTING YOUR FRIENDS FOR THIS POWERMAN, WHOEVER HE IS!
IT'S ALL RIGHT, ROBIN-- WE'LL GO!

AND AS THE DEPRESSED DUO DEPART...
TO TREAT YOU LIKE THAT, AFTER THE RISKS YOU TOOK FOR HIM, IN OUR FIRST CASE! I REMEMBER YOUR RISKY BLUFF--
METROPOLIS

"...GOING RIGHT INTO THE CROOKS' HIDEOUT, DISGUISED AS SUPERMAN..."
IT'S SUPERMAN!
THIS KRYPTONITE-GUN WILL STOP HIM AGAIN!

"AGAIN, THEY USED THE KRYPTONITE WEAPON, BUT THIS TIME..."
IT DOESN'T AFFECT HIM THIS TIME!
NOT A BIT-- I CAN PROTECT MYSELF AGAINST IT NOW!

"BUT, ALL AT ONCE..."
LOOK, THE SPRAY WASHED MAKE-UP OFF HIS FACE! HE'S NOT SUPERMAN!
SO THAT'S WHY KRYPTONITE DIDN'T STOP HIM-- BUT THE MACHINE-GUN WILL!

"THAT'S WHEN I WENT INTO ACTION!"
SUPERMAN! NOW'S YOUR CHANCE--
GUN THEM DOWN! GET THAT KRYPTONITE-GUN BACK TO USE ON THE REAL SUPERMAN!
10

BATMAN! I'D NEVER HAVE LET YOU TAKE THE RISK IF I'D KNOWN!
THE BLUFF WORKED, THOUGH! WE'VE ROUNDED THEM UP!
"LATER, WHEN WE PARTED..."
I'LL NEVER FORGET HOW WE WORKED TOGETHER, BATMAN -- BUT I NEVER WANT YOU TO RISK YOUR LIFE FOR ME AGAIN!
MAYBE YOU CAN PAY BACK THE FAVOR SOME DAY, SUPERMAN!
AND NOW THAT'S HOW HE REPAYS YOU -- CASTING YOU OFF FOR THIS POWERMAN!
ROBIN, YOU JUST REMINDED ME OF SOMETHING THAT SUGGESTS WHY SUPERMAN HAS BEEN ACTING THIS WAY!
SUPERMAN WOULD ONLY REJECT US BECAUSE, AS IN OUR FIRST CASE, HE WOULDN'T ENDANGER US TO HELP HIM! I'VE GOT AN IDEA -- I WANT TO SEE HOW LUTHOR ESCAPED FROM JAIL!
METROPOLIS PRISON
AND, SHORTLY AFTER, IN THE METROPOLIS PRISON...
SUPERMAN ASKED ME NOT TO TELL ANYONE, BUT, OF COURSE, THAT WOULDN'T INCLUDE YOU, BATMAN! LUTHOR SECRETLY MADE A DESTRUCTIVE RAY DEVICE, AND CUT RIGHT OUT THROUGH THE WALL!
I SEE BITS OF SILICON WERE LEFT, SO HIS RAY DIDN'T AFFECT THAT ELEMENT!
BECAUSE LUTHOR'S RAY COULD DESTROY US, SUPERMAN WOULDN'T LET US HELP! BUT I KNOW HOW WE STILL CAN!
I DON'T GET IT! IF HE WOULDN'T ENDANGER US, WHY WOULD HE IMPERIL POWERMAN?
11

SHORTLY, AS SUPERMAN AND HIS NEW ALLY CLOSE IN ON LUTHOR'S HIDEOUT...
THAT'S LUTHOR'S RAY, WHICH HE'LL USE TO TAKE REVENGE ON METROPOLIS! BUT IT CAN'T HURT ME! I'M GOING IN!
BUT LUTHOR WILL USE KRYPTONITE ON YOU, SUPERMAN-- SO WE'RE GOING IN INSTEAD!
METROPOLIS WAREHOUSE COMPANY
BATMAN! THAT RAY WILL DESTROY YOU---
I LEARNED THAT IT DOESN'T AFFECT SILICON, SO I IMPROVISED SOME SILICON SHIELDS! COME ON, ROBIN!
METROPOLIS WAREHOUSE COMPANY
AND BEFORE SUPERMAN CAN STOP THEM...
THEIR SHIELDS DEFLECT THE RAY, BUT OUR KRYPTONITE WILL STOP SUPERMAN!
YOU WON'T GET A CHANCE TO USE IT, LUTHOR!
I'VE GOT THE KRYPTONITE, SUPERMAN!
COVER IT, SO I CAN GET HIM!
SOON...
IT'S LIKE OUR FIRST CASE TOGETHER, BATMAN!
BUT YOUR FRIEND POWERMAN DIDN'T DO ANYTHING--
12
HE'S A ROBOT, WITH A TAPE-PLAYER SPEECH DEVICE, THAT I OPERATED BY REMOTE CONTROL. RATHER THAN ENDANGER YOU TWO, I PLANNED TO USE HIM IF I RAN INTO KRYPTONITE!
WE MIGHT HAVE KNOWN YOU'D NEVER REPLACE US WITH A REAL NEW PARTNER!
THE END

Art by Sheldon Moldoff & Charles Paris/Coloring by Carl Gafford

"WHERE IS BATMAN?" ROBIN WONDERS! AND THE FAMED CRIME-FIGHTER SOON WONDERS, TOO-- FOR HIS WHEREABOUTS IS A MYSTERY TO HIMSELF!

ALL BATMAN KNOWS IS THAT HE IS BEING SWEPT ALONG BY SWIRLING LIGHTS THROUGH VAST REACHES OF SPACE...

THEN SAND CRUNCHES UNDER HIS FEET--AND AN UNFAMILIAR LANDSCAPE ENCIRLES HIM!
TWIN MOONS! I'M ON AN ALIEN PLANET!

THOSE SWIRLING LIGHTS-- WERE THEY AN ALIEN ENERGY THAT TRANSMITTED ME HERE? I--I CAN'T REMEMBER! MAYBE ALIENS DELIBERATELY ERASED MY MEMORY! BUT WHY? WHAT IS IT THEY DON'T WANT ME TO REMEMBER?

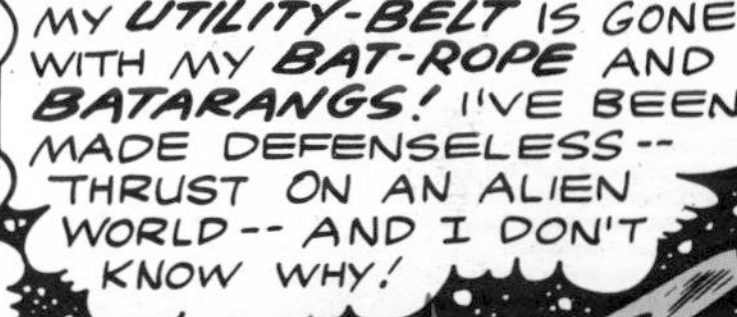

MY UTILITY-BELT IS GONE-- WITH MY BAT-ROPE AND BATARANGS! I'VE BEEN MADE DEFENSELESS-- THRUST ON AN ALIEN WORLD-- AND I DON'T KNOW WHY!

THEN BATMAN IS TOUCHED BY A TINY FEAR--THE INSTINCTIVE FEAR OF ANY MAN WHO IS ISOLATED AND WEAPONLESS--AND CONFRONTED BY THE UNKNOWN!
IT'S NOT KNOWING THAT'S SO DISQUIETING! AND SOMEHOW I SENSE TERRIBLE DANGER-- WAITING! I--I'VE NEVER FELT SO ALONE IN ALL MY LIFE...
2

SO, BATMAN TRUDGES ON THROUGH THE ALIEN LAND, UNTIL ...
THE RUINS OF A DESERTED CITY! IT'S SO ANCIENT THE PLANTS HAVE TAKEN OVER!

WITHOUT WARNING, SOMETHING SHOOTS OUT AT HIM ...
GREAT SCOTT! THAT PLANT'S TENDRIL HAS ELONGATED AND WRAPPED ITSELF AROUND ME! GOT TO YANK MYSELF LOOSE!

BUT BEFORE BATMAN CAN MOVE ...
UH--CAN'T FREE MY ARM! I'M HELPLESS!
THEN AS THE TERRIBLE PLANT RELENTLESSLY TIGHTENS ITS GRIP...
IF ONLY ROBIN WERE HERE TO HELP ME! ROBIN! WHERE ARE YOU, ROBIN? ROBIN!

SUDDENLY, A FAMILIAR, STURDY FIGURE RACES FORWARD ...
I'LL GET YOU FREE!
ROBIN!
3

ALL RIGHT NOW?
CRACK
YES-- THE TENDRILS HAVE RELAXED THEIR GRIP!
ROBIN--HOW DID YOU GET HERE?
NO TIME TO TALK NOW! MORE PLANTS ARE COMING! THEY CAN WALK! LET'S GET AWAY FROM HERE--FAST!
LATER...
THE SUN! DAWN'S APPROACHING!
WHY DO I FEEL SO UNEASY? WHY DO I FEEL THAT THERE ARE EYES WATCHING-- EYES WITH HUMAN INTELLIGENCE?
LOOK! A GIANT STATUE!
IT MUST BE AN IDOL THAT THE ALIENS WORSHIP!
THEN, AMAZINGLY, THE STONE FIGURE SUDDENLY REARS ERECT!
IT'S ALIVE-- AND COMING AFTER US! RUN, ROBIN-- RUN!
4

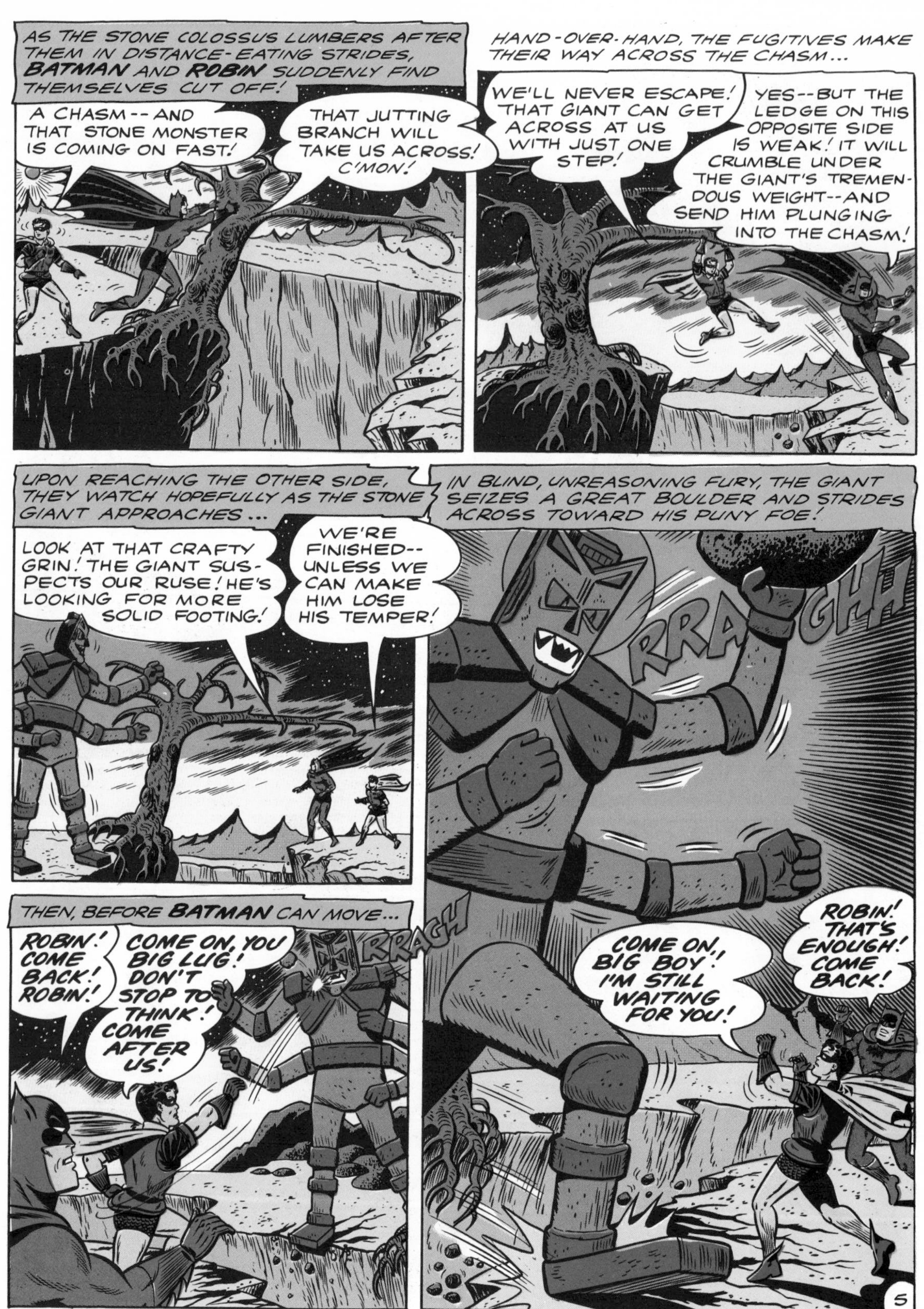

AS THE STONE COLOSSUS LUMBERS AFTER THEM IN DISTANCE-EATING STRIDES, BATMAN AND ROBIN SUDDENLY FIND THEMSELVES CUT OFF!
A CHASM--AND THAT STONE MONSTER IS COMING ON FAST!
THAT JUTTING BRANCH WILL TAKE US ACROSS! C'MON!
HAND-OVER-HAND, THE FUGITIVES MAKE THEIR WAY ACROSS THE CHASM...
WE'LL NEVER ESCAPE! THAT GIANT CAN GET ACROSS AT US WITH JUST ONE STEP!
YES--BUT THE LEDGE ON THIS OPPOSITE SIDE IS WEAK! IT WILL CRUMBLE UNDER THE GIANT'S TREMENDOUS WEIGHT--AND SEND HIM PLUNGING INTO THE CHASM!
UPON REACHING THE OTHER SIDE, THEY WATCH HOPEFULLY AS THE STONE GIANT APPROACHES...
LOOK AT THAT CRAFTY GRIN! THE GIANT SUSPECTS OUR RUSE! HE'S LOOKING FOR MORE SOLID FOOTING!
WE'RE FINISHED--UNLESS WE CAN MAKE HIM LOSE HIS TEMPER!
THEN, BEFORE BATMAN CAN MOVE...
ROBIN! COME BACK! ROBIN!
COME ON, YOU BIG LUG! DON'T STOP TO THINK! COME AFTER US!
RRAGH
IN BLIND, UNREASONING FURY, THE GIANT SEIZES A GREAT BOULDER AND STRIDES ACROSS TOWARD HIS PUNY FOE!
RRAGHH
COME ON, BIG BOY! I'M STILL WAITING FOR YOU!
ROBIN! THAT'S ENOUGH! COME BACK!
5

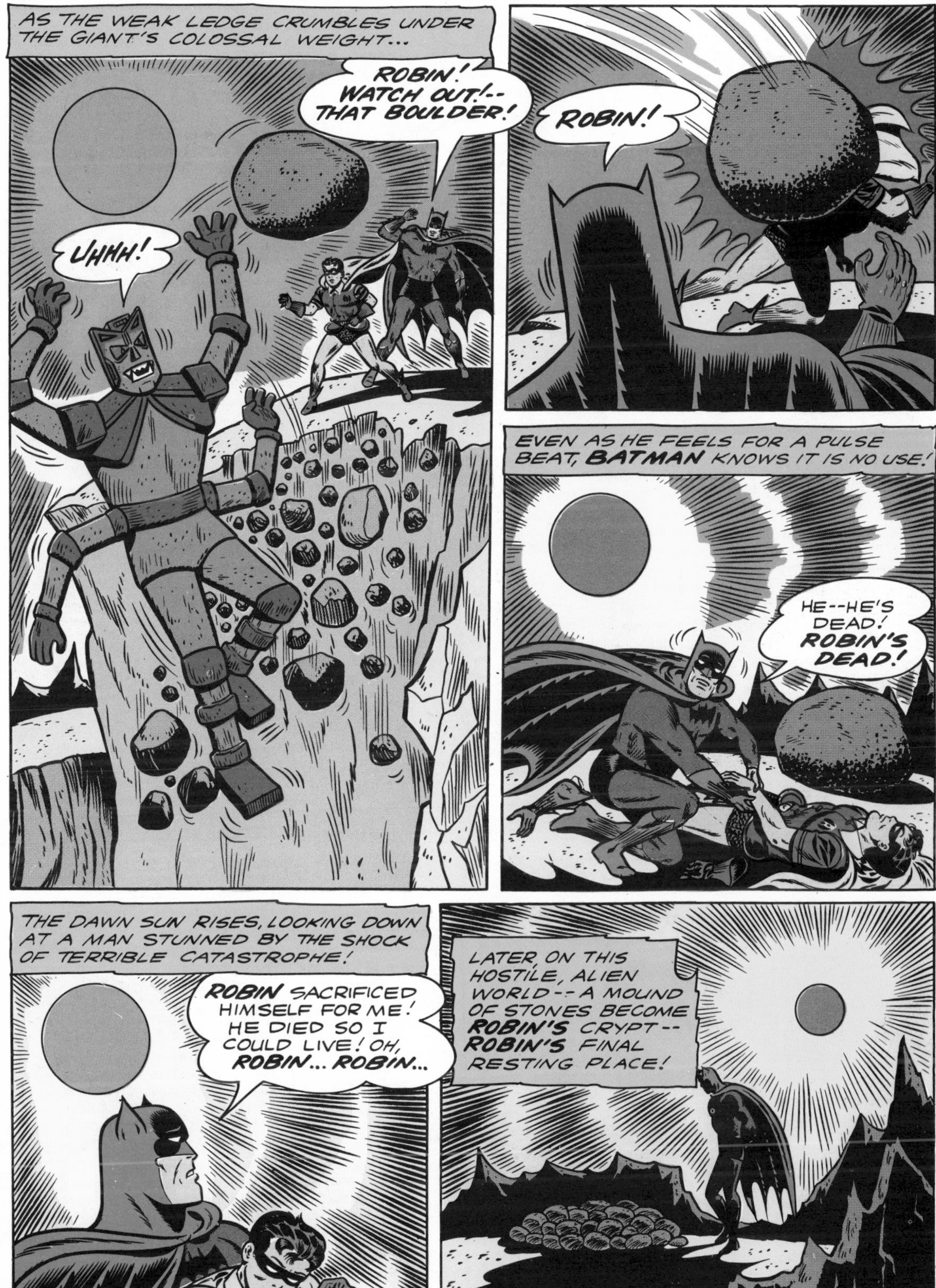
AS THE WEAK LEDGE CRUMBLES UNDER THE GIANT'S COLOSSAL WEIGHT...
ROBIN! WATCH OUT!-- THAT BOULDER!
UHHH!
ROBIN!
EVEN AS HE FEELS FOR A PULSE BEAT, BATMAN KNOWS IT IS NO USE!
HE--HE'S DEAD! ROBIN'S DEAD!
THE DAWN SUN RISES, LOOKING DOWN AT A MAN STUNNED BY THE SHOCK OF TERRIBLE CATASTROPHE!
ROBIN SACRIFICED HIMSELF FOR ME! HE DIED SO I COULD LIVE! OH, ROBIN... ROBIN...
LATER ON THIS HOSTILE, ALIEN WORLD-- A MOUND OF STONES BECOME ROBIN'S CRYPT-- ROBIN'S FINAL RESTING PLACE!
6

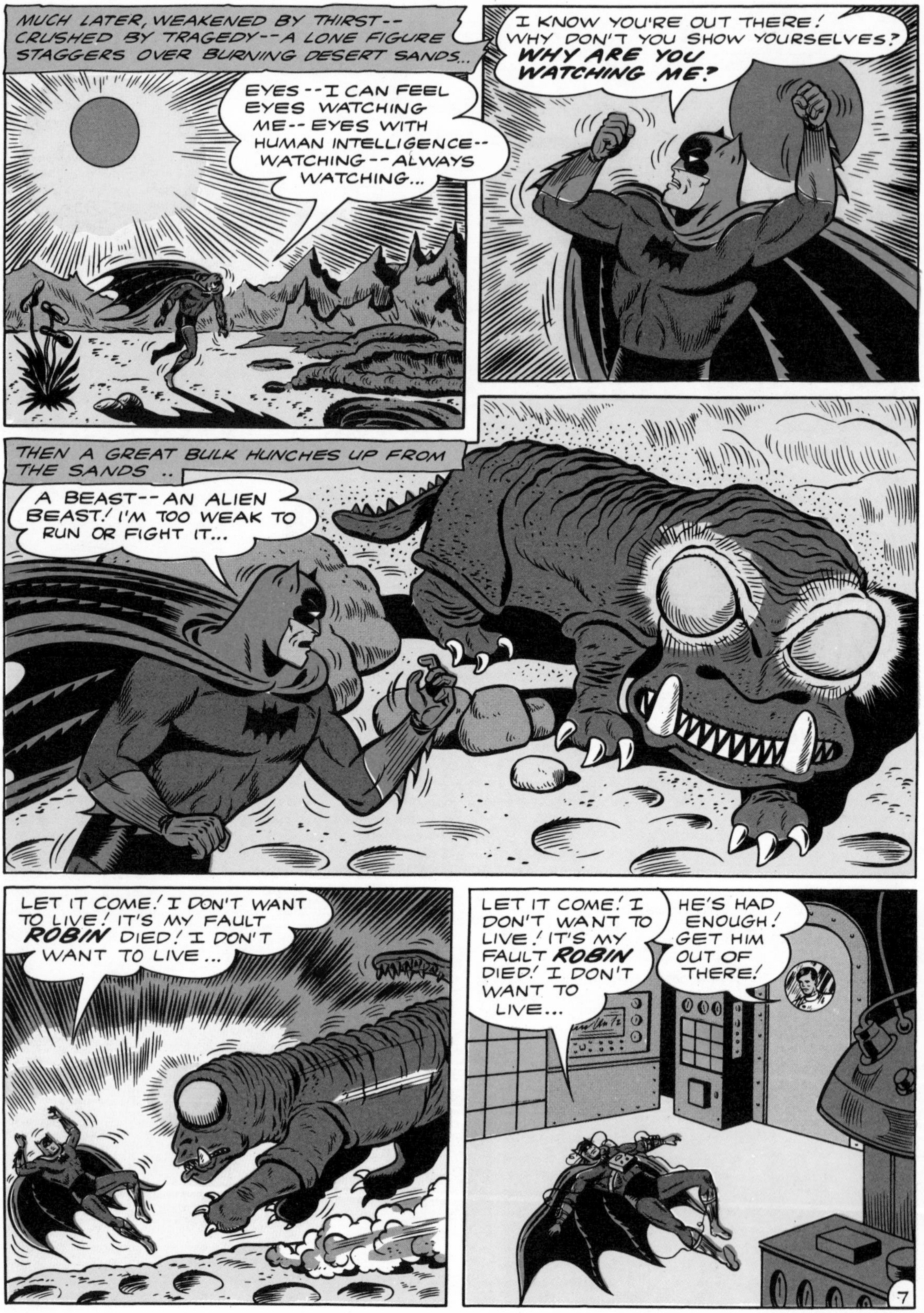

MUCH LATER, WEAKENED BY THIRST-- CRUSHED BY TRAGEDY--A LONE FIGURE STAGGERS OVER BURNING DESERT SANDS...

EYES--I CAN FEEL EYES WATCHING ME--EYES WITH HUMAN INTELLIGENCE--WATCHING--ALWAYS WATCHING...

I KNOW YOU'RE OUT THERE! WHY DON'T YOU SHOW YOURSELVES? ***WHY ARE YOU WATCHING ME?***

THEN A GREAT BULK HUNCHES UP FROM THE SANDS ..

A BEAST--AN ALIEN BEAST! I'M TOO WEAK TO RUN OR FIGHT IT...

SWIFTLY, A HATCH OPENS--FIGURES HURRY TO BATMAN'S SIDE...
WHAT...? ROBIN--ALIVE! I--I...
EASY, BATMAN--EVERYTHING'S UNDER CONTROL! YOU'RE IN THE TEST CHAMBER--REMEMBER?
THE TEST--I REMEMBER NOW! I DIDN'T WANT YOU TO WORRY--I LEFT A LETTER WITH GORDON FOR YOU--TO BE GIVEN TO YOU AFTER TWO DAYS...
YES--I GOT THE NOTE--AND I'VE BEEN COMING HERE EVERY DAY SINCE THEN, TO LOOK IN ON YOU!
WELL, DOC--HOW DID I DO?
YOU DID FINE! YOU MADE A SIMULATED "FLIGHT" INTO SPACE IN THIS CHAMBER THAT DUPLICATES CONDITIONS AN ASTRONAUT MIGHT UNDERGO IF HE FOUND HIMSELF ALONE ON SUCH A SPACE FLIGHT!
BATMAN, BY VOLUNTEERING FOR THIS TEST, YOU'VE MADE A GREAT CONTRIBUTION TO SPACE MEDICINE!
YES, INDEED! THE DATA COLLECTED ON THESE SENSITIVE RECORDING INSTRUMENTS WILL ENABLE US TO GAUGE EFFECTS ON AN ASTRONAUT'S NERVOUS SYSTEM!
YOUR REACTIONS WILL HELP US DETERMINE HOW LONG, AND WHAT KINDS OF STRAINS AN ASTRONAUT CAN ENDURE IN LONELINESS, BEFORE HIS MIND STARTS IMAGINING THINGS...
IMAGINING THINGS...I HAD AN HALLUCINATION...
WE GUESSED THAT WHEN WE HEARD YOU YELLING! YOU CAN TELL ME ABOUT IT TOMORROW--BUT RIGHT NOW YOU NEED SLEEP!
8

THE FOLLOWING DAY, AFTER MANY TESTS, BATMAN DICTATES HIS HALLUCINATION INTO A TAPE RECORDER...
THOSE EYES I SENSED WATCHING ME-- NOW I REALIZE THEY WERE YOUR EYES WATCHING THROUGH THE OBSERVATION WINDOW! STRANGE, HOW AFRAID I WAS OF BEING ALONE...
NOT SO STRANGE!...
ONE OF MAN'S MOST PRIMITIVE FEARS IS LONELINESS! WHEN A MAN IS ISOLATED TOO LONG, THE MIND PLAYS STRANGE TRICKS... IN YOUR CASE, YOU IMAGINED THAT YOU WERE INDIRECTLY GUILTY OF ROBIN'S DEATH... YOUR CONSTANT CONCERN ABOUT THE BOY'S SAFETY CAME TO THE SURFACE IN YOUR HALLUCINATIONS!

LATER, AS BATMAN LEAVES FOR HOME...
DOCTOR, YOU LOOK WORRIED...
I AM! BATMAN'S A HARDY SPECIMEN, WITH AN ABOVE-AVERAGE MIND-- BUT EVEN A BATMAN CAN SUCCUMB TO STRESS AND SHOCK! I JUST HOPE THERE WON'T BE ANY AFTER-EFFECTS...
US
9
CONTINUED IN CHAPTER 2

SUPERMAN DC NATIONAL COMICS
APPROVED BY THE COMICS CODE AUTHORITY
Detective COMICS
"BATMAN'S FIRST CASE!"
GOLLY! WHAT A MESS BATMAN GOT HIMSELF INTO BEFORE HIS CAREER HAD EVEN STARTED!
THIS COSTUMED CHARACTER WALKED RIGHT INTO MY TRAP!
R
BATMAN'S DIARY

For The VERY BEST
SUPERMAN DC NATIONAL COMICS
in COMICS READING

SUPERMAN DC NATIONAL COMICS
10¢
OCT. NO. 127
APPROVED BY THE COMICS CODE AUTHORITY
BATMAN
Featuring "THE HAMMER of THOR!"
YOU DARE TO DEFY THOR, THE THUNDERGOD! LET THIS BE A WARNING!

CHAPTER 2 ROBIN DIES AT DAWN

HOMEWARD BOUND, ROBIN BRIEFS BATMAN ON THE ANT-MAN CASE, WHEN...
ACME LOAN CO.
ROBIN, DO YOU SEE WHAT I SEE? GORILLAS ESCAPING WITH MONEY FROM THAT LOAN COMPANY!

THEY'RE ONLY MEN WEARING GORILLA COSTUMES, BATMAN! ACCORDING TO POLICE REPORTS, THE GORILLA GANG HAS BEEN OPERATING IN VARIOUS CITIES! NOW THEY'VE COME TO GOTHAM CITY-- SO LET'S GIVE THEM A FITTING "WELCOME"!

SWIFTLY, SILENTLY, BATMAN AND ROBIN DART UP THE FIRE-ESCAPE--AND CHARGE INTO THE GORILLA GANG!

NOW LET'S MAKE MONKEYS OUT OF THESE APES!

BATMAN AND ROBIN! QUICK-- WE'LL HAVE TO ESCAPE TO THE NEXT BUILDING, OVER THE DANGLING GIRDER!

ACME LOAN

10

AS ROBIN RACES AHEAD TOWARD THE FLEEING BANDITS, BATMAN SUDDENLY STARES AT THE TALL CONSTRUCTION CRANE...

...AND IT SEEMS TO ALTER...

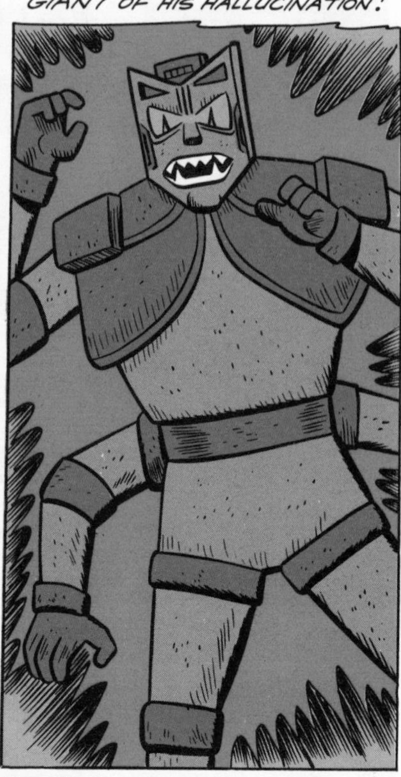
...TO BECOME THE STONE GIANT OF HIS HALLUCINATION!

ONCE AGAIN BATMAN SEEMS TO SEE ROBIN IN PERIL, AND ACTS INSTINCTIVELY!
NO, ROBIN--NO!

BUT, TO ROBIN'S EYES, THE SCENE IS A VERY DIFFERENT ONE!
BATMAN! YOU'RE TAKING US OVER THE EDGE OF THE ROOF!

ROBIN'S SUDDEN SHOUT JOLTS BATMAN'S LAPSE OF MEMORY--AND HE INSTANTLY FLINGS OUT A HAND THAT CLINGS WITH AN IRON GRIP!
IT'S OKAY, ROBIN--WE'RE SAFE NOW!
WOW!
11

LATER, AFTER BATMAN TELLS OF HIS MOMENTARY HALLUCINATION...
SORRY, ROBIN--I GUESS I'M STILL A LITTLE SHAKY FROM THE TEST! I--I'LL BE BACK TO NORMAL BY TOMORROW!
I SURE HOPE SO--FOR BATMAN'S SAKE

LATER, AT THE WAYNE MANSION, BRUCE'S RETURN IS EAGERLY AWAITED BY TWO LOYAL FRIENDS!
ALFRED! ACE! AH, IT'S GOOD TO BE BACK HOME AGAIN!
WE ALL MISSED YOU, SIR!

FOUR O'CLOCK IN THE MORNING! THE HOUSE IS QUIET--UNTIL A SHOUT SENDS DICK BURSTING INTO BRUCE'S ROOM...
THE TENTACLES--TIGHTENING ABOUT ME! HELP! ROBIN! HELP!
GOSH! HE'S DREAMING ABOUT THE TENTACLE-PLANT!
CLICK

AS THE SUDDEN ILLUMINATION AWAKENS BRUCE...
UH...? I'M HOME! OH, I HAD A NIGHTMARE! IT WAS AWFUL--AWFUL...
BRUCE, I'LL HAVE ACE SLEEP IN HERE TONIGHT--SO YOU WON'T FEEL SO ALONE...

Y-YES... MAYBE THAT WOULD BE BETTER...

THE FOLLOWING NIGHT, AS DICK DESCENDS TO THE BAT-CAVE...
YOU'RE NOT REALLY GOING ON PATROL?
I CERTAINLY AM! I FEEL FINE TODAY! BESIDES, WITH THE GORILLA GANG IN TOWN, THE POLICE MAY NEED OUR HELP! GET DRESSED, DICK!
12

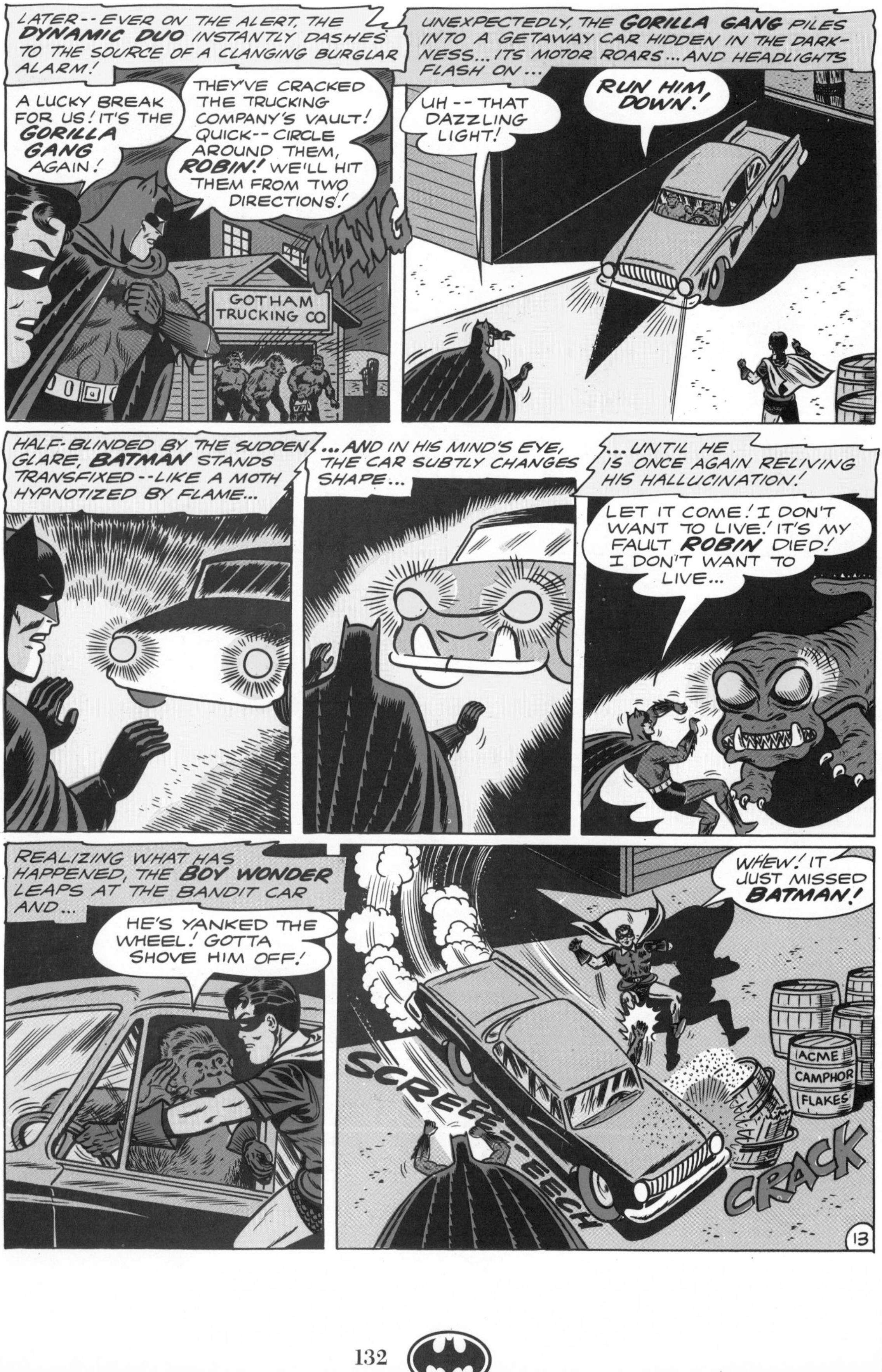

LATER--EVER ON THE ALERT, THE **DYNAMIC DUO** INSTANTLY DASHES TO THE SOURCE OF A CLANGING BURGLAR ALARM!

A LUCKY BREAK FOR US! IT'S THE **GORILLA GANG** AGAIN!

THEY'VE CRACKED THE TRUCKING COMPANY'S VAULT! QUICK--CIRCLE AROUND THEM, **ROBIN!** WE'LL HIT THEM FROM TWO DIRECTIONS!

CLANG

GOTHAM TRUCKING CO.

UNEXPECTEDLY, THE **GORILLA GANG** PILES INTO A GETAWAY CAR HIDDEN IN THE DARKNESS...ITS MOTOR ROARS...AND HEADLIGHTS FLASH ON...

UH--THAT DAZZLING LIGHT!

RUN HIM DOWN!

HALF-BLINDED BY THE SUDDEN GLARE, **BATMAN** STANDS TRANSFIXED--LIKE A MOTH HYPNOTIZED BY FLAME...

...AND IN HIS MIND'S EYE, THE CAR SUBTLY CHANGES SHAPE...

...UNTIL HE IS ONCE AGAIN RELIVING HIS HALLUCINATION!

LET IT COME! I DON'T WANT TO LIVE! IT'S MY FAULT **ROBIN** DIED! I DON'T WANT TO LIVE...

REALIZING WHAT HAS HAPPENED, THE BOY WONDER LEAPS AT THE BANDIT CAR AND...
HE'S YANKED THE WHEEL! GOTTA SHOVE HIM OFF!

WHEW! IT JUST MISSED BATMAN!
SCREEE-EECH
ACME
CAMPHOR
FLAKES
CRACK
13

IT IS THE SPLINTERING OF THE CAMPHOR BARREL THAT SNAPS BATMAN OUT OF HIS MOMENTARY TRANCE...
I--I MUST HAVE BLACKED OUT AGAIN! ROBIN-- WHAT HAPPENED?
I'LL TELL YOU ABOUT IT WHEN WE GET HOME...
LATER, BATMAN AT LAST REALIZES THERE IS SOMETHING VERY, VERY WRONG WITH HIM...
LET'S FACE REALITY! WHILE I HAVE THESE MENTAL BLACKOUTS, I ENDANGER YOUR LIFE! I CAN'T EVER LET THAT HAPPEN AGAIN! THERE'S ONLY ONE THING I CAN DO...
...I MUST PUT AWAY MY BATMAN COSTUME AND RETIRE FROM CRIME-FIGHTING!
OH, BATMAN! SOB
THE FOLLOWING NIGHT--ONLY ONE MEMBER OF THE FAMED TEAM DONS CRIME-FIGHTING GARB...
I'VE AN APPOINTMENT WITH PROFESSOR CARSON--ABOUT THE TESTIMONY WE'LL GIVE AT THE ANT-MAN'S TRIAL! I--I'LL BE BACK AS SOON AS I CAN!
I-IF YOU RUN INTO CRIMINAL ACTIVITY, BE EVEN MORE CAREFUL THAN YOU WOULD BE IF I WERE ALONG!
BUT ONE THING ROBIN KEEPS FROM BATMAN IS A SECRET APPOINTMENT WITH THE ARMY DOCTOR...
I WAS AFRAID OF THIS! BATMAN WILL NEED TREATMENT! THEN, EVENTUALLY, HE WILL BE HIMSELF AGAIN-- BUT IT WILL TAKE TIME...
HOURS PASS, AND KEEPING HIS VIGIL IN THE BAT-CAVE, BRUCE IS GETTING WORRIED, WHEN...
THE EMERGENCY BAT-SIGNAL FROM COMMISSIONER GORDON! I'D BETTER CONTACT HIM AT ONCE ON THE BATMOBILE'S TWO-WAY RADIO!
BBZZZZZZ
14

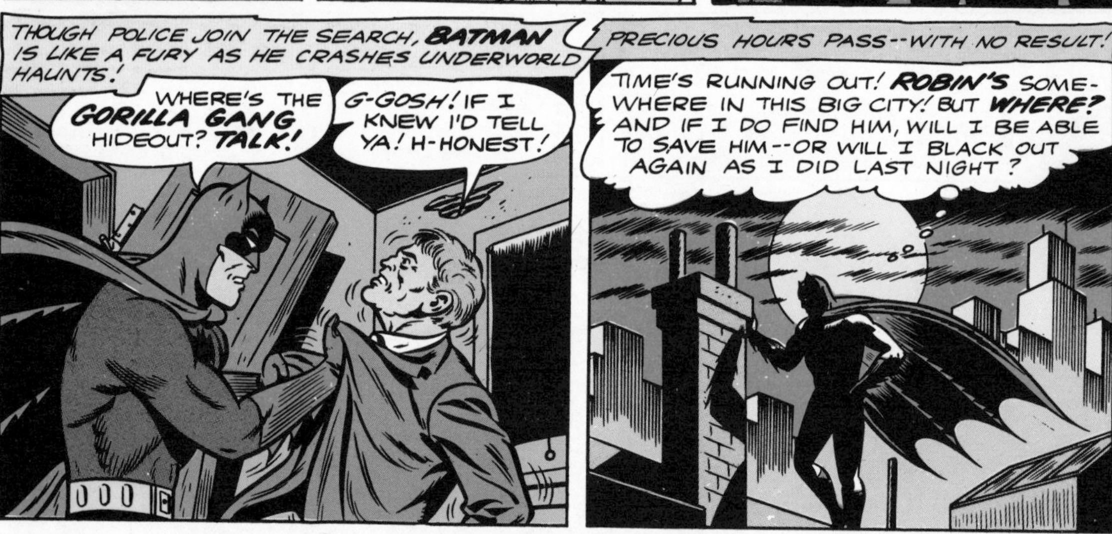

"LAST NIGHT"! THOSE WORDS SUDDENLY HELP BATMAN RECALL SOMETHING THAT OCCURRED THE PREVIOUS NIGHT!

THE GETAWAY CAR TIRES PASSED THROUGH SPILLED CAMPHOR FLAKES! CAMPHOR SCENT IS VERY STRONG--TAKES QUITE A WHILE TO FADE AWAY COMPLETELY! THAT CAMPHOR SCENT WOULD BE TOO FAINT FOR ME TO TRAIL--BUT NOT FOR A DOG'S KEEN SENSE OF SMELL!

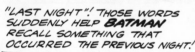

SOON--DAWN! SHAFTS OF SUNLIGHT PROBE EVERYWHERE--ESPECIALLY THROUGH A SLIDING ROOFTOP...
SUNRISE--AND ROBIN'S GONNA RISE UNTIL HE'S OUTA THIS WORLD! ¡HA, HA,! ONE WHACK OF THIS SHARP AX AND...
HOLD IT, PETE! I HEARD SOMETHING--SOUNDS LIKE FOOTSTEPS! LUKE, TAKE A LOOK OUTSIDE AND SEE IF ANYBODY'S SNOOPING AROUND!
CHECK!
MINUTES PASS AS THE CRIMINALS WAIT FOR THE RETURN OF THEIR COMPANION...
WELL? ANYBODY OUTSIDE?
YES...
...ME!
BATMAN! HE KAYOED LUKE--AND GOT INTO LUKE'S SUIT TO CATCH US OFF-GUARD! I'LL FIX HIM!
THEN, A SHAGGY SHAPE HURTLES FORWARD LIKE A MISSILE...
THE AX--IT'S CUT THE MOORING ROPES!
FREED, THE BALLOON STARTS TO RISE, THE ROPES TRAILING LIKE TENTACLES AROUND BATMAN'S SHOULDERS!..
"LIKE TENTACLES"! WILL THOSE ROPES CAUSE BATMAN TO BLACK OUT AGAIN? WILL HE IMAGINE HE IS IN THE GRIP OF THE TENTACLE-PLANT?
16

SO IT SEEMS AS BATMAN SWEEPS THE ROPES ASIDE, LUNGES DESPERATELY FOR THE FALLEN AXE, AND HURLS IT UPWARD...
IS BATMAN WILDLY BATTLING THE "TENTACLES" OF HIS IMAGINARY WORLD?

THE ANSWER COMES IN THE NEXT INSTANT...
MY AIM WAS PERFECT! AS THE GAS ESCAPES, THE BALLOON WILL COLLAPSE --AND GENTLY FLOAT DOWN TO THE FLOOR!
HISS-SSS

LATER, WHEN POLICE ARE SUMMONED TO JAIL THE GORILLA GANG...

GOSH! YOU WERE LIKE YOUR OLD SELF! YOU DIDN'T BLACK OUT THIS TIME!

NO! YOU SEE, ROBIN, IN MY HALLUCINATION, I ONLY IMAGINED YOU DIED AT DAWN! BUT THIS WAS A REAL DAWN --AND YOU FACED A REAL DEATH! WELL, THE REALITY OF THE SITUATION WAS SO TERRIBLE, IT SHOCKED ME RIGHT BACK TO NORMAL!

17

DAWN--ONCE AN OMEN OF ROBIN'S DEATH--IT IS NOW A FITTING SIGN THAT BATMAN'S CRIME-FIGHTING CAREER HAS RETURNED TO LIFE!

"The NEGATIVE BATMAN!"
ROBIN... THOSE HEADLIGHTS... ARE WEAKENING ME!
GOLLY! SINCE BATMAN TURNED INTO A NEGATIVE MAN, LIGHT BEAMS ARE GRADUALLY DESTROYING HIM!

BATMAN and ROBIN DEFY
"The MENACE of CLAY-FACE!"
THAT FANTASTIC CHARACTER, CLAY-FACE, CAN MOLD HIS BODY INTO ANY SHAPE!

Story by Gardner Fox/Art by Carmine Infantino & Joe Giella/Coloring by Helen Vesik

THROUGH THE SURGE AND HEAVE OF A STORM-BATTERED SEA, A CABIN CRUISER LIFTS AND DIPS HELPLESSLY IN THE TROUGH AND SWELL OF MADDENED WATERS...

THE YELLOW SCRATCH OF LIGHTNING AGAINST A BLACKENED SKY HIGHLIGHTS THE RENDING CRASH AND SPLINTERING OF A WOODEN PROW ON JAGGED, KNIFE-LIKE ROCKS...
HAVE TO ABANDON SHIP! WHAT A MISERABLE WIND-UP TO A DAY OF DEEP-SEA FISHING!
CRAACK!

LIGHTNING SPOTLIGHTS THE FIGURE OF BRUCE (BATMAN) WAYNE AS HE SPLITS THE WAVES IN A CLEAN DIVE FROM THE DECK OF THE TOSSING, DYING VESSEL BEING POUNDED TO PIECES AGAINST THE RUTHLESS ROCKS...
SPOTTED AN ISLAND CLOSE BY! GOT TO MAKE A SWIM FOR IT!

A WET, BEDRAGGLED FIGURE STAGGERS ASHORE A LITTLE LATER AS THE FULL FURY OF THE STORM SMASHES OVERHEAD IN A DIAPASON OF DEADLY DESTRUCTION!...
PANT!
WONDER IF THERE'S ANY SHELTER FURTHER INLAND? ANYTHING'D BE BETTER THAN THIS!

THEN IN A LULL BETWEEN THE OMINOUS CRESCENDO OF CRASHING THUNDER, BRUCE WAYNE HEARS A CRY, A WAIL OF DESPAIR, OF UTTER HOPELESSNESS...
HELP!...HELP! PLEASE--SOMEBODY... HELP ME!
GOOD GOSH! SOUNDS LIKE SOMEONE'S WORSE OFF THAN I AM!

HE LURCHES FORWARD BLINDLY THROUGH THE AWESOME DOWNPOUR--AND COMES TO A DEAD STOP WHEN HE SEES...
A BOY--CAUGHT IN A QUICKSAND BED! KEEP CALM, YOUNGSTER--DON'T THRASH ABOUT SO MUCH! YOU'RE ONLY MAKING YOURSELF SINK DEEPER...

HIS POWERFUL HANDS BREAK OFF A BRANCH AND THRUST IT OUT OVER THE GRIPPING QUAGMIRE! HIS VOICE SOOTHES AND COMFORTS...
JUST RELAX...AND YOU WON'T STIR UP THE SANDS THAT DRAW YOU DOWNWARD! ATTABOY! NOW--GRAB HOLD OF THIS BRANCH AND I'LL HAVE YOU OUT IN A JIFFY!
2

THEN, WITH HIS ARM ABOUT THE BOY FOR SUPPORT, BRUCE HEADS INLAND--AND COMES UPON ANOTHER WANDERER OF THE ISLAND WOODLANDS, HIS FACE DISTORTED WITH PANIC, HIS VOICE THICK WITH FEAR...
MARK! MARK--IS THAT YOU? I WAS SO WORRIED! WHAT HAPPENED TO YOU?
HE FELL INTO A QUICKSAND BOG--BUT HE SHOULD BE OKAY BY MORNING!

AND IN THE MORNING A GRATEFUL ROLAND DESMOND GRIPS **BRUCE** WAYNE BY THE HAND **AS CLEAR** SKIES REVEAL A CHANGE IN WEATHER...

THANKS AGAIN FOR SAVING MY BROTHER MARK'S LIFE! IF THERE'S ANYTHING I CAN DO--

THE OVER-NIGHT SHELTER YOU PROVIDED SQUARED THINGS AS FAR AS I'M CONCERNED! NOW IF YOU'LL JUST TAKE ME BACK TO THE MAINLAND...

THE DAYS SLIP INTO WEEKS AND THE WEEKS INTO MONTHS. THEN ONE EVENING AS ***BATMAN*** AND ***ROBIN*** MAKE THEIR PATROL OF THE BUSINESS DISTRICT OF ***GOTHAM CITY...***
TAKE A GANDER AT THAT! A BIG HOLE IN THAT WALL--AND POLICE PROWL CARS GATHERED TO INVESTIGATE IT!
ODD THAT WE DIDN'T HEAR ANY EXPLOSION ON OUR ROUNDS!

THERE WAS NO EXPLOSION, ***BATMAN!*** A SINGLE MAN MADE THAT OPENING--WITH SHEER BRUTE STRENGTH!
WHAT?!

"YES, HE SLAMMED INTO THAT WALL LIKE A FULLBACK RAMMING THE LINE--CLEAVING A PATH THROUGH BRICK AND CONCRETE AS IF MADE OF TISSUE PAPER!..."
CRASSH!

"INSIDE THE BANK HE STUFFED A DOUBLE KNAPSACK FULL OF MONEY! WE SAW HIM COMING OUT--AND WHEN HE IGNORED OUR WARNING TO STOP..."

OUR BULLETS FLATTEN OUT WHEN THEY HIT HIS BODY--AND BOUNCE OFF!

THINGS LIKE THIS ARE ONLY SUPPOSED TO HAPPEN IN HORROR MOVIES!

POW! POW!

3

"AS IF TO SHOW HIS DEFIANCE OF US, HE LIFTED MY PARKED SQUAD CAR HIGH INTO THE AIR WITH ONE HAND..."

GHAAGH!

"THEN, SETTING THE CAR DOWN, HE RACED OFF INTO THE NIGHT..."

MAN, WHAT A NIGHT-MARE EVENING THIS HAS TURNED OUT TO BE!

A STUNNED **ROBIN** GIVES VOICE TO THE THOUGHTS THAT SWIRL ABOUT IN EVERYONE'S MIND...

WOWEE! HOW DOES ANYONE FIGHT A **BLOCKBUSTER** LIKE THAT!

BLOCKBUSTER!! SAY, THAT'S A TERRIFIC HEADLINE NAME FOR HIM! THE "**BLOCK-BUSTER BANDIT**"! YEAH!

SOON AFTERWARD IN THE **BATCAVE**, THE **MASKED MANHUNTER** AND THE **BOY WONDER** BUCKLE DOWN TO SEVERAL HOURS' WORK...

IF THAT **BLOCK-BUSTER** IS GOING TO HAUNT OUR NIGHTLY PATROLS--WE'D BETTER BE READY TO DEAL WITH HIM!

WITH SOME **VERY** SPECIAL WEAPONS AND EQUIPMENT TO HANDLE HIS VERY **SPECIAL** CASE!

ONE NIGHT--TWO NIGHTS--A THIRD NIGHT SLIPS BY WITH-OUT INCIDENT! THEN ON THE SHORT-WAVE RADIO OF THE **BATMOBILE** COMES THE ALARM THEY HAVE BEEN WAITING FOR...

ATTENTION, ALL UNITS! AN OFFICER ON THE BEAT HAS REPORTED SEEING THE **BLOCKBUSTER BANDIT** CRASHING INTO THE **TOLLIVER ART GALLERY!**

WE'RE ONLY A COUPLE OF BLOCKS FROM THERE, **ROBIN!**

MOMENTS AFTERWARD, TWO GRIM FIGURES VAULT FROM THE **BATMOBILE**--LADEN WITH THEIR **BLOCKBUSTER-BANDIT-CONTROL-GEAR...**

MY ORDERS WERE NOT TO INTERFERE WITH THE **BLOCK-BUSTER**--JUST GIVE THE ALARM!

HOLD THE POLICE RE-INFORCEMENTS OUT HERE WHEN THEY ARRIVE--WHILE WE TAKE A CRACK AT HIM WITH OUR SPECIAL WEAPONS!

TOWERING LIKE A COLOSSUS IN THE ART GALLERY, THE BLOCKBUSTER BANDIT TURNS A SAVAGE FACE TOWARD THE ON-RUSHING CRIME-FIGHTERS...
GYAAGH!
WOW! COMPARED TO THIS BABY, FRANKENSTEIN'S MONSTER WAS A LITTLE LORD FAUNTLEROY!

AS DEFTLY AS A WELL-OILED MACHINE, THE DARING DUO MOVES INTO ACTION! A LEAPING BATMAN RAMS A FIST INTO A JUTTING JAW...
HAD TO THROW A PUNCH AT HIM FIRST--JUST TO SATISFY MYSELF THAT IT WOULDN'T WORK! IT DIDN'T--!
SOK!

AND AS THE CREATURE REACHES OUT TO GRASP AND CRUNCH HIM, ROBIN DARTS BENEATH THOSE ARMS TO SNAP TIGHT THE SPECIAL STEEL MANACLES PREPARED FOR THIS MOMENT..

GOT HIM!

A GLARE OF INSENSATE RAGE CROSSES THE FEATURES OF THE TITANIC TERROR AS HIS MUSCLES BULGE AND BUNCH! STEEL STRAINS--CRACKS--FLIES WIDE APART...

GYAAGH!

SHADES OF SUPERMAN! THOSE LINKS ARE MADE OF THE STRONGEST STEEL POSSIBLE! WE'LL HAVE TO GO THROUGH WITH OUR FOLLOW-UP PLAN!

CRAAK!

NOW THE TEEN-AGE THUNDERBOLT HURLS A GAS PELLET--EVEN AS THE COWLED CRUSADER WHIRLS A STEEL-CABLED BOLA...

GYAAGH!
SEEMS LIKE BLOCKBUSTER HAS ONLY A ONE-WORD VOCABULARY!
BATMAN AND I ARE PROTECTED FROM THIS TEAR-GAS--BUT BLOCKBUSTER ISN'T!
5

ONCE AGAIN THE BELLOW OF THE MADDENED GIANT SOUNDS IN THE GALLERY AS STEEL CABLES SNAP AND FLY...

GYAAGH!
NOT A TEAR IN HIS EYE! DOESN'T ANYTHING BOTHER THIS FREEP*?
*Editor's Note; SLANG FOR A COMBINATION FREAK AND CREEP!

A MASSIVE HAND DARTS OUT-- AND CLOSES IN A GRIP OF UNIMAGINABLE POWER...
HE'S GOT ROBIN! IF THIS BRUTE HAS A WEAK SPOT, I'D BETTER FIND IT FAST!
THUD!

FISTS THAT HAVE NEVER MET THEIR EQUAL BASH AND THUD UP AND DOWN THAT ROCK-LIKE BODY! BATMAN FIGHTS AS HE HAS NEVER FOUGHT BEFORE--TO FREE HIS YOUNG COMPANION FROM THAT AWESOME GRIP...
LIKE BANGING ONE'S HEAD AGAINST THE PROVERBIAL WALL...
POW!

THE BLOCKBUSTER DRAWS BACK A FEW STEPS--AS HE RAISES A HAND TO A CHEEK THAT HAS TAKEN BATTERING PUNISHMENT! HE TOUCHES HIS FLESH GINGERLY, AS IF IN PAIN...
I'M GETTING TO HIM! HE ISN'T AS INVULNERABLE AS I THOUGHT!
GYAAGH!

AGAIN THE COWLED CRUSADER HITS-- AND YET AGAIN--WITH BLOWS THAT WOULD FELL AN OX! AND STUNG TO A WILD, ANIMALISTIC FURY--THE BLOCKBUSTER BANDIT ROARS WITH ANGER...
GYAAAGH
THUNNK!
THUNNK!

OUTSIDE THE GALLERY WAITS A FORCE OF EAGER, WELL-TRAINED POLICEMEN...
DON'T INTERFERE! GIVE BATMAN AND ROBIN A CHANCE TO "GET THEIR MAN"!
WHAT A BATTLE THEY MUST BE PUTTING UP!
BLAPPP!
VOOOMP!

AND THEN-- WITH A CRASH OF MASONRY AS HE KICKS THROUGH BRICK AND MORTAR-- COMES THE CRIME COLOSSUS...
CRASH!
MAN ALIVE! HE GOT 'EM BOTH!

HIGH ABOVE HIS HEAD ARE LIFTED THE MASKED MANHUNTER AND TEEN-AGE THUNDERBOLT-- INERT WEIGHTS IN THE MIGHTY HANDS OF THE BLOCKBUSTER BANDIT...
GYAAAGH!

THEN THEY ARE FLUNG LIKE CANNON-BALLS AT THE STUNNED POLICE-- BOWLING THEM OVER LIKE TENPINS...
WHAM
7

THE BLOCKBUSTER RACES OFF--SMASHING HIS WAY THROUGH ANOTHER BUILDING WALL--THEN BLASTING DOWN INTO A CELLAR...
CRAK!

HE MAKES HIS WAY INTO A SEWER-WAY, SPLASHING ALONG AT EVERY STEP...

UNTIL HE COMES TO AN ABANDONED SUBWAY TRACK, WHERE HE SCAMPERS OFF INTO THE DISTANCE...

BEHIND HIM HE LEAVES A SERIES OF GAPING HOLES, CRUNCHED-THROUGH BUILDING WALLS, THAT POINT A PATH TO THE NOWHERE INTO WHICH THE CRIME COLOSSUS HAS DISAPPEARED...
THE TRAIL HAS PETERED OUT! HE'S GONE!
BUT HE'LL BE BACK--AND NEXT TIME WE'LL REALLY BE READY FOR HIM! LET'S GO SEE COMMISSIONER GORDON, ROBIN!
8

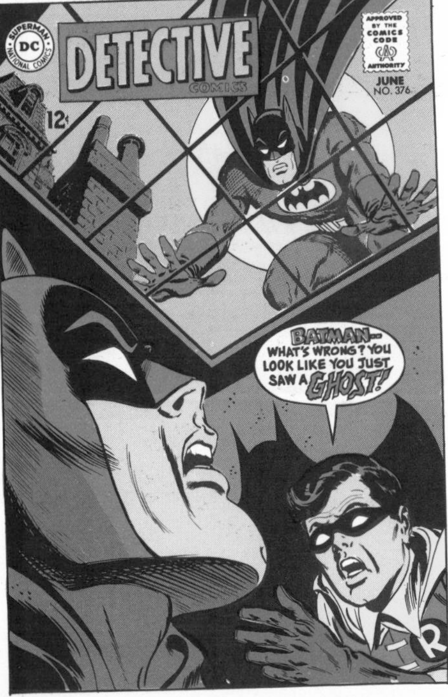
SUPERMAN DC NATIONAL COMICS
DETECTIVE COMICS
APPROVED BY THE COMICS CODE AUTHORITY
JUNE NO. 376
12¢
BATMAN-- WHAT'S WRONG? YOU LOOK LIKE YOU JUST SAW A GHOST!

For The
VERY
BEST
SUPERMAN
DC
NATIONAL COMICS
in
COMICS
READING

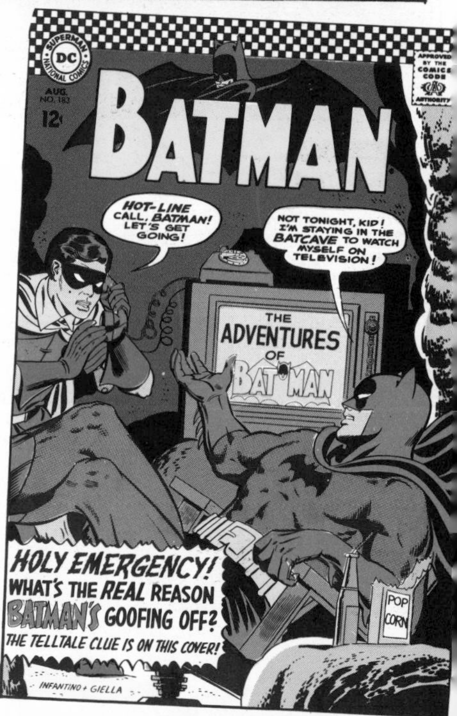
SUPERMAN DC NATIONAL COMICS
AUG. NO. 183
12¢
APPROVED BY THE COMICS CODE AUTHORITY
BATMAN
HOT-LINE CALL, BATMAN! LET'S GET GOING!
NOT TONIGHT, KID! I'M STAYING IN THE BATCAVE TO WATCH MYSELF ON TELEVISION!
THE ADVENTURES OF BATMAN
POP CORN
HOLY EMERGENCY! WHAT'S THE REAL REASON BATMAN'S GOOFING OFF? THE TELLTALE CLUE IS ON THIS COVER!
INFANTINO + GIELLA

DURING THE NEXT SEVERAL HOURS, THE DISGRUNTLED DUO CONFERS WITH THE ***GOTHAM CITY*** POLICE COMMISSIONER...

THEN IT'S AGREED! NEXT TIME HE APPEARS-- WE LET HIM STEAL WHAT HE WANTS!

WHILE WE'LL BE ABOVE THE CITY IN THE ***BAT-COPTER***-- TO FOLLOW AND SEE WHERE HE GOES!

FOR THE NEXT TWO NIGHTS THE DARK, GRIM SHAPE OF THE ***BATCOPTER*** HOVERS LIKE A GREAT BIRD OF PREY ABOVE THE CITY ROOFTOPS...

WE'LL FIGHT HIM ON HIS HOME GROUND--AND HOLD HIM UNTIL THE POLICE ARRIVE WITH ELECTRIFIED NETS!

THEN ON A CLOUDY NIGHT, WHEN DARKNESS CLOAKS THE CITY-- THE ***BEHEMOTH OF BANDITRY*** CRASHES INTO A CITY MUSEUM..

THERE HE GOES! NOW KEEP YOUR EYES PEELED FOR HIM WHEN HE COMES OUT!

RIGHTO, ***BATMAN***! MY PUPILS ARE ALREADY PANTING!

ALL ***GOTHAM CITY*** HAS BEEN ALERTED TO THE TERRIBLE DANGER! LET THE ***BLOCKBUSTER BANDIT*** COME AND GO WITHOUT INTERFERENCE...
GYAAGH!

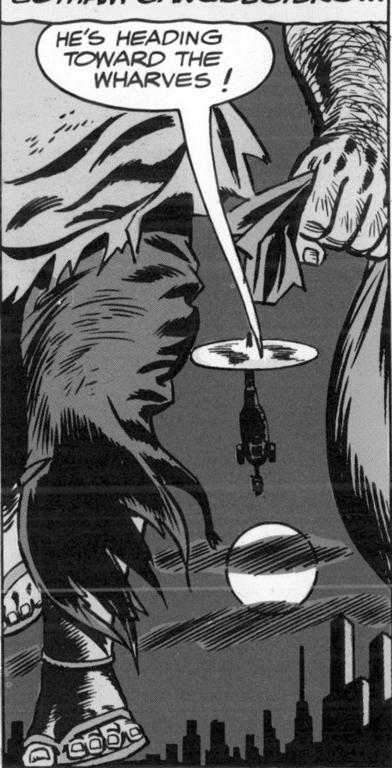

MINUTES LATER, HOLLOW FOOT-FALLS ***SPEED*** ALONG THE DESERTED CITY STREETS-- WHILE OVERHEAD THAT DREAD FORM IS SHADOWED BY THE ***GOTHAM GANGBUSTERS***...
HE'S HEADING TOWARD THE WHARVES!

INTO THE SEA HE PLUNGES, SWIMMING WITH POWERFUL STROKES AS THE ALMOST SILENT ROTORS OF THE ***BATCOPTER*** FOLLOW OVER-HEAD...
SAY, HE'S HEADING TOWARD THE ISLAND WHERE I RESCUED THAT BOY, MARK DESMOND! I WONDER IF THERE CAN BE ANY CONNECTION?
9

THEN ABOVE THE ISLAND--CRIES ARE WRUNG FROM STARTLED THROATS AS THE WHIRLYBIRD DIPS AND BEGINS TO FALL!...
THE COPTER'S OUT OF CONTROL! WE'VE RUN INTO SOME SORT OF HIGH-FREQUENCY INTERFERENCE THAT'S JAMMED THE MOTOR!
OUR RADIO'S GONE DEAD! WE CAN'T CONTACT THE POLICE! BATMAN-- WE'RE ON OUR OWN!

A BLADE SNAPS AS THE GALLANT CRAFT HITS THE UPPER BRANCHES OF A WOODLAND GIANT--AND SPILLS ITS HUMAN OCCUPANTS...
LIKE THIS IS JOURNEY'S END, MAN! WOWW!
SAVE YOUR BREATH, ROBIN-- REAL TROUBLE IS ON ITS WAY!

FROM A FOOTPATH BELOW THE WRECKED BATCOPTER THE BLOCKBUSTER BANDIT RECOGNIZES HIS FIGHTING FOES! A MAD SHRIEK TEARS FROM HIS THROAT...
GYAAGH!
SOUNDS LIKE HE HASN'T INCREASED HIS VOCABULARY ANY! BOY, WHAT I WOULDN'T GIVE TO MAKE HIM CRY "UNCLE"!

HIS HUGE HANDS GRIP AND SHAKE THE TREE BOLE! AND LIKE OVER-RIPE FRUIT THE DUO COMES TUMBLING TO THE GROUND...
I FEEL LIKE AN APPLE ABOUT TO BE SQUASHED!
IT WOULDN'T DO ANY GOOD TRYING TO REASON WITH HIM! HE DOESN'T SEEM TO COMPREHEND US--

NOW BEGINS A RUNNING BATTLE--A DESPERATE ENCOUNTER WITH CRUDE, IMPROVISED WEAPONS--A VERITABLE STRUGGLE FOR SURVIVAL...
KEEP RUNNING, ROBIN--! I'M GETTING AN IDEA HOW TO HANDLE THIS GUY!
IT'D BETTER BE A GOOD ONE...
10

DODGING AROUND TREES--CHANGING DIRECTION ABRUPTLY--THEY COME IN SIGHT OF...
A HOUSE!
THE ONE I'VE BEEN LOOKING FOR--WHERE ROLAND DESMOND LIVES WITH HIS BROTHER MARK!

ON FEET THAT FLY LIKE THOSE OF OLYMPIC SPRINTERS, THE CRIME-FIGHTING COUPLE DASHES INTO THE CELLAR-WAY OF THE HOUSE...
OKAY! NOW I CAN GET SET TO STOP THE BLOCKBUSTER!
LET ME KNOW WHEN YOU'RE SET-- AND I'LL CALL GO!
SLAM

THE MADDENED MIGHT OF THE CRIME COLOSSUS IS NOT TO BE DENIED! HE LUNGES FOR-WARD--AND THE HEAVY OAK DOOR SPLINTERS BEFORE HIM..
NOW, BATMAN?
NOT YET, ROBIN!
CRUNCH

JELLING IN THE ALERT, DEDUCTIVE BRAIN OF BATMAN IS THE ONE POSSIBLE HOPE OF VICTORY IN THIS UNEQUAL STRUGGLE...
ROBIN--I THINK THE BLOCKBUSTER IS THE SAME FELLOW I SAVED FROM THE QUICKSAND BED--MARK DESMOND! THERE'S JUST ENOUGH FACIAL STRUCTURE LEFT SO THAT THEY LOOK ALIKE! IF THAT'S SO--I CAN STOP HIM!
BUT YOU TOLD ME MARK WAS A SCRAWNY KID! THIS ONE'S A--A BLOCK-BUSTER!

DESPERATELY THE BOY WONDER FLINGS HIMSELF UPON THE MASKED MANHUNTER! HIS VOICE PLEADS AS HIS HANDS RESTRAIN...
NO, NO, BATMAN! YOU CAN'T FIGHT THE BLOCK-BUSTER! HE'S TOO TOUGH AN OPPONENT!
TOO TOUGH FOR BATMAN--BUT NOT FOR BRUCE WAYNE!
11

AS BATMAN THROWS OFF HIS UNIFORM TO STAND IN SLACKS AND SHIRT--THE BEHEMOTH BANDIT PAUSES! ACROSS HIS FACE FLITS A STRANGE EXPRESSION! IS HE REMEMBERING THAT NIGHT MONTHS AGO, WHEN THIS VERY MAN SAVED HIS LIFE--AS MARK DESMOND?...
NO SIGN OF RECOGNITION YET! ROBIN, GO FIND THE OTHER MAN-- HIS BROTHER ROLAND! IF MY HUNCH IS RIGHT, HE'S THE BRAINS BEHIND THIS CHARACTER! THE SAME ONE WHO BROUGHT DOWN OUR 'COPTER AND CUT OFF OUR RADIO!
GYAAGH!

THEN THAT EXPRESSION FADES AS A MAMMOTH FIST BASHES OUT! ONLY THE INSTANT REFLEXES OF BRUCE (BATMAN) WAYNE SAVE HIM...
GYAAGH!
POW!

MOMENTS LATER, BRUCE IS RUNNING FOR HIS LIFE ALONG AN ISLAND TRAIL! BEHIND HIM COMES THE THUDDING FOOTBEATS OF THE BLOCKBUSTER..
GOT TO--GET TO THAT QUICKSAND...

A SPLASH OF SANDY WATERS! A THUMP OF HEAVY FEET! AND NOW IT IS BRUCE WAYNE HIMSELF WHO WILDLY THRASHES IN THE STEADY TUG OF THE DEADLY BOG...
I MUST DUPLICATE EVERY MOVE MARK MADE WHEN HE WAS IN THE QUICKSAND-- TO HELP HIM REMEMBER OUR FIRST MEETING --THAT HE OWES HIS LIFE TO ME--AND WILL SPARE MINE!
THE COLOSSUS SWAYS! HIS EYES GLAZE OVER! HIS DAZED BRAIN STRUGGLES FOR THOUGHT, FOR MEMORY...
GYAH? GYAAGH?! GYAAGH!!

SUDDENLY HIS HANDS HOLD OUT THE VERY SAME BRANCH WHICH BRUCE WAYNE USED TO RESCUE HIM!...
HE REMEMBERED! HE KNOWS-- BRUCE WAYNE IS HIS FRIEND!

AND YET--I'M IN A QUANDARY! I CAN'T BECOME BATMAN AGAIN--OR BLOCKBUSTER WILL ATTACK ME! BUT IF I REMAIN AS BRUCE WAYNE--HIS BROTHER ROLAND WILL TUMBLE ON TO THE SECRET OF MY DOUBLE IDENTITY!
12

AT THIS MOMENT, **ROBIN** IS ON THE ATTACK! HE, TOO, REALIZES THE DILEMMA CONFRONTING BRUCE WAYNE--AS HIS FIST THUNDERS AGAINST THE JAW OF ROLAND DESMOND...

ZOK!

I MUST KAYO HIM--FAST!

THEN, AS BRUCE APPEARS IN THE DOORWAY, THE **TEEN-AGE THUNDERBOLT** IS STARTLED BY HIS COMMAND...

TAKE ROLAND TO HIS BOAT! AND HURRY! THE THREE OF US ARE GETTING OUT OF HERE!

B-BUT WHAT ABOUT THE **BLOCKBUSTER**? I GUESS HE'S YOUR *"FRIEND"* NOW--BUT WE CAME HERE TO CAPTURE **HIM**!

WHILE **ROBIN** LUGS ROLAND TO THE BOAT, BRUCE RETURNS TO THE CELLAR WHERE...

WHEN **ROBIN** GIVES IT SOME THOUGHT, HE'LL REALIZE THAT **BLOCKBUSTER** MUST STAY ON THE ISLAND UNTIL WE CAN RETURN, AND THAT ROLAND MUSTN'T SEE ME--AS **BATMAN**!

WHILE **BLOCKBUSTER** WANDERS AROUND THE ISLAND, **BATMAN** SNEAKS OFF TO THE WAITING BOAT...

YEAH, YOU CAUGHT ME! AND YOU'RE RIGHT ABOUT MARK! HE'S THE **BLOCKBUSTER**--BUT HE ONLY OBEYS **ME**! AND HE'LL GET YOU YET--BECAUSE I'LL NEVER TELL HIM NOT TO!

MARK WAS ALWAYS THE GENIUS OF THE FAMILY, BUT HE WAS A SCRAWNY KID! SO HE WORKED OUT A SERUM THAT WOULD AFFECT CERTAIN ENDOCRINE GLANDS TO MAKE HIM GROW BIG AND STRONG! BUT HE WAS OVER-ANXIOUS--HE NEVER BOTHERED TO TEST HIS DISCOVERY FIRST!

WHAT NATURE GAVE WITH ONE HAND, IT TOOK AWAY WITH THE OTHER! AN OVER-ACTIVE ANTERIOR LOBE OF THE PITUITARY GLAND MADE HIM SHOOT UP LIKE A GIANT--WITH TREMENDOUS STRENGTH! BUT SIMULTANEOUSLY, A FAULTY *ENDOCRINE* GLAND RETARDED HIS MENTAL DEVELOPMENT...

13

IN THE BATCAVE, AFTER ROLAND DESMOND HAS BEEN TURNED OVER TO THE AUTHORITIES...
I'LL BET I KNOW WHERE WE'RE GOING NOW--BACK TO THE ISLAND TO ROUND UP THE BLOCKBUSTER!
THAT WASN'T HARD TO FIGURE OUT! THE TRICK IS HOW TO DO IT!

AS SOON AS I HEARD ROLAND DESMOND SAY THAT HIS BLOCKBUSTER BROTHER ONLY OBEYED HIM--WHICH IS WHY HE ROBBED, TO MAKE ROLAND DESMOND RICH--I TUMBLED TO THE FACT THAT YOU'D DISGUISE YOURSELF TO LOOK LIKE HIM, IMITATE HIS VOICE--AND SO GET BLOCKBUSTER TO OBEY YOU!

AND SO BRUCE WAYNE--DISGUISED AS ROLAND DESMOND--RETURNS ONCE MORE TO BLOCKBUSTER ISLAND...
HIS FOOTPRINTS--LEADING INTO THE SEA! SOME ANIMAL INSTINCT MUST HAVE WARNED HIM IT WOULD BE DANGEROUS TO STAY HERE!
WHEREVER HE'S GONE, THE BLOCKBUSTER HAS CUT HIMSELF OFF FROM THE WORLD--DOOMED HIMSELF TO LIVE APART FROM HIS FELLOW HUMAN BEINGS! IN THIS MANNER, IRONICALLY ENOUGH, HE IS SERVING A SENTENCE OF SOLITARY CONFINEMENT FOR HIS CRIMES!
A FORTHCOMING ISSUE OF DETECTIVE COMICS WILL REVEAL THE SURPRISING AND THRILLING WIND-UP TO THE CASE OF THE BLOCKBUSTER BANDIT!
The End
14

SUPERMAN NATIONAL COMICS DC
JULY NO. 353
STARRING
12¢
DETECTIVE COMICS
BATMAN
WITH ROBIN THE BOY WONDER
Out of the pages of the FLASH storms the WEATHER WIZARD...
FLASH
...to unleash a blistering ATTACK against BATMAN AND ROBIN!
CRAAACK
INFANTINO + GIELLA

For The VERY BEST
SUPERMAN DC NATIONAL COMICS
in COMICS READING

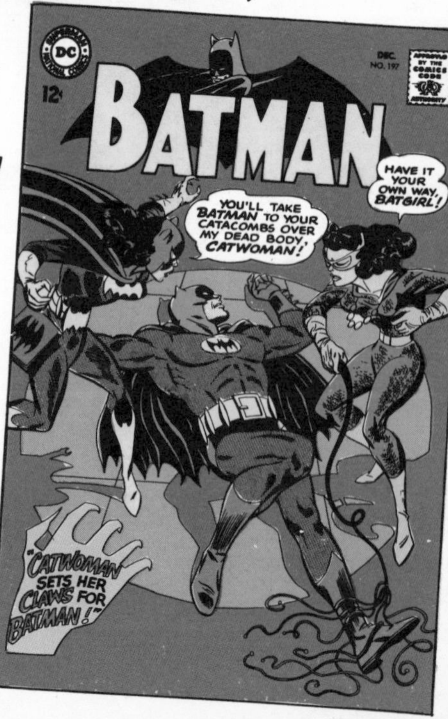
DEC. NO. 197
12¢
BATMAN
HAVE IT YOUR OWN WAY, BATGIRL!
YOU'LL TAKE BATMAN TO YOUR CATACOMBS OVER MY DEAD BODY, CATWOMAN!
"CATWOMAN SETS HER CLAWS FOR BATMAN!"

YOU ARE STANDING ON A WINDSWEPT CLIFF SOMEWHERE IN CENTRAL **SPAIN**, LOOKING THROUGH THE EYES OF A SOLITARY WATCHER... OBSERVING A SPECK OF AN AIR-CRAFT IN THE DISTANCE...

IT IS CLOSER, AND YOU HEAR ITS ENGINE SPUTTERING--YOU SEE THAT IT IS A FRENCH-MADE **NIEUPORT 17**-- A MOTORIZED KITE THAT WAS USED IN THE WORLD'S FIRST AIR-COMBAT IN 1916...

SUDDENLY IT FLIPS OVER AND HURLS TOWARD THE ROCKS BELOW YOU... AND YOU KNOW, WITH CHILL CERTAINTY, THAT YOU ARE WITNESSING A **MURDER**--

THE GROUND SHUDDERS AS THE PLANE SPLINTERS AGAINST THE CLIFF'S SNOWY FACE...
LEAVE, NOW THE EYES OF THE DREAD--
BATMAN
AND FOLLOW THE CAPED AVENGER THROUGH A TANGLE OF CRIME AND INTO THE BLEAKEST CORNER OF A MAN'S SOUL... A MAN WHO MUST BECOME...
"GHOST OF THE KILLER SKIES!"
1

Coloring by Tatjana Wood

SWIFT AS HIS FLYING NAME-SAKE, THE BATMAN SWOOPS TO THE BROKEN CRAFT...

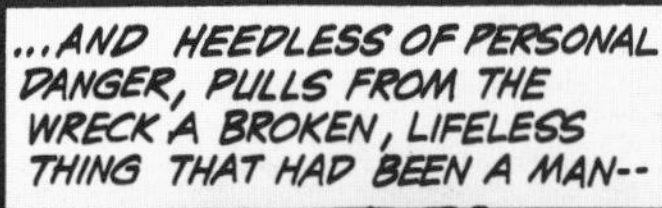
...AND HEEDLESS OF PERSONAL DANGER, PULLS FROM THE WRECK A BROKEN, LIFELESS THING THAT HAD BEEN A MAN--

INCREDIBLE--! I SAW THERE'D BEEN FOUL PLAY... BUT NOT THE KIND I THOUGHT!
THE PILOT'S BEEN... STRANGLED! HE MUST HAVE BEEN DEAD BEFORE THE CRASH...
STRANGLED IN MID-AIR...IN A SINGLE-SEATER PLANE...

UP THERE, MR. ANSON!
YOU THINK I DON'T KNOW, BOOB? SO WE CLIMB!
THE FILM CREW--! IT WON'T DO TO LET THEM SEE THE BATMAN HERE IN SPAIN... AT LEAST NOT JUST YET!

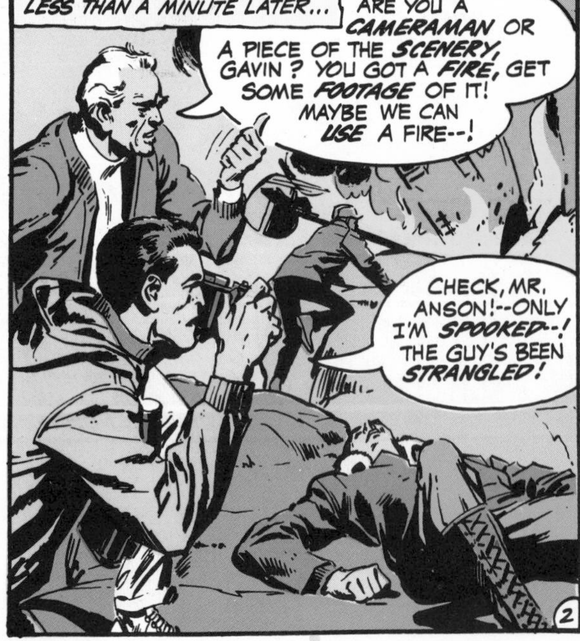
LESS THAN A MINUTE LATER...
ARE YOU A CAMERAMAN OR A PIECE OF THE SCENERY, GAVIN ? YOU GOT A FIRE, GET SOME FOOTAGE OF IT! MAYBE WE CAN USE A FIRE--!
CHECK, MR. ANSON!--ONLY I'M SPOOKED--! THE GUY'S BEEN STRANGLED!
2

DID SOMEONE SAY DEAD?
LIKE A DOORNAIL, MR. WAYNE!
BRUCE, BABY, WHAT THIS PICTURE IS...IS JINXED! THAT PILOT WAS ONE OF THE FEW LEFT WHO CAN FLY THOSE WORLD WAR I CRATES!

NOTHIN' BUT TROUBLE SINCE WE STARTED--! WE COME TO SPAIN 'CAUSE WE CAN MAKE IT CHEAP HERE, AND WHAT HAPPENS?
PROPS ARE MISSING... FILM-STOCK CATCHES FIRE... SOUND TRACKS GET ACCIDENTALLY ERASED...AND NOW THIS!
I'M READY TO GIVE UP!
PERHAPS WE SHOULD RETURN TO THE SET AND CALL A MEETING!

SHORTLY, ON THE MAIN SET OF THE MOVIE-IN-PROGRESS, TENTATIVELY TITLED "THE HAMMER OF HELL"...

YOU WANT REASONS WHY WE SHOULD PACK OUR BAGS AND SCOOT, I'LL GIVE 'EM, BRUCE!

NOT ONLY HAVE WE HAD SETBACKS WHICH ALREADY PUT US A LOT OVER OUR BUDGET, BUT I HEAR ANOTHER OUTFIT IS MAKIN' A GERMAN WAR PIC! IT'LL KILL OUR MARKET!

...BUT THE OTHER COMPANY DOESN'T HAVE A DIRECTOR LIKE YOU, ANSON-- A THREE-TIME ACADEMY AWARD WINNER...

AND...THEY AREN'T TELLING THE STORY OF BARON HANS VON HAMMER ...THE MOST ENIGMATIC FLYER WHO EVER LIVED!

3

I BELIEVE IN "THE HAMMER OF HELL"-- AND THE THINGS IT CAN SAY TO AUDIENCES ABOUT THE NATURE--AND FOLLY--OF WAR!
THAT'S WHY I PUT MONEY INTO IT...AND WHY I'LL CONTINUE TO FINANCE IT!
PARDON ME, PLEASE!
COME ON IN, FRANZ!

I HAVE HEARD ABOUT... ACCIDENT, NO? MY FELLOW PILOT KILLED?
MORE THAN KILLED... STRANGLED!

BRUCIE, MEET HEINRICH FRANZ --OUR TECHNICAL EXPERT! HEINRICH, THIS IS BRUCE WAYNE--ONE OF THE BANK-ROLLERS OF THIS MESS WE'RE WORKING ON!
YOU'VE DONE A FINE JOB KEEPING OUR ANTIQUES IN THE AIR, HERR FRANZ!

I AM SORRY FOR TROUBLES, MEIN HERR! PERHAPS WE ARE NOT FATED TO COMPLETE ZIS FILM, EH?
VON HAMMER VAS A GREAT BELIEVER IN FATE... THE DESTINY OF THE KILLER SKIES, HE CALLED IT!
PERHAPS... VON HAMMER'S GHOST IS OUR ENEMY, EH?

UMMM, WELL... I HAVE SOME BUSINESS TO ATTEND TO!
MAYBE THE BATMAN CAN FIND THE ANSWER TO THAT...ON THE MOVIE SET!
4

AND SO, IN BRUCE WAYNE'S HOTEL ROOM...
I THOUGHT THERE WAS SOMETHING FAMILIAR ABOUT FRANZ... THE RESEMBLANCE IS UNCANNY!

HE LOOKS ALMOST EXACTLY LIKE THE MAN IN THIS OLD PHOTO... THE REAL BARON HANS VON HAMMER!
AS ALICE SAID, "CURIOUSER AND CURIOUSER..."

NIGHT, THICK AS A VELVET CLOAK, ENSHROUDS THE CARDBOARD AND CANVAS CASTLE, AND THE MAKE-SHIFT AIRFIELD WHICH LIES NEARBY...
HURRY... LIGHT THE FUSES AND RUN--
SI, SEÑOR HAMMER!
THEN YOU WILL GIVE US THE PESOS YOU PROMISED, SEÑOR?

SOMETHING MOVES IN THE DARKNESS!
USE YOUR FLASH, IDIOT!
MY ASKING YOU TO SURRENDER-- IN ENGLISH OR SPANISH-- WOULD DOUBTLESSLY FALL ON DEAF EARS-- SO...
5

AIEEE! EL HOMBRE MURCIELAGO!*
* TRANS: LITERALLY, THE BATMAN!

MARTINEZ... THE FUSE! DESTROY THE PLANES!
SI, SEÑOR HAMMER!
AND I SHALL PLACE MY BLADE IN THIS... THIS MONSTER!

UGGNH
HE MOVES SWIFTLY AS THE SHARK--!

NO... MORE SWIFTLY THAN A SHARK, THIS RELENTLESSLY TRAINED BODY, POWERED BY UNQUENCHABLE WILL... STRIKES--

...AND STRIKES AGAIN, WITH DEVASTATING PRECISION...

FOR THIS IS THE BATMAN... ONE WHO KNOWS A SPECIAL SORT OF GREATNESS!
6

AT LEAST TWO OF MY PLAYMATES WERE HIT HARD ENOUGH TO STAY COOLED--
--BUT THAT THIRD ONE MIGHT STILL BE UP TO ANOTHER ROUND--
--COULDN'T GIVE BOTH HIM AND THE EXPLOSIVE ATTENTION THEY NEEDED!
AS I THOUGHT... HE'S TRYING FOR A QUICK EXIT!

HE RUNS LIKE A REJECT FROM AN OLD FOLKS HOME--
UN MOMENTO, HOMBRECITO!

DEAR FRIEND, IF YOU VALUE YOUR FINE TEETH, YOU WILL SPEAK OF THE MAN WHO HIRED YOU TO DO EVIL THINGS! HIS NAME, OR--*
THIS I KNOW NOT, MAN OF THE BATS! ALWAYS, HE IS MASKED IN GOGGLES AND SCARF--EVEN AS YOU ARE MASKED! *
* TRANSLATED FROM THE SPANISH!

HE PAYS US MANY PESOS TO RUIN THE WORK OF THE AMERICAN FILM-MAKERS--
--BUT I SWEAR ON THE GRAVE OF MY MOTHER, I HAVE NOT HIS TRUE IDENTITY!
DID HE REQUIRE YOU TO TAMPER WITH THE AIRPLANE?
THIS WE DID NOT DO...

I CHOOSE TO BELIEVE YOU--FOR THE MOMENT! GO... SEEK A POLICEMAN AND SURRENDER YOURSELF AND YOUR COMPANIONS!
SHOULD YOU ATTEMPT TO FLEE, I WILL HUNT YOU THOUGH YOU HIDE AT THE END OF THE EARTH!

MOTIVE... OPPORTUNITY... AND ONE VERY BAD SLIP OF THE TONGUE--
IT'S GOT TO BE HIM MASQUERADING AS "VON HAMMER"!-
7
SO, THE BATMAN IS CERTAIN HE HAS SOLVED THE MYSTERY! ARE YOU AS CERTAIN...

I HAVE NO WAY OF KNOWING EXACTLY WHERE HE FLED--BUT IT IS PROBABLE HE RETURNED HERE... TO THE COMPANY'S LIVING AREA--
YES--! THERE'S A LIGHT IN HIS TRAILER--

AS I HOPED... HE'S STOPPED TO COLLECT HIS BLOOD MONEY..

FINISH COUNTING... I'M CURIOUS TO LEARN EXACTLY HOW MUCH THE RIVAL MOVIE OUTFIT PAID YOU TO SABOTAGE "THE HAMMER OF HELL"--
THE BATMAN?

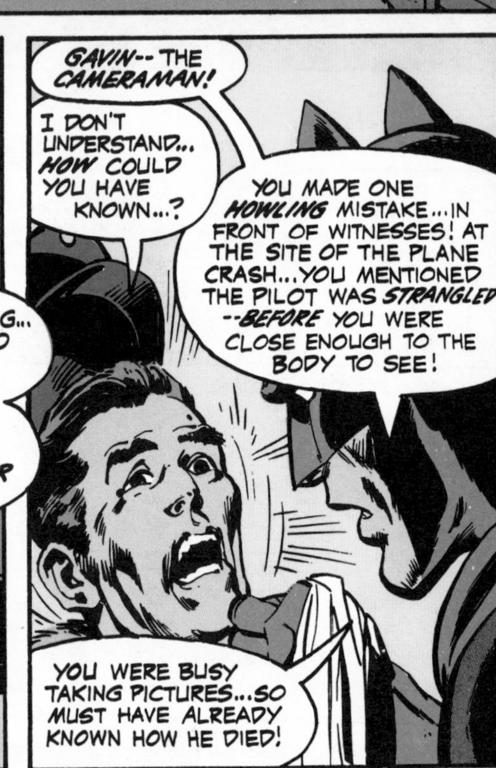
GAVIN-- THE CAMERAMAN!
I DON'T UNDERSTAND... HOW COULD YOU HAVE KNOWN...?
YOU MADE ONE HOWLING MISTAKE... IN FRONT OF WITNESSES! AT THE SITE OF THE PLANE CRASH... YOU MENTIONED THE PILOT WAS STRANGLED --BEFORE YOU WERE CLOSE ENOUGH TO THE BODY TO SEE!
YOU WERE BUSY TAKING PICTURES... SO MUST HAVE ALREADY KNOWN HOW HE DIED!

BUT... I WASN'T ANYWHERE NEAR THAT PLANE...
NO... BUT ONE OF THOSE SPANISH GOONS YOU HIRED COULD'VE HIDDEN IN THE COCKPIT OF THE NIEUPORT 17, PUT A GUN ON THE PILOT, FORCED HIM TO TAKE OFF-- THEN STRANGLED HIM IN THE AIR AND BAILED OUT BEHIND THE MOUNTAIN! YOU ALSO HAD A THUG SABOTAGE THE PLANE AS INSURANCE! I NOTICED THAT ONE OF THE NIEUPORT'S FLAPS WAS STUCK IN THE HALF-DOWN POSITION...
8

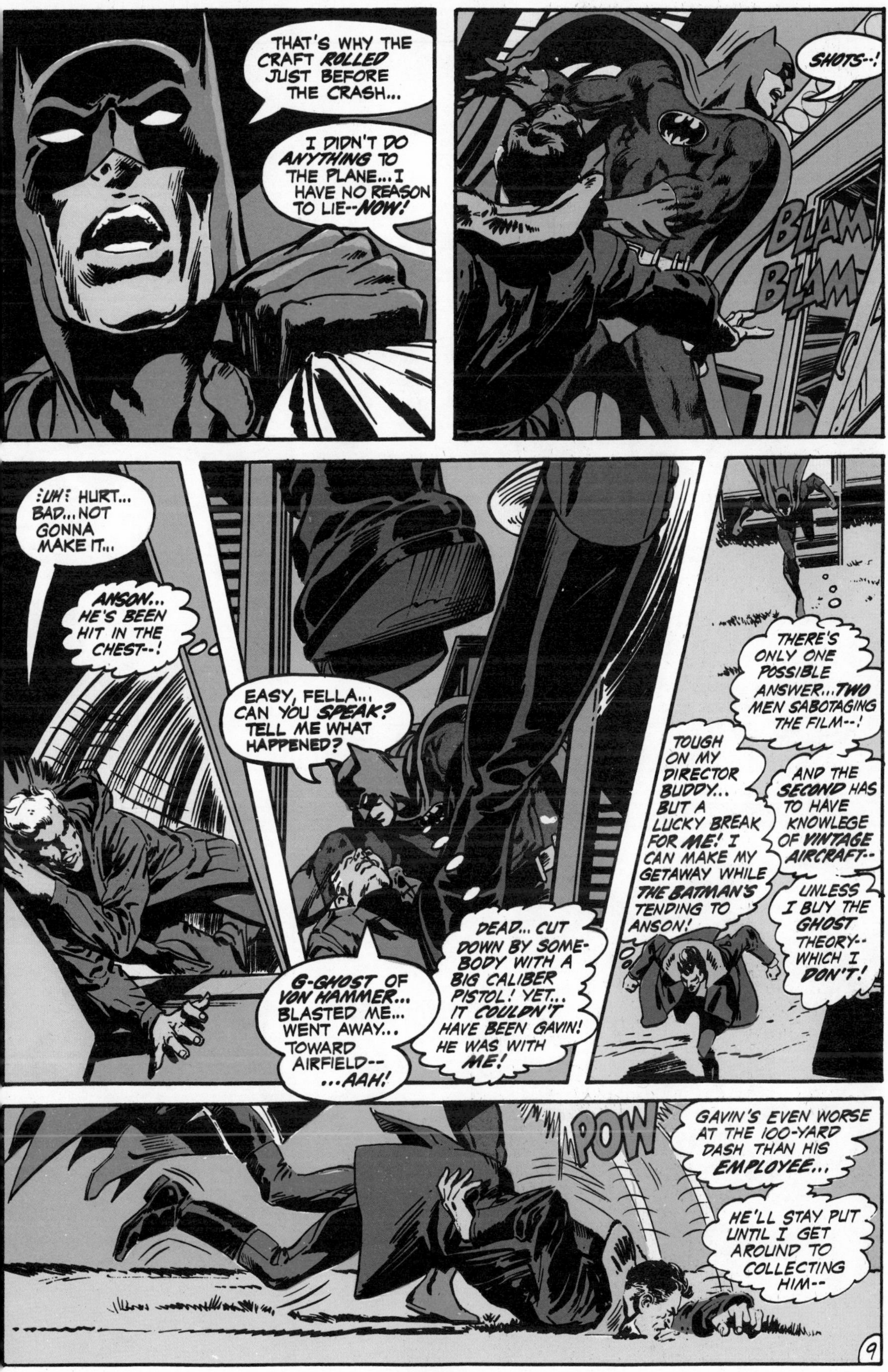

:*UH*: HURT... BAD... NOT GONNA MAKE IT...

ANSON... HE'S BEEN HIT IN THE CHEST--!

EASY, FELLA... CAN YOU *SPEAK?* TELL ME WHAT HAPPENED?

G-GHOST OF *VON HAMMER*... BLASTED ME... WENT AWAY... TOWARD AIRFIELD-- ...*AAH!*

DEAD... CUT DOWN BY SOMEBODY WITH A BIG CALIBER PISTOL! YET... IT COULDN'T HAVE BEEN GAVIN! HE WAS WITH ME!

THERE'S ONLY ONE POSSIBLE ANSWER... TWO MEN SABOTAGING THE FILM--!

AND THE SECOND HAS TO HAVE KNOWLEGE OF VINTAGE AIRCRAFT--

UNLESS I BUY THE GHOST THEORY-- WHICH I DON'T!

TOUGH ON MY DIRECTOR BUDDY... BUT A LUCKY BREAK FOR *ME!* I CAN MAKE MY GETAWAY WHILE *THE BATMAN'S* TENDING TO ANSON!

SOMEBODY'S STARTING AN ENGINE... SOUNDS LIKE THE OLD FOKKER TRIPLANE--
ANSON SAID HIS KILLER WENT TOWARD THE STRIP... GOT TO RUN LIKE I'VE NEVER RUN BEFORE!

THE FOKKER'S READY TO GO! BUT I DON'T SEE A PILOT--!
PLEASE, TURN AROUND SLOWLY SO I MAY LOOK AT YOU!

YOU ARE THE AMERICAN LAWMAN-- THE BATMAN!
YES... I DON'T BELIEVE WE'VE MET!
YOU MAY CALL ME THE GHOST OF HANS VON HAMMER--!

I'D RATHER NOT--! I'D RATHER CALL YOU BY YOUR NAME!
HEINRICH FRANZ AT YOUR SERVICE!
YOU'RE THE ONE WHO'S BEEN SABOTAGING THE MOVIE!

GUILTY AS CHARGED! THIS... FILTHY AMERICAN FILM IS AN INSULT TO THE MEMORY OF GERMANY'S FINEST HERO--
--VON HAMMER WAS AS A GOD! THE AMERICANS SHOW HIM AS A SOFT, SNIVELING WEAKLING...
...PUTTING INTO HIS MOUTH WORDS OF COMPASSION ...OF MERCY... OF RESPECT FOR THE ENEMY!

BAH! HE WAS RUTHLESS, WAS MY ANCESTOR-- MAGNIFICENTLY RUTHLESS!
NOT THE WAY I READ HIS STORY! I SEE THE BARON AS A MAN CAUGHT BETWEEN HIS FEELING OF DUTY AND HIS OWN BEST INSTINCTS... A TRAGIC, TORMENTED AND SOMEWHAT PITIFUL SOLDIER--
10

AS YOU WILL! I AM NOT GOING TO ARGUE HISTORY! RATHER, I AM GOING TO KILL!
SHOOT AN UNARMED ENEMY? IS THAT HOW VON HAMMER WOULD'VE ACTED? OR WOULD HE HAVE WELCOMED A FAIR FIGHT?

YES, YES... YOU ARE RIGHT! A CONTEST OF SKILL--THAT IS THE WAY OF VON HAMMER!
THE NIEUPORT IS FUELED AND READY--
I SHALL MEET YOU-- IN THE KILLER SKY!

ONCE, A LONG TIME AGO, AN OLD STUNT-PILOT SHOWED ME HOW TO FLY THESE CRATES...
I HOPE I REMEMBER ALL HE SAID! BECAUSE IF I DON'T--
THAT MANIAC WILL GO FREE... AND I'LL BE DEAD!

AS THE FIRST LIGHT OF THE DAY BREAKS OVER THE CLOUDS EAST OF THE FIELD, TWO FRAIL THINGS-- BARELY MORE THAN STICKS COVERED WITH CANVAS-- CLIMB SLOWLY AWAY FROM THE EARTH...

...THEY TURN IN SCREAMING ARCS AND BEGIN A DEATH-DUEL--!
11

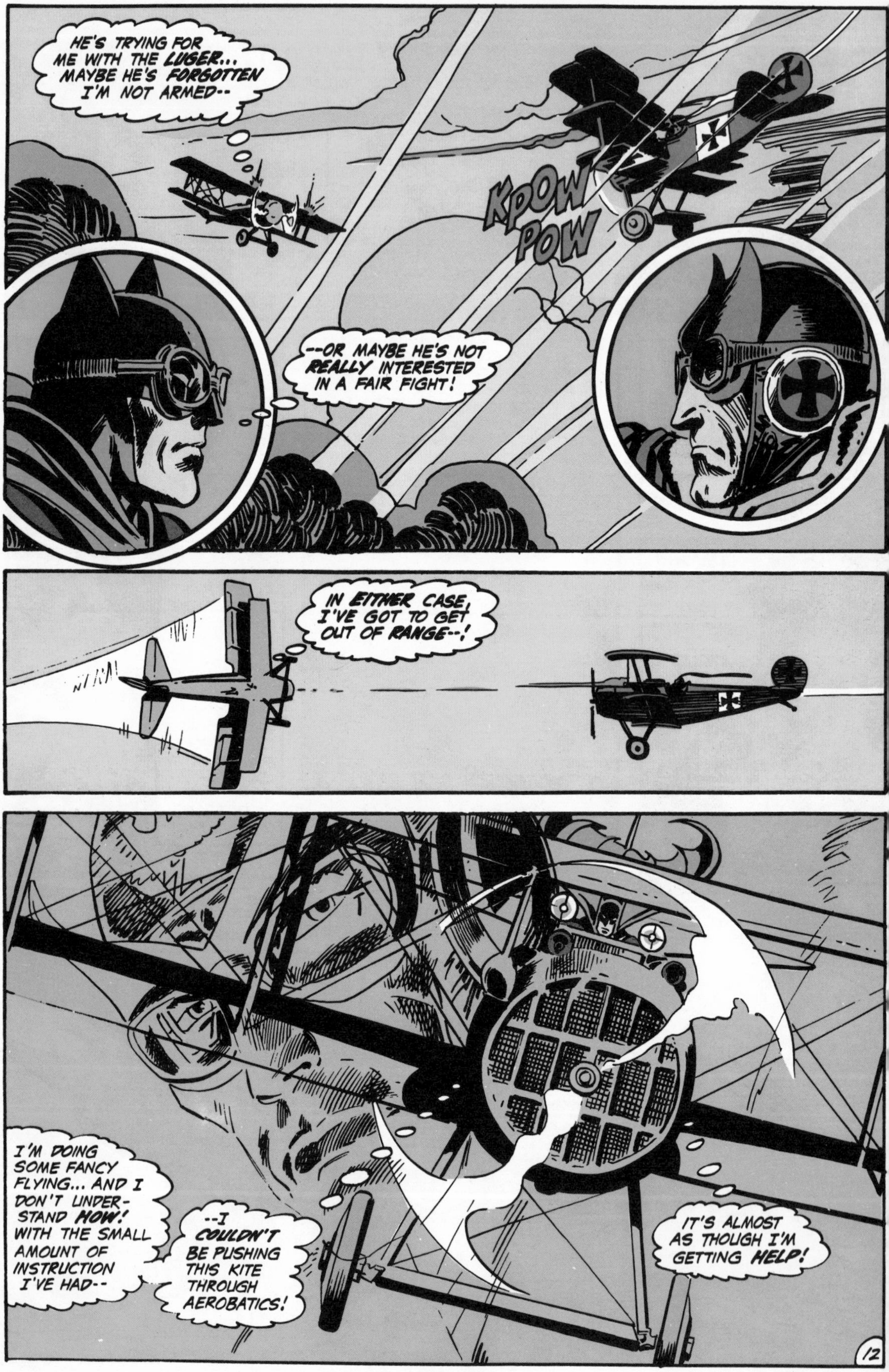

HE'S TRYING FOR ME WITH THE LUGER... MAYBE HE'S FORGOTTEN I'M NOT ARMED--
KPOW POW
--OR MAYBE HE'S NOT REALLY INTERESTED IN A FAIR FIGHT!

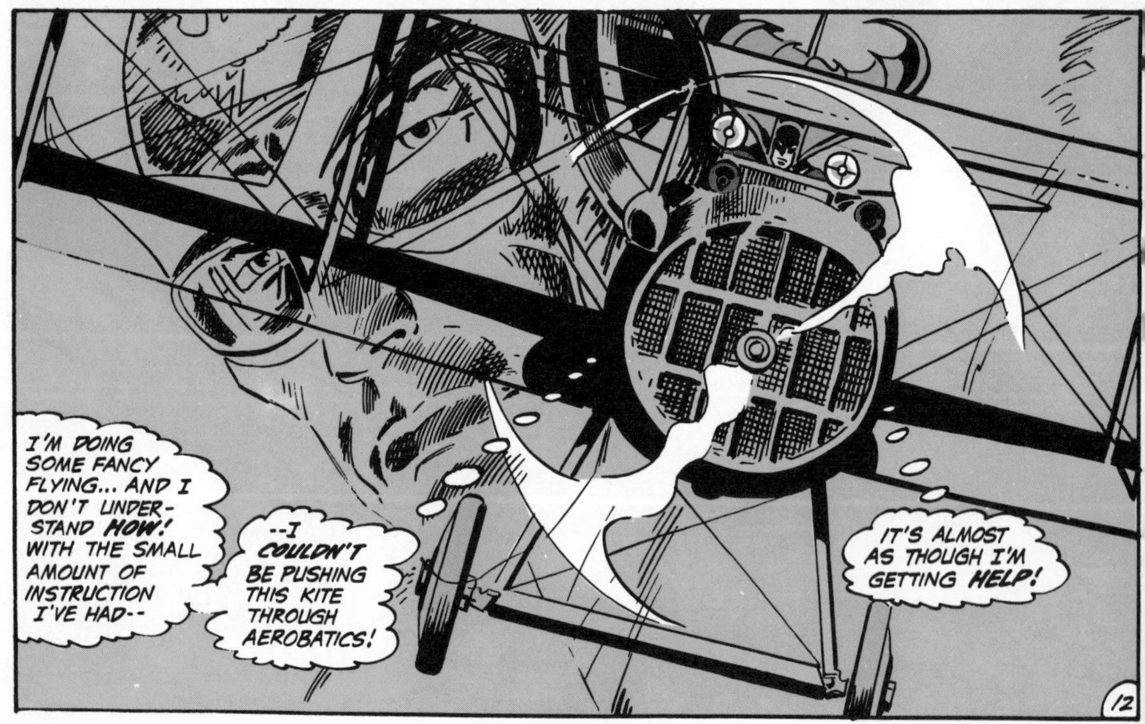

HE'S DIVING... STRAIGHT AT ME--! DOES HE PLAN TO CRASH--?

NO...HE'S USING HIS PROP TO CAUSE TURBULENCE... HOPING THAT I'LL BE BOUNCED AROUND UNTIL I MAKE A MISTAKE...
--A FATAL MISTAKE!

IF THE PLANE CAN TAKE IT--SO CAN I! FIRST JOB IS TO GET OUT OF HIS BACK-WASH...BY GOING UPSTAIRS--

...AND THEN I'LL TRY A STUNT OF MY OWN--HUH? THE ENGINE'S QUITTING...
ONE OF THE SLUGS MUST HAVE CUT THE FUEL-LINE...

I'M A SITTING DUCK... BUT HE CAN'T HAVE MORE THAN ONE BULLET LEFT--
GOT TO MAKE HIM WASTE IT...

--BY DOING THE TOTALLY... UNEXPECTED!
13

YOU ARE A COURAGEOUS FOE! IT IS ALMOST WITH RESPECT THAT I DESTROY YOU!

I SHALL SALUTE YOU AS YOU FALL-- AS THE GREAT BARON SALUTED VALIENT ENEMIES!

THUNK!

SURELY THIS IS NOT WORTHY OF THE BATMAN...EXPECTING ME TO BELIEVE I AM ATTACKED FROM BEHIND--
FRANZ... BEHIND YOU!
--WHILE WE RIDE THE WINDS HIGH ABOVE THE GROUND--!

NO... YOUR SCARF--!
G-EHHH!!
14

IT CAUGHT IN THE PROP.. YANKED HIM OUT OF THE COCKPIT--
YAAAARRRRGGHHH
I WONDER IF FRANZ WAS REALLY VON HAMMER'S DESCENDANT-- OR JUST ANOTHER VICTIM OF THE MOST TERRIBLE OF LOVES--
--THE LOVE OF WAR!
I GUESS I'LL NEVER KNOW...
End
A TRIBUTE TO THE GREAT
Joe Kubert & Robert Kanigher
FROM
DENNY O'NEIL (SCRIPTER)
NEAL ADAMS DICK GIORDANO (ART)
JULIUS SCHWARTZ (EDITOR)
15

Coloring by Gene D'Angelo

IT BEGINS AT THE ANNUAL *GOTHAM CITY MERCHANTS'* PARADE... A MERRY PROCESSION OF FLOATS THROUGH THE BUSINESS DISTRICT, CELEBRATING THE PRODUCTS AND SERVICES OF THE MIGHTY METROPOLIS...

NONE OF THE GRINNING SPECTATORS ARE AWARE THAT A *CRIME* IS BEING COMMITTED BEFORE THEIR EYES...

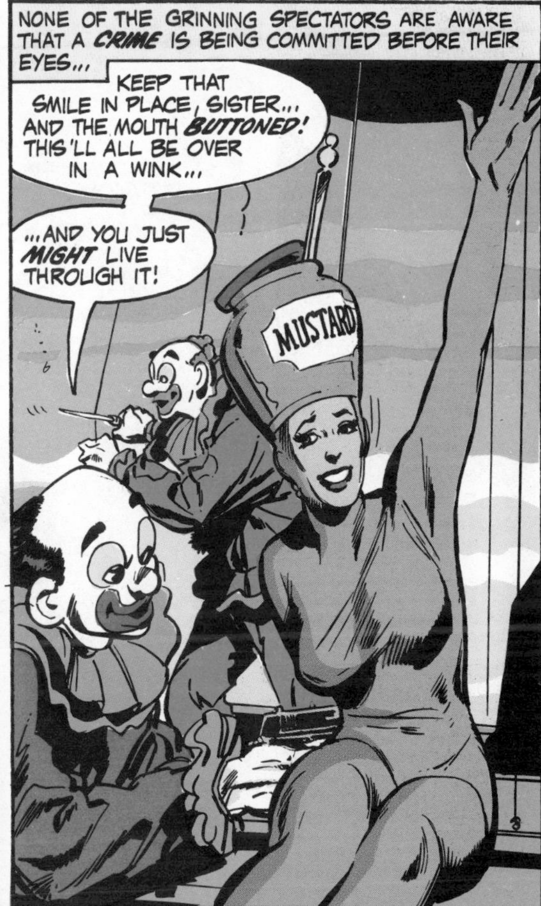

KEEP THAT SMILE IN PLACE, SISTER... AND THE MOUTH *BUTTONED!* THIS'LL ALL BE OVER IN A WINK...
...AND YOU JUST *MIGHT* LIVE THROUGH IT!
MUSTARD

THERE! IT'S *CUT!*
OKAY! LET'S SPLIT, BEFORE SOMEBODY TUMBLES TO WHAT'S HAPPENIN'!

SOME ONLOOKERS ARE PUZZLED... MOST THINK THE BALLOON'S DISAPPEARANCE INTO THE BELLY OF A HOVERING HELICOPTER IS MERELY PART OF THE SHOW...

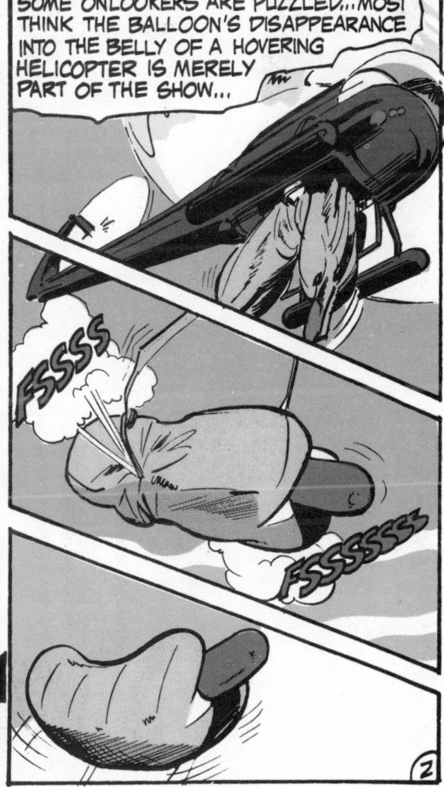

THAT NIGHT, A FAMILIAR SHAPE APPEARS ON THE STARLESS NIGHT-SKY--A SILENT CALL FOR THE BATMAN!

AND INSIDE THE OFFICE OF POLICE COMMISSIONER GORDON, A CERTAIN PUBLIC SERVANT IS WAVING HIS ARMS... AND SCREECHING JUST A BIT--
I DO NOT UNDERSTAND WHY YOU FEEL COMPELLED TO SUMMON THAT... THAT MASKED BLACKGUARD!
BECAUSE, MR. REEVES, THE THEFT OF A FRANKFURTER--SHAPED HELIUM BALLOON IS AN UNUSUAL CRIME... TO SAY THE LEAST!
AND THE UNUSUAL IS THE SPECIALTY OF THE BATMAN!

WELL, I HOPE HE SHOWS UP-- THAT'S ALL! I'M TIRED OF HIS MEDDLING IN CITY AFFAIRS...
I MAY DECIDE TO SEE HOW TOUGH HE REALLY IS! AN ARTHUR REEVES LEFT... FOLLOWED BY A REEVES RIGHT!

...I'LL TAKE HIM DOWN A PEG OR TWO... OHH!

BOO!

3

YOU CALLED ME ABOUT THAT ODD ROBBERY THIS AFTERNOON, COMMISSIONER!
YES...IT SEEMED TO BE YOUR SORT OF CASE! ANY IDEAS?
A DIM ONE, SIR! SO UNLIKELY IT'S HARDLY WORTH MENTIONING!
COMMISSIONER! THE ALARM AT THE NAUTICAL MUSEUM IS RINGING!
HAVE MY CAR BROUGHT TO THE FRONT DOOR!
COME ON, BATMAN! I'LL DRIVE YOU...
YOU HAVE YOUR TRANS-PORTATION... AND I HAVE MINE! SEE YOU THERE!
BANG BANG BANG
BARE MINUTES LATER...
THE GUARDS ARE SHOOTING AT THE GETAWAY CAR...AND NOT DOING MUCH GOOD!
THEY'RE DUMB CROOKS... SHOWING THEMSELVES ON THE STREET! UNLESS...
...THEY PLANNED ON BEING SEEN!...TO DIVERT THE GUARDS FROM WHERE THE REAL ACTION IS... INSIDE!
YES...THERE'S A FLASHLIGHT MOVING IN THE NEXT GALLERY!
WILL YOU GET IT IN GEAR? THIS JOINT GIVES ME THE CREEPY-CRAWLIES!
GO CHEW YOUR TONGUE! I GOT THE JUNK WE WAS SENT FOR!
EXACTLY WHAT JUNK, FUNNY-FACE?
4

THE BATMAN?
DON'T GAB... BLAST HIM!
NOT LIKELY!
THE OTHER ONE-- PITCHING A SMOKE-GRENADE! THEY'RE WELL-EQUIPPED FOR COMMON RIP-OFF ARTISTS!
SSSSSSSSS
UN!...
I'VE GOT TO COUNT THE GRENADE-TOSSER AS A DEAD LOSS... NO WAY OF FOLLOWING HIM THROUGH THE FUMES!
BUT THIS CHARMER ISN'T GOING ANYWHERE... EXCEPT INTO A ROOM OF FRESH AIR!
WAK
STAY BACK, BATMAN... OR SO HELP ME, I'LL SCRAMBLE YOUR BRAINS! I DON'T WANNA MIX WITH YOU--!
JUST... KEEP AWAY!
NO NEED TO GET UPSET!...
...YOU'RE NO DANGER--NONE AT ALL!
5

THE POLICE WILL ARRIVE SHORTLY! IF YOU'D CARE TO BE HEALTHY WHEN THEY TAKE YOU AWAY, YOU'LL ANSWER MY QUESTIONS!
S-SURE... ANYTHING!

WHOM ARE YOU WORKING FOR?
I DUNNO...I SWEAR I DON'T! HE'S A WEIRDO... FACE HIDDEN ALL 'A TIME...
...AN' HE KEEPS TOSSIN' SOME KINDA COIN!

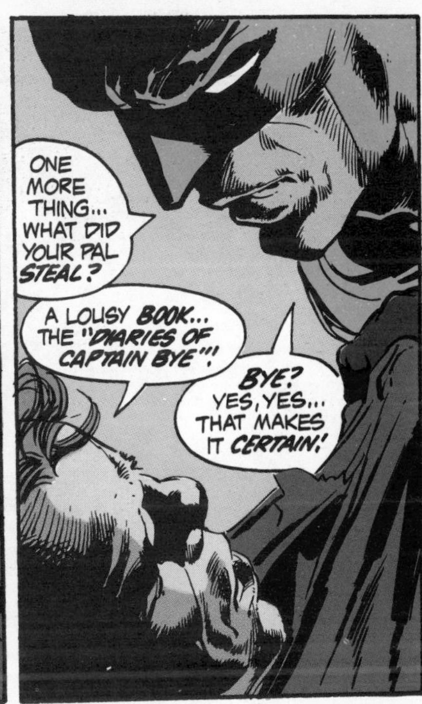
ONE MORE THING... WHAT DID YOUR PAL STEAL?
A LOUSY BOOK... THE "DIARIES OF CAPTAIN BYE"!
BYE? YES, YES... THAT MAKES IT CERTAIN!

YOUR BOSS IS ONE OF THE STRANGEST CRIMINAL GENIUSES WHO EVER LIVED! ONE OF THE MOST TRAGIC...AND ONE OF THE DEADLIEST!

AT THAT MOMENT, IN A SHACK NEAR THE GOTHAM CITY DOCKS...
YOU GOT IT?... THE DIARY?
YEAH...ONLY MY BUDDY WAS NABBED!

THAT'S VERY UNFORTUNATE... FOR HIM! IT'S NO CONCERN OF MINE, HOWEVER! THIS IS THE IMPORTANT THING...
...THIS WRITING! A CIPHER-EXPERT I MET IN PRISON TOLD ME THERE IS IN THESE PAGES THE CODED CLUE TO A FORTUNE!

AND I HAVE THE KEY TO THE CODE! BUT WILL I USE IT? WILL I ACTUALLY COMMIT THE CRIME?
THAT IS FOR THE COIN TO DECIDE!

WHICH FACE WILL IT SHOW? WHICH SIDE... THE WHOLE...

...OR THE RUINED?
6

THE COIN HAS DECIDED! THE EVIL PART OF MY NATURE WINS... AND SO TWO-FACE MUST STRIKE!
AS THE BELLS OF GOTHAM CITY TOLL MIDNIGHT, WEALTHY SOCIALITE BRUCE WAYNE STANDS ON THE BALCONY OF HIS PENTHOUSE, CONFERRING WITH HIS BUTLER, ALFRED...
A KNOTTY PROBLEM, MASTER BRUCE?
WORSE, ALFRED! I SUSPECTED THAT OUR OLD ENEMY TWO-FACE WAS BEHIND THE BALLOON THEFT...
...HE COULDN'T RESIST THE SLOGAN ON THE FLOAT--"DOUBLY DELICIOUS!" OR THE NAME "JANUS"... THE TWO-FACED ROMAN GOD!
ARE YOU SURE, SIR? ISN'T TWO-FACE STILL IN JAIL?
HE ESCAPED... SEVERAL MONTHS AGO! HOW COULD ANY JAIL HOPE TO HOLD A MAN SO CLEVER AND DEVIOUS AS HARVEY?
TSSSSS
"REMEMBER, ALFRED, HOW TWO-FACE CAME TO BE? HOW MANY YEARS AGO WAS IT WHEN THAT TWO-BIT GANSTER HURTLED A VIAL OF ACID INTO THE FACE OF GOTHAM'S MOST BRILLIANT DISTRICT ATTORNEY, HARVEY DENT..."
7

"...WHAT A MAD AND DIABOLICAL CHASE HE LED ROBIN AND ME WHEN HIS HALF-RUINED FACE TWISTED HIS MIND TOWARD CRIME..."
"IT WAS ONLY THANKS TO MODERN METHODS OF PLASTIC SURGERY THAT THE PERSONALITY OF HARVEY DENT WAS BROUGHT BACK FROM THE EDGE OF MADNESS..."
"ONCE AGAIN HE RE-ENTERED LAWFUL SOCIETY AND SPENT HIS ENERGIES ON THE SIDE OF JUSTICE... UNTIL ONE UNHOLY DAY HARVEY ATTEMPTED TO STOP A ROBBERY..."
ALL RIGHT, YOU TWO! STAND WHERE YOU ARE--!
"SO INTENT WAS HE ON CAPTURING THE THIEVES, HE FAILED TO SPOT THE SPUTTERING FUSE THEY HAD SET..."
BLAM
"IT WASN'T UNTIL HE STAGGERED HOME AND LOOKED INTO A MIRROR THAT THE FULL EXTENT OF HIS TRAGEDY TOOK HOLD OF HIS MIND ONCE AGAIN..."
THE PLASTIC SURGERY! IT'S ALL BEEN UNDONE! IT CAN NEVER BE REPAIRED THIS TIME! I'M DOOMED TO REMAIN TWO-FACE... FOREVER...
TWO-FACE... FOREVER!
8.

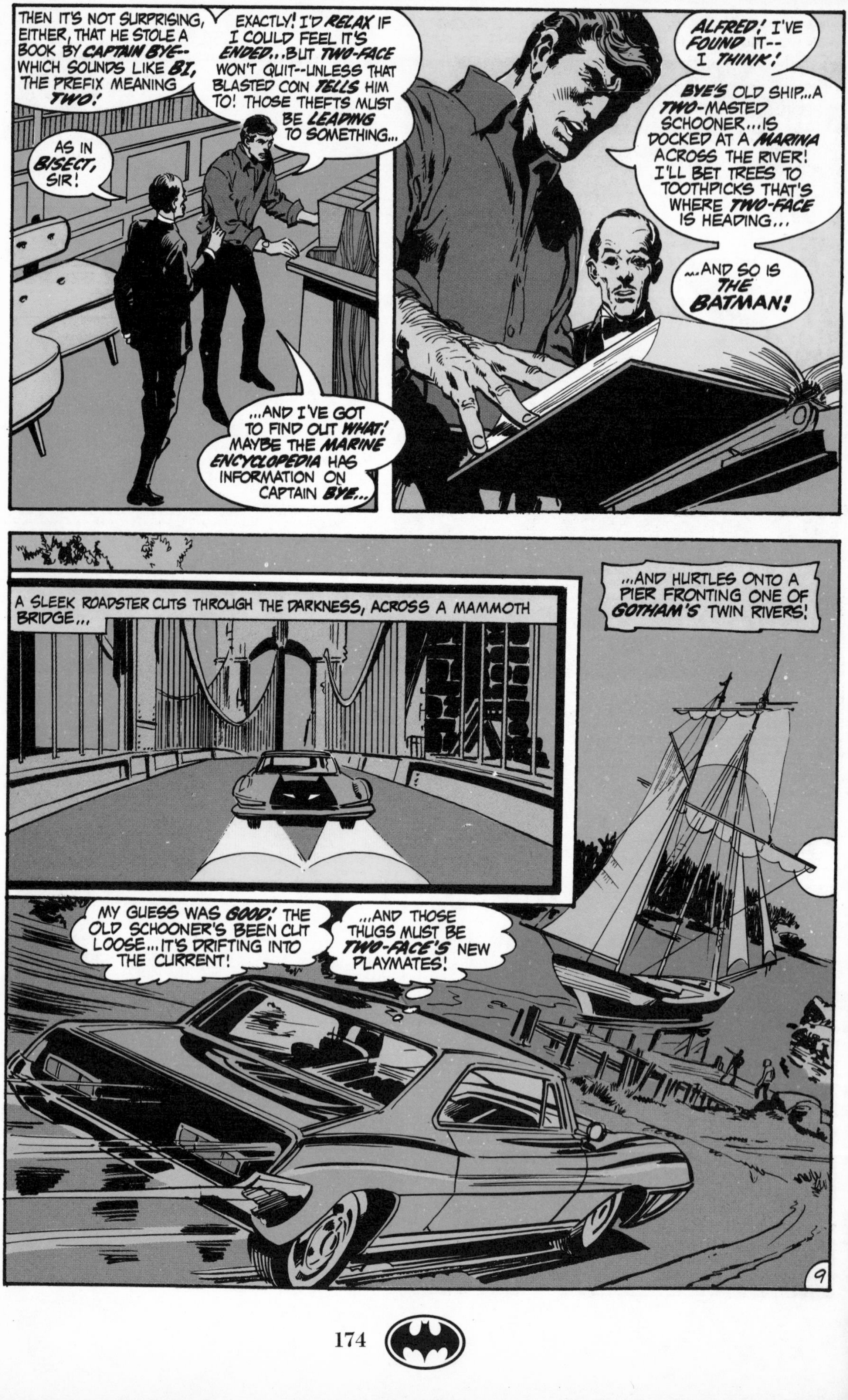

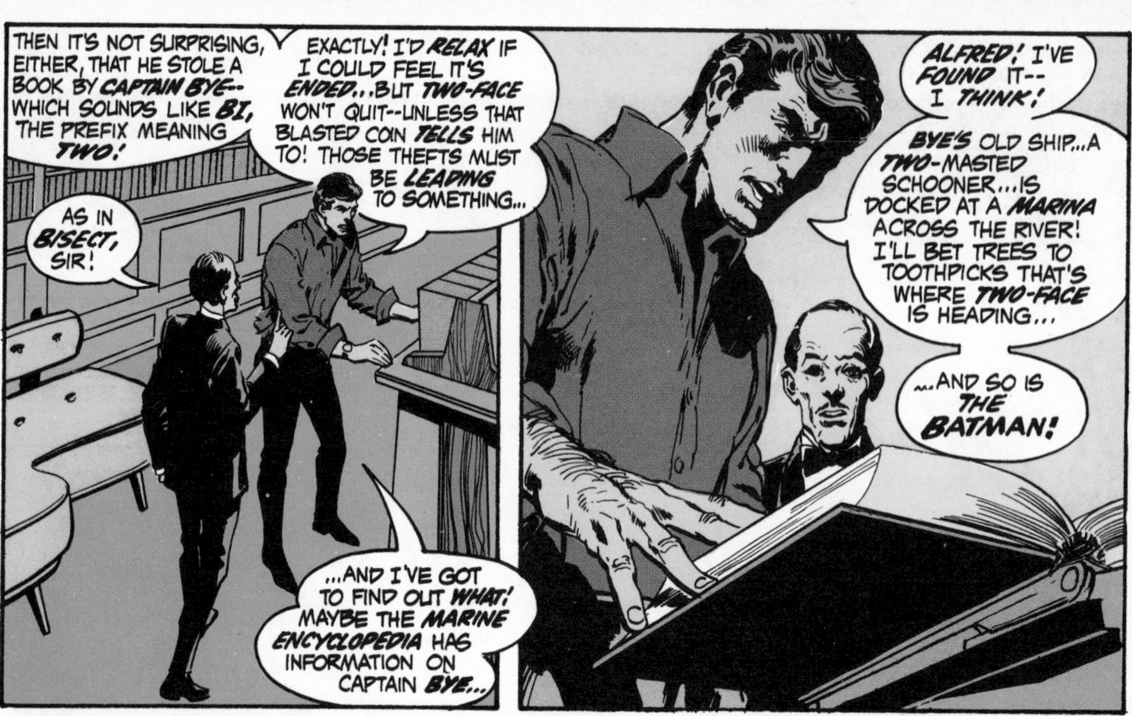

A SLEEK ROADSTER CUTS THROUGH THE DARKNESS, ACROSS A MAMMOTH BRIDGE...

...AND HURTLES ONTO A PIER FRONTING ONE OF GOTHAM'S TWIN RIVERS!

MY GUESS WAS GOOD! THE OLD SCHOONER'S BEEN CUT LOOSE...IT'S DRIFTING INTO THE CURRENT!

...AND THOSE THUGS MUST BE TWO-FACE'S NEW PLAYMATES!

9

THAT CAR AIN'T ONE OF *OURS!*
PROB'LY THE *HEAT!* GIVE IT TO 'EM!

HE CAN'T *SEE...* HE'S FIRING AT WHERE HE *FIGURES* I AM! THE AUTOMATIC PILOT-TYPE CONTROLS IN THAT MODEL BAT-MOBILE ARE PRECISION PERFECT!

I'VE BEEN IN THIS SITUATION TOO *OFTEN* TO DO THE *OBVIOUS!*
AYIEEEE

BRAKATAK
NUMBER *TWO'S* GETTING INTO THE ACT! THIS CALLS FOR A *SUBTERRANEAN* ATTACK!
CHOK

10

THE SHIP HASN'T REACHED SWIFT WATER YET... DRIFTING SLOWLY!
I SHOULD BE ABLE TO SWIM TO IT...
AN EXPLOSION--?!
BLADOOOOM
THE ANCIENT VESSEL LISTS, SHUDDERS, SINKS!
NUMB WITH ASTONISHMENT, THE BATMAN TURNS, HIS MIND SEEKING... DESPERATELY SEEKING!...
IT DOESN'T MAKE SENSE--NONE! WHY WOULD TWO-FACE GO TO ALL THAT TROUBLE... STAGE THE THEFT OF A SHIP...
...AND THEN SINK HIS PRIZE?!
GOT TO CONCENTRATE... CONSIDER ALL FACTORS OF THE CASE--AND COME UP WITH AN ANSWER!
THE FACTS ARE IN...AND THERE IS A SOLUTION! HAVE YOU DEDUCED TWO-FACE'S INTENTION?
11

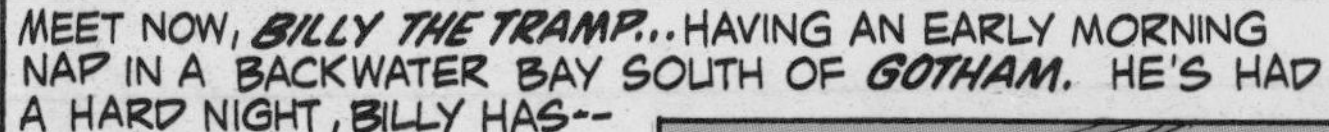
MEET NOW, BILLY THE TRAMP... HAVING AN EARLY MORNING NAP IN A BACKWATER BAY SOUTH OF GOTHAM. HE'S HAD A HARD NIGHT, BILLY HAS--

BUT NOT NEARLY AS HARD AS HIS MORNING WILL BE! FOR THE TOP-MAST OF A SHIP POKES ABOVE THE BAY NEAR HIS HEAD...

...AND...

NEARBY, THE BATMAN LURKS...
RIGHT ON TIME! THE TIDE-CHARTS SHOWED THAT IF A FLOATING OBJECT WERE SUNK NEAR THE PIER WHERE I COOLED TWO-FACE'S HENCHMEN...
...BUT NOT ENTIRELY SUNK-- IT WOULD DRIFT HERE!

TWO-FACE HASN'T ARRIVED YET! I'LL BE WAITING FOR HIM WHEN HE DOES!
AND ON HIS WAY TO JAIL, I'LL EXPLAIN THAT I DEDUCED WHY HE NEEDED A BIG BALLOON--
--TO PUT IN THE HOLD OF THIS TUB, RIGGED TO INFLATE AFTER A PROPER INTERVAL!
--TO RAISE IT IN A QUIET COVE WHERE HE CAN WORK UNDISTURBED!
12

EH? WHO THE DEUCE IS THAT IN THE RIGGING? LOOKS LIKE A HOBO! HOW IN THE NAME OF ALL THAT'S HOLY DID HE GET THERE?

KAK
I'LL HAUL HIM DOWN...
I DON'T WANT ANY DISTRACTIONS WHEN THE FIREWORKS BEGIN... UNNNGH!

QUICKLY, THE WET-SUITED CRIMINAL PRODUCES A LENGTH OF WIRE-ROPE, AND BEGINS LASHING THE CAPED CRUSADER TO A MAST...

I WAS SURE THE BATMAN WOULD TAKE A HAND! SO I HID IN THE SHIP'S HOLD, BREATHING WITH AN OXYGEN MASK...

GROGGY... BUT... NOT OUT... GOT TO EXPAND MY MUSCLES ..., PREVENT HIM TYING LINE TIGHTLY--

DON'T PRETEND YOU'RE NOT AWAKE, OLD FOE! I WANT YOU TO SEE-- HOW YOU'LL DIE! UGLY, YOU'LL DIE... UGLY AS THE ACCIDENT THAT MADE ME A FREAK!

I PUT A HOT EMBER TO THE BALLOON WHICH HELD THIS SCOW AFLOAT ONCE--AND FOR THE SECOND TIME...
PAWOO

...AND WHILE THE GAS ESCAPES, I SMASH AWAY THIS MOLDING...
13

BEHOLD, A FORTUNE IN GOLD COMES SPILLING... GOLD DOUBLOONS, JUST AS CAPTAIN BYE'S DIARY PROMISED!

HAVING FILLED HIS SACK, TWO-FACE WHIRLS TO A LIFEBOAT, AND...
WITHIN MOMENTS, THIS SCOW WILL HAVE SUNK...TAKING A BATMAN WITH IT!
NOT ONLY ME! LOOK-- UP IN THE RIGGING!

ARE YOU GOING TO LET HIM DROWN-- AN INNOCENT, OLD MAN?
HIS MISFORTUNE, BATMAN...AND NO CONCERN OF MINE!

YOU'VE ALWAYS PRIDED YOURSELF ON BEING AS GOOD AS YOU ARE EVIL! WAS YOUR PRIDE A MERE POSE?
QUIET, BATMAN! MY DECISION IS FINAL!

ONCE MORE CAPTAIN BYE'S SCHOONER SETTLES, WATER CREEPING RAPIDLY UP ITS HULL--! TWO-FACE TRIES TO IGNORE IT...

...BUT CAN'T! RELUCTANTLY, HE REMOVES THE DOUBLE-HEADED COIN FROM HIS POUCH, FLIPS IT... AND...

14

BATMAN-- YOU'RE FREE?!
I MIGHT HAVE KNOWN--
IT WASN'T DIFFICULT! I EXPANDED MY MUSCLES WHILE YOU WERE ROPING ME! BY CONTRACTING THEM, I GOT ENOUGH SLACK TO SLIP OUT OF THE KNOTS!
DO YOU WANT TO SURREN-DER?

NEVER! THE COIN DICTATED I SAVE THE OLD MAN... YOU REMAIN MY ENEMY!
AND THUS IT ENDS... PERHAPS!
15

SOMETHING NEW HAS BEEN ADDED TO THE FEARSOME ARMAMENT OF MAN-BAT... THE POWER OF AN ANCIENT EVIL... WHICH MAKES THIS AWESOME NIGHT CREATURE THE MOST FORMIDABLE FOE THE BATMAN HAS EVER FOUGHT!

"MAN-BAT over VEGAS!"

STORY+ART by FRANK ROBBINS

EDITED by JULIUS SCHWARTZ

SKREEEEEEK!

WITH ALL THE "SMART MONEY" IN VEGAS ON MAN-BAT...

...HOW DO I BEAT THE ODDS?

S-1296

1

Coloring by Tatjana Wood

DAWN... AND A DESERT IN NEW MEXICO IS SHAKEN BY...
... A MASSIVE UNDERGROUND NUCLEAR TEST-
BLAST!
A.E.C. STA-72A 7
SHORTLY, FAR TO THE WEST... STILL SHUDDERING FROM THE FIRST SHOCK-WAVES...
... MIGHTY HOOVER DAM IS STRUCK AGAIN... BY SWARMS OF PANIC-BLINDED BATS!
?!
THEY DIDN'T EVEN "SEE" IT!-- AS IF THEIR "SONAR-GUIDANCE SYSTEMS" WERE...
KNOCKED OUT!
LATE THAT NIGHT...
... A SILENT LOOMING HORROR STRIKES AT VEGAS!
CASA
DRIVE-IN
INN
EVEN LATER, AS BIG SPENDERS OF THE "STRIP'S" ROUND-THE-CLOCK GAMBLING CASINOS CALL IT A NIGHT...
DON'T LOOK LIKE SLEEP, THELMA -- NOT THE WAY HE'S SPRAWLED!
COLLAR RIPPED OPEN-- AND... LOOK!
WELL, I NEVER...! SOME FOLKS DON'T CARE WHERE THEY SLEEP IT OFF...
AGH-!
THOSE UGLY MARKS IN HIS NECK-- THAT DEAD-WHITE SKIN!
J-JUST LIKE-- LIKE...
DON'T DARE SAY IT, SAM!
THAT SORT OF STUFF ONLY HAPPENS IN -- "DRACULA" MOVIES!
2

WITHIN THE HOUR, ALL OF VEGAS IS ABUZZ...
YOU SURE, QUINT?
NO OTHER POSSIBILITY?
NONE, CHET! I DON'T BELIEVE IN THESE "THINGS", EITHER, BUT...
...ESPECIALLY THE USUALLY DEAD-SILENT POLICE-MORGUE!
...WITH EYEWITNESS REPORTS FLOODING IN OF A KING-SIZE "VAMPIRE-BAT" FLYING OFF-- HOW ELSE DO YOU EXPLAIN IT?

WILD THEORIES QUICKLY FILL THE AIR-WAVES...
...THE LATEST GUESSES NOW LINK UP THREE SEEMINGLY "ISOLATED" EVENTS!
ONE: THE NUCLEAR BLAST!
TWO: IT'S FAR-FLUNG SHOCK-WAVES WHICH SPLIT OPEN AN UNDISCOVERED NETWORK OF CAVES...

WHILE IN GOTHAM, HOME OF ANOTHER "CREATURE OF THE NIGHT"... ...THE BATMAN...
VAMPIRES? IN NEVADA-- SO FAR NORTH OF THEIR NATURAL HABITAT?
ALFRED-- I WONDER IF KIRK LANGSTROM HAS HEARD OF THIS YET...?
...RELEASING SWARMS OF PANICKED VAMPIRE-BATS TO SMASH INTO HOOVER DAM!
AND THREE: HERE IN VEGAS...

SHOULD BE RIGHT DOWN HIS ALLEY, SIR...
...AS CURATOR OF NOCTURNAL MAMMALS AT GOTHAM NATURAL HISTORY MUSEUM!
...THE SMART MONEY HAS IT THAT THE "VEGAS RAIDER" IS A NUCLEAR-CREATED...
...MONSTER-MUTANT VAMPIRE-BAT!

THE "SMART MONEY" HAS BEEN SEEING TOO MANY "HORROR MOVIES"!
A "MUTANT" BAT-- HUH!
MIGHT I SUGGEST, MASTER BRUCE-- THAT LANGSTROM HIMSELF WAS ONCE A "MUTANT" BAT?
IN SPECIFIC-- A MAN-BAT!

TRUE-- BUT HE BROUGHT THAT ON HIMSELF... AND HIS WIFE... BY RECKLESS EXPERIMENTS!
...TO SHED SCIENTIFIC LIGHT ON THESE THEORIES...
...WE TAKE YOU TO THE CAVE-SITE WHERE VISITING BAT-SPECIALIST, PROFESSOR KIRK LANGSTROM...
LANGSTROM-- DOWN THERE?
3

YOU WERE NEAR HERE AT THE TIME, PROFESSOR--ON AN EXPLORATORY FIELD-TRIP...
SHEER NONSENSE!
FACT: THE NUCLEAR SHOCK-WAVES DID UNCOVER THESE POSSIBLY "PREHISTORIC" CAVES...
WHAT IS YOUR OPINION OF THESE "MUTANT" THEORIES?
LVC

...REVEALING A SURVIVING SPECIES OF BAT-- THE "DIPHYLLA VAMPYRUS"-- NEVER SEEN THIS FAR NORTH!
A TROPIC-ZONE VAMPIRE PREYING MAINLY ON ANIMALS, AND RARELY--ON MEN!

THEN, IN YOUR CONSIDERED VIEW, SIR-- THE "CREATURE" OVER VEGAS WAS...
...A FIGMENT OF MASS-HYSTERIA!
A MIND-TRIP... DIG?
YOU MEAN...?
...YOUR "MUTANT" WAS A TINY STRAGGLER FROM THIS CAVE--CRAZED BY HUNGER--WHO HAPPENED UPON A LONE MAN!

THANK YOU, PROFESSOR-- AND YOUR LOVELY WIFE, FRANCINE!
HE'S COVERING, ALFRED-- I'D SWEAR IT!

LANGSTROM CAN DISCREDIT "EYEWITNESS" REPORTS OF A GIANT VAMPIRE-BAT...
...BUT CAN HE EXPLAIN AWAY THE BODY OF A FULL-GROWN MAN-- DRAINED DRY...

...BY A TINY VAMPIRE-BAT? I THINK NOT!
AND... LANGSTROM'S PRESENCE IN THE AREA-- MERE COINCIDENCE? HARDLY, ALFRED-- HARDLY!
THEN YOU SUSPECT...

...THAT HIS "BAT-MADNESS" HAS MADE HIM TRY IT AGAIN?
YES!
MAN-BAT HIMSELF IS-- THE VAMPIRE OVER VEGAS!
4

THE FOLLOWING NIGHT, HIGH ABOVE THE VEGAS "STRIP"...
WHO ELSE CAN IT BE? YET... I MUST BE SURE BEFORE I "NAB" LANGSTROM!
AND IF IT IS HIM... IS HE FULLY RESPONSIBLE FOR HIS ACTIONS?
HAD A DEVIL OF A TIME PERSUADING THE POLICE HERE NOT TO SHOOT ON SIGHT... GIVING ME FIRST CRACK AT THE "VAMPIRE"!
ACES

BRAVE KID! SHE DIDN'T HAVE TO BUY MY SCHEME...
...BUT I HAD TO HAVE A LIVE TARGET TO LURE MAN-BAT WITHIN STRIKING DISTANCE!
HERE HE COMES NOW!
I'M COUNTING ON THIS NEON-GLARE TO BLIND HIM TO MY PRESENCE...
...FORCE HIM TO FOCUS ON DEBBIE!
SKEEEK!
EEEEEEE!
GOTTA EVEN THE ODDS...!
...BRING HIM DOWN!
THE EQUALIZER... A BATARANG FOR THE MAN-BAT!
KRANGG
6

GET BELOW, DEBBIE! THAT THING IS STILL DANGEROUS...

--MORE THAN THE BATMAN REALIZES! AND ONCE ALONE...
LANGSTROM! WHAT MAD CRAVINGS MADE YOU GO THIS FAR?
MAN-BAT WAS EVIL ENOUGH! BUT NOW... A VAMPIRE-BAT?

YAAGHH

SKREEK
DON'T FIGURE...! MY BATARANG HEAD-SHOT SHOULD'VE PUT HIM OUT FOR HOURS!

WHAT NEW POWERS DOES THIS FIEND HAVE...?

IT'S BREAK... NOW OR NEVER!
SKRAK!
7

RISING TO ATTACK... FROM THE AIR?!

JUST HOPE MY WEIGHT CAN COUNTERACT HIS WINGS!

PULLING HIM BACK DOWN-BUT...
... WHAT'S HE DOING NOW?

USING THE LADDER AS LEVERAGE...
... TO SHAKE ME LOOSE!

SLIPPING...
GRIP SLIPPING...
8

CRASHING DOWNWARD, THE BATMAN CLUTCHES DESPERATELY AT COLD-LIGHT NEON-TUBES...
...SNAPPING THEM OFF LIKE — FRAGILE ICICLES!...

BUT A RAVENING MAN-BAT INTENT ONLY ON SATISFYING HIS VAMPIRE-TASTES...
SKREEE
...FOLLOWS HIS PREY DOWN IN A CRASH-DIVE!...

...GIVING THE MASKED MAN-HUNTER ONE LAST GRAB AT LIFE...!
ONLY HOPE... HIS BATWINGS BREAK OUR FALL!

KARAASH!
9

STARK HORROR...
...IN THE GAMBLING CASINO!...
...AS FLAILING BATWINGS CUSHION THE MASSIVE IMPACT!
WHOMP!

MASS-PANIC SCATTERS THE PATRONS... BLOCKING THE BATMAN!
GOTTA GRAB HIM-- 'FORE HE...

BUT A FAST-REACTING "BOUNCER" HAS THE SAME IDEA!...
I'LL GIT 'IM, BATMAN...!

MAN-BAT IS FASTER THAN BOTH!
?!

CRIPES! DIDN'T MEAN TO...
LANGSTROM! CAN'T LOSE HIM NOW! MUSTN'T...
KNOW YOU DIDN'T...!
10

INSTANTS LATER...
HAD EVERY CONTINGENCY COVERED... EVEN MAN-BAT'S ESCAPE!
... WITH A BORROWED POLICE-COPTER TO MATCH HIS WINGS!
POLICE

LANGSTROM'S GOT A BIG LEAD, BUT I'VE GOT TO RUN HIM TO EARTH... BEFORE HE RAVAGES THE COUNTRYSIDE!
HE'S BLOOD-HUNGRY NOW... FRUSTRATED... AT HIS MOST DANGEROUS!

MANY FEVERED MILES LATER...
HE'S STYMIED ME -- CAN'T FOLLOW HIM INTO THAT NARROW CRACK WITH THIS!

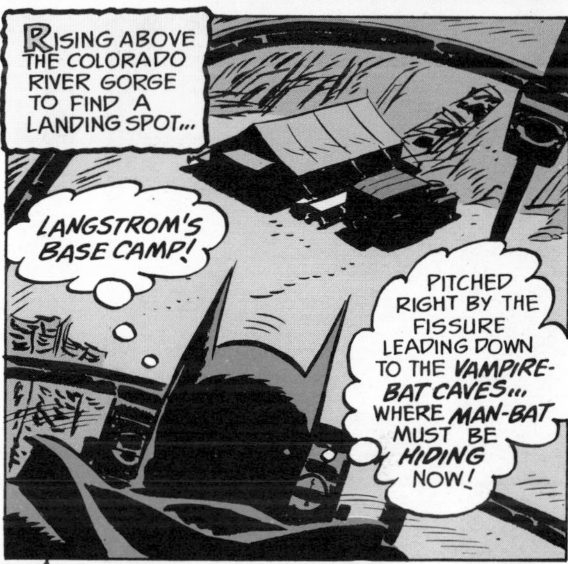
RISING ABOVE THE COLORADO RIVER GORGE TO FIND A LANDING SPOT...
LANGSTROM'S BASE CAMP!
PITCHED RIGHT BY THE FISSURE LEADING DOWN TO THE VAMPIRE-BAT CAVES... WHERE MAN-BAT MUST BE HIDING NOW!

THEN, SPURRED BY A SUDDEN HORRIFYING THOUGHT...
WHAT'S THIS?...
COULD HE BE FAR GONE ENOUGH NOW TO MAKE A TRY FOR HIS OWN WIFE, FRANCIE? MUST WAKE HER BEFORE...

... CLINGING TO MY GLOVE...
... A BANDAID!?
NOW WHERE DID THAT COME FROM...?
11

MMM... ONLY ONE PLACE I COULD'VE PICKED THIS UP!
--DURING MY BATTLE WITH MAN-BAT! BUT... WAS IT HIM?
WAIT!
I RECALL WHEN I FIRST SAW THIS... DURING THAT TV INTERVIEW WITH THE LANGSTROMS!*
* REMEMBER, READER? Ed.

GOOD G--! IF I REMEMBER RIGHTLY...
...KIRK LANGSTROM CAN'T POSSIBLY BE THE VAMPIRE OF VEGAS!

THIS PROVES IT!
B-BATMAN...?! WHAT'RE YOU DOING HERE...?

TRYING TO SAVE YOUR WIFE'S LIFE!
FRANCIE? WHY, SHE'S PERFECTLY SAFE...
...HERE IN BED...
?!

UH-UH! AS OF NOW SHE'S HIDING IN THE BAT-CAVES... AN INNOCENT VICTIM OF YOUR EVIL "MAN-BAT" EXPERIMENTS!
DON'T PUT ME ON, KIRK-- I KNOW NOW THAT FRANCIE IS THE "VAMPIRE"!
THE-- WHAT?!
NO!
IT'S NOT POSSIBLE! I'VE DONE NOTHING... NOTHING...
...I SWEAR!

THEN EXPLAIN THIS BANDAID TORN OFF YOUR WIFE'S WRISTS-- WHEN SHE TRIED TO KILL ME OVER VEGAS TONIGHT!
OH, LORD-- FRAN WAS WEARING A BANDAID!
EVER SINCE THAT SCRATCH SHE GOT-- HANDLING OUR FIRST DEAD SPECIMENS OF THE "HOOVER-DAM" BATS!
UGH!
THOSE UGLY VAMPIRE FANGS--COULD THEY HAVE...?
12

WHAT COUNTS NOW IS FINDING FRANCIE-- SOMEWHERE IN THESE UNEXPLORED CAVES!
I'LL BRING "SPELUNKING"* GEAR, BATMAN-- WE'LL NEED IT!
*CAVE-EXPLORATION GEAR.

WHILE SEEKING AN EXIT DEEP INSIDE THE DARK CAVERNS... A BEWILDERED HUMAN "VAMPIRE" FINDS HERSELF COMPLETELY LOST!...
SKREEEKKKK
EEEK
SKREEEK

FINALLY... EXHAUSTED... THE FORLORN "CREATURE" COLLAPSES INTO A DEEP SLEEP!...

...UNAWARE THAT OUTSIDE DAWN IS BREAKING...

...SIGNALLING AN END TO THE EVIL SPELL THE FULL MOON HAS OVER HER!...

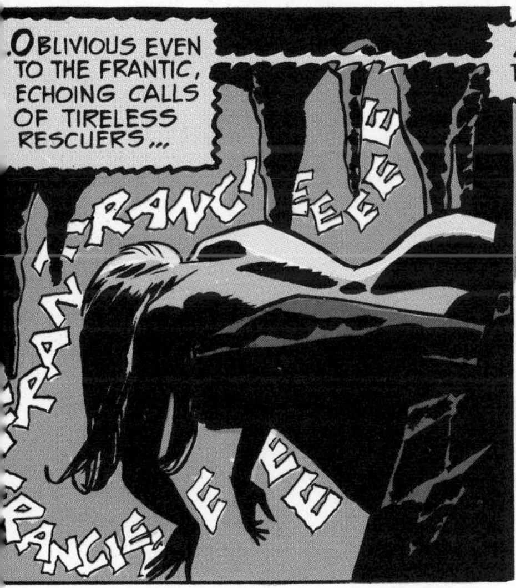
OBLIVIOUS EVEN TO THE FRANTIC, ECHOING CALLS OF TIRELESS RESCUERS...
FRANCIEEEE
FRANCIEEE

...WHICH LAST TILL SUNDOWN...

UH-H, BATMAN-- WILL WE EVER FIND HER? WILL I EVER SEE FRAN AGAIN...?
NOT UNLESS WE KEEP GOING, KIRK! I'VE MARKED OUR WAY TO THIS FORK...
...BUT HERE WE SPLIT! NO OTHER CHOICE...
13

WHILE IN THE TIMELESS DARKNESS... A DAZED, VERY HUMAN GIRL NOW... AWAKENS TO A TERRIFYING SITUATION!
WH-WHERE AM I...?
S-SO COLD... D-DAMP...
... LIKE AN ICY TOMB!

OH-H, KIRK-- KIRK! HELP MEEEE... PLEASE?
HELP
PLEASE
KIRK
FRAN?

HERE!
...UP HERE-- KIRK, DEAREST!
HANG ON, LOVE! I'LL GET YOU DOWN-- FAST AS I CAN!
DARLING... WHERE ARE YOU?

WHILE OUTSIDE...

NEAR EXHAUSTION, A DEVOTED HUSBAND FIGHTS HIS WAY UPWARD... UNTIL...
ALMOST THERE, FRAN...
GASP
... A LITTLE MORE...
PANT
...AND WE'RE TOGETHER AGAIN!

SKREEEK
NO!
ARGHH
14

ONCE MORE UN-HUMAN... STARVED FROM HER LONG "FAST"!...
...NO LONGER AWARE IT'S HER OWN HUSBAND'S THROAT SHE HUNGERS FOR...
...THE MOONSTRUCK VAMPIRE...
STRIKES!
SKREEEK
YAHHHH!!
SUDDENLY, FROM THE BLACKNESS BELOW... A SEARCHING GRAPNEL SNAKES UPWARD... AND...!
FOLLOWED BY...
CAME AS FAST AS I COULD, KIRK...
...AFTER HEARING YOUR ECHOING SHOUTS!
15

SHE'S AFTER MY THROAT NOW...!
YAGHHHH
GOTTA BE STOPPED ANY WAY I CAN...

Y-YOU'RE SO RIGHT, BATMAN...
SOB
...FRAN'S NO LONGER RESPONSIBLE FOR WHAT SHE DOES... CAN NEVER BE NOW!
MUST BE STOPPED-- FOREVER!

NO, KIRK-- NO!
WE DO IT-- MY WAY!

SWIFTLY TWIRLING THE TRAILING BATROPE INTO RESTRAINING LOOPS...
GOT HER-- ALIVE!
NOW FRAN'S VAMPIRE NIGHTMARE IS ABOUT OVER-- IF WE CAN FIND ENOUGH OF HER BLOOD-TYPE IN A VEGAS HOSPITAL!

AND... AS THEY SPEED BACK TOWARD THE "STRIP"...
A FULL TRANSFUSION, BATMAN?
THEN TAKE MINE-- WE'RE THE SAME TYPE!
NONE OF YOURS, KIRK! MY GUESS IS...
...THAT YOUR "BAT-SERUM" ORIGINALLY CONTAMINATED HER BLOOD-- LEAVING HER VULNERABLE TO THE MERE SCRATCH OF A TINY VAMPIRE-BAT!
POLICE
16
NO--IF YOU LOVE HER, LANGSTROM-- YOU'LL REALIZE THAT ONLY A TRANSFUSION OF FRESH, PURE BLOOD CAN SAVE HER NOW!
I HOPE... AND PRAY!
THE END

"The BATMAN NOBODY KNOWS!"

Story by Frank Robbins Art by Dick Giordano Edited by Julius Schwartz

DEEP IN THE WOODS FAR FROM *GOTHAM*, THREE GHETTO-HARDENED KIDS -- GUESTS OF MILLIONAIRE *BRUCE WAYNE* -- GET THEIR FIRST BREATH OF SMOG-FREE AIR, THEIR FIRST SIGHT OF THE GREAT OUTDOORS...

...AND THEIR FIRST EARFUL OF THE *UNKNOWN!*...

HOOOT! HOOO-OOOT!

W-WHAT WAS *THAT?*

A *OWL*, YA DUMMY! AIN'T IT, *MR. WAYNE?*

RIGHT, *RONNIE!*

HUH! A LUCKY GUESS!

TH' ONLY BIRDS *RONNIE* EVER SEEN WAS *JAIL*-BIRDS AN' *SNOW*-BIRDS!

S-1473

YEAH? WELL, I KNOW LOTSA THINGS *YOU* DON'T, *ZIGGY!*
YE-AH? LIKE ANY JERK KNOWS *THAT* IS A PLAIN OL' *BAT!*

SHOWS HOW MUCH YOU TWO WISE GUYS KNOW!
THAT WAS *THE BATMAN!* HISSELF... IN *PERSON!*

YOU *SURE, MICKEY?* WAY OUT HERE -- SO FAR FROM *GOTHAM?*
FOR *SURE! THE BATMAN* IS *EVERYWHERE* -- AN' *NOWHERE!*
...'CAUSE HE AIN'T EVEN *HUMAN!*
THAT'S WHAT *YOU* SAY!

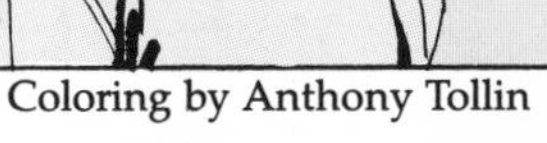
Coloring by Anthony Tollin

I'LL *PROVE* IT TO YUH ABOUT *THE BATMAN!* INNA FIRST PLACE-- IF YUH EVER SAW HIM...

"...HE'S SO BIG-- HE COVERS *ALL O' GOTHAM!* LIKE A KING-SIZE BLANKET!..."

HE'S GOT *X-RAY EYES!* SEES THRU WALLS AN' STUFF! *NOTHIN'* ESCAPES HIM!

"MAN, *BATS* SLIPS RIGHT THRU WALLS-- LIKE THEY WASN'T EVEN THERE!"

HEY! THOUGHT YOU SAID HE WAS AS BIG AS THE WHOLE CITY?
LIKE... HOW COME HE SHRINKS DOWN SMALL ENOUGH TO GET INSIDE A BUILDING?

'CAUSE, LIKE I SAID-- HE AIN'T HUMAN!

"EVEN BULLETS ZIP THRU HIM LIKE NOTHIN'!"

"BUT-- HEH!-- WHEN THE BATMAN CONNECTS, IT'S WITH A FIST OF IRON!"
"SENDS THOSE CREEPS STRAIGHT INTO JAIL-- NON-STOP!"
2

OH, MAN, MICKEY-- WHAT YOU DON'T KNOW 'BOUT THE BATMAN WOULD FILL A BOOK!
YE-AH? LIKE WHAT DO YOU DIG-- THAT I DON'T?

THAT OL' BATWINGS IS A REAL LIVE DUDE!
NOTHIN' SPOOKY 'BOUT HIM--
'CEPT HOW HE COMES ON!

"HE'S LOADED WITH TRICK-GADGETS! GOT SHINY PLASTIC WINGS RUN BY MOTORS--JET-PROPELLED BY TINY ROCKETS!"

"AN' HE JUST SNIFFS OUT TROUBLE--LIKE A HOUNDDOG--USIN' ONE O' THEM ELECTRONIC SNIFFIN' GIZMOS..."

SO YOU SEE THE BATMAN AS A SUPER-MOD CRIME-FIGHTER, RONNIE?
NOT SUPER, MR. WAYNE! HE'S ONE DOWN-TO-EARTH HIP-DUDE!

"...A ONE-MAN ARMY! THE BATMAN IS MUHAMMED ALI--JIM BROWN--SHAFT--AN' SUPER-FLY ALL ROLLED INTO ONE!"
3

LIKE WOW, RONNIE-- YOU MAKE THE BATMAN SOUND LIKE A "BROTHER"!
WHAT ELSE COULD A COOL CAT LIKE HIM BE, ZIGGY?

NOT ACCORDING TO TH' WAY I HEAR IT-- RIGHT FROM THE HORSE'S MOUTH!
IN FACT, FROM WILLIE THE HORSE HIMSELF!

Y'MEAN THE CON WHAT ONCE GOT SENT UP BY THE BATMAN?
YE-AH! HANGS 'ROUND MY BLOCK, FEEDS US KIDS THE INSIDE INFO--TO KEEP US "STRAIGHT," HE SAYS!
HMM, MAYBE NOW WE'LL GET A TRUE PICTURE OF "ME"!
WILLIE THE HORSE SHOULD KNOW... I COLLARED HIM!

"LIKE WILLIE TELLS IT... HE WAS CASIN' THE ROOFS ONE NIGHT, LOOKIN' FOR AN 'EASY-ENTRY'! THAT'S WHAT BURGLARS CALL A HEIST WHERE YUH DON'T GOTTA BREAK IN..."

"...WHEN SUDDENLY--FROM OUTA NOWHERE--COMES THIS GIANT SHADOW!"

"TEN FEET TALL HE WAS! WITH BIG BAT-EARS-- WHAT COULD HEAR A PIN DROP MILES AWAY!"
"THAT'S HOW HE SPOTTED WILLIE-- EVEN THOUGH WILLIE WAS WEARIN' HUSH-SNEAKERS!"
4

BUT THE "HORSE" WASN'T GONNA GET NABBED SO EASY-- NOT WITHOUT A FIGHT!...

"...HE HITS THAT GIANT BATGUY WITH A RUNNIN' SHOULDER-BLOCK-- RIGHT OFF THE ROOF!"

"WHICH MAKES NO NEVER-MIND TO THE BATMAN! 'CAUSE HE BOUNCES RIGHT BACK UP FROM A CLOTHESLINE BELOW..."

OH...NO! WILLIE SURE PILED IT ON THICK TO MAKE HIMSELF LOOK GOOD!
FIRST, ME "TEN FEET" TALL WITH "BAT'S EARS"... AND NOW MY HANDY BATROPE TURNS INTO A BOUNCING CLOTHESLINE!

SO WHA' HAPPEN THEN, ZIGGY?
"...COMIN' UP LIKE A BAT OUTA HELL, HE UPPERCUTS WILLIE--IN MID-AIR, YET!"
"POOR GUY DIDN'T KNOW WHAT HIT HIM--TILL HE'S STANDING IN FRONT OF THE JUDGE! LIKE WILLIE SAYS NOW--NEVER MESS AROUND WITH THE BATMAN!"
5

AND THAT'S WHAT THE REAL "BATMAN" IS LIKE!
WHOO-HOO! LIKE MAN, ZIGGY-- HOW STRAIGHT CAN Y' GET? BELIEVIN' A CON-MAN LIKE "THE HORSE"...
WELL, I DUNNO, RONNIE...
LET'S ASK MR. WAYNE WHAT HE THINKS! HE'S KINDA GROWN-UP...

MR. WAYNE-- WHERE'D HE GO?
LET ME TELL YOU WHAT I THINK, FELLAS...

...THE BATMAN LOOKS LIKE THIS!

AW, C'MON--MR. WAYNE! YOU'RE TOO BIG FOR THAT KINDA KID-STUFF!
NO WAY, MAN--NO HOW! EVERY COSTUME-CAT THINKS HE CAN BE THE "MAN"-- THE REAL "BLACK BATMAN"!
YUH WANTA PLAY, MR. WAYNE :YAWN: YOU'RE ON YOUR OWN! I'M GONNA TURN IN...
6

SHORTLY...
HMM, WHATEVER ELSE IT PROVES-- THE BATMAN'S FRIGHTENING IMAGE SCARES THE GUILTY...
...NOT THE INNOCENT!
THE END

The GOTHAM MUSEUM invites
THE BATMAN
to the preview showing of a
rare and unusual exhibit:
"The ART of the XOCHIPECS"
A NIGHT WIND BLOWS OVER THE GOTHAM MUSEUM, WARM WITH THE PROMISE OF AUGUST HEAT. WITH IT COME VISITORS. MOST ARRIVE BY LIMOUSINE AT THE RAMBLING STRUCTURE'S MAIN ENTRANCE... BUT NOT ALL! YET EVEN THESE HAVE BEEN DRAWN BY THE SAME ATTRACTION; A NEWLY UNEARTHED ART TREASURE OF A LONG EXTINCT CENTRAL AMERICAN TRIBE: THE...
WRITER/EDITOR ARCHIE GOODWIN
ART JIM APARO
DEATHMASK!
L-211
1

Coloring by Petra Scotese

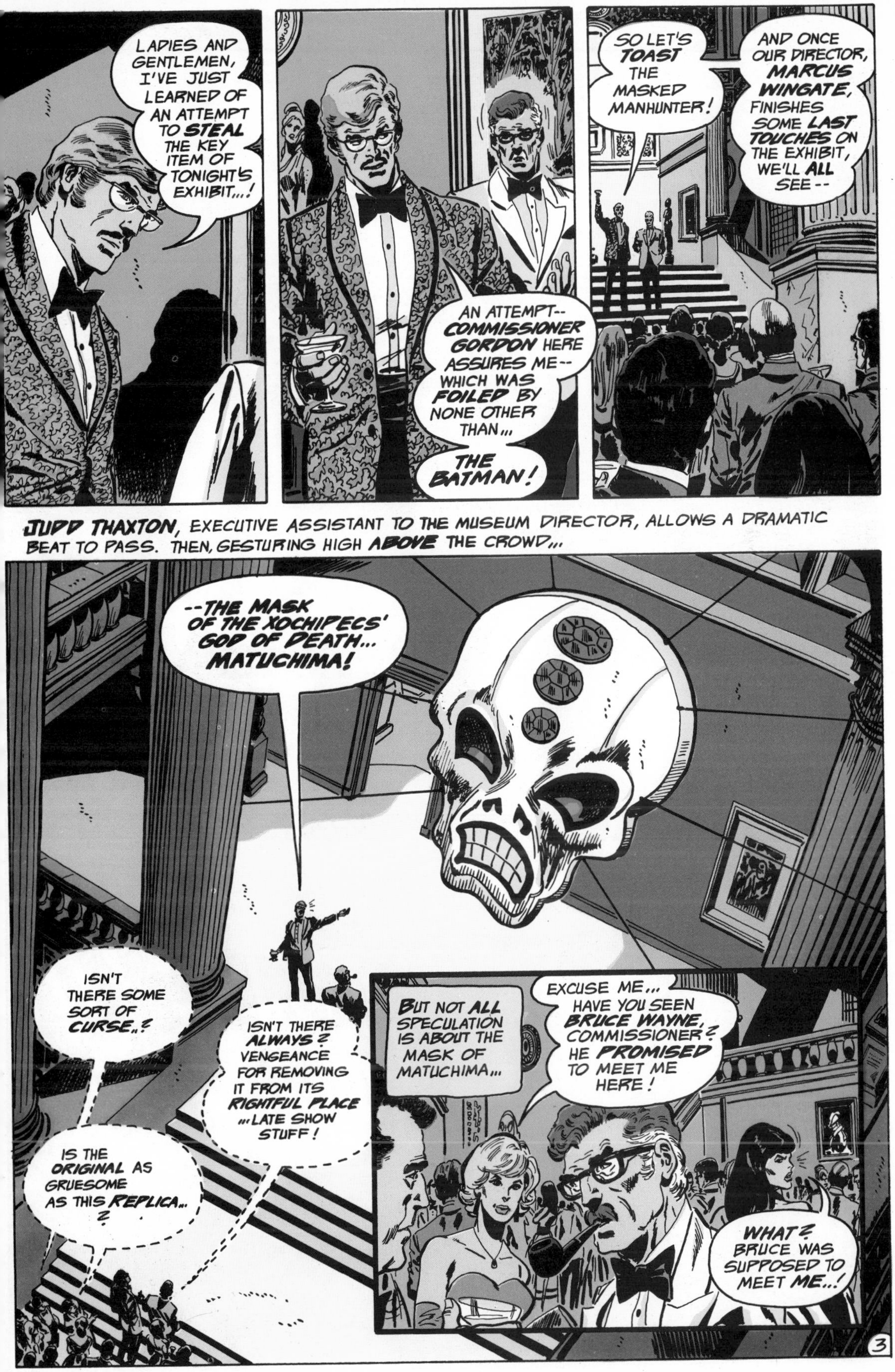

LADIES AND GENTLEMEN, I'VE JUST LEARNED OF AN ATTEMPT TO **STEAL** THE KEY ITEM OF TONIGHT'S EXHIBIT...!

AN ATTEMPT-- **COMMISSIONER GORDON** HERE ASSURES ME-- WHICH WAS **FOILED** BY NONE OTHER THAN...
THE BATMAN!

SO LET'S **TOAST** THE MASKED MANHUNTER!
AND ONCE OUR DIRECTOR, **MARCUS WINGATE**, FINISHES SOME **LAST TOUCHES** ON THE EXHIBIT, WE'LL **ALL** SEE --

JUDD THAXTON, EXECUTIVE ASSISTANT TO THE MUSEUM DIRECTOR, ALLOWS A DRAMATIC BEAT TO PASS. THEN, GESTURING HIGH **ABOVE** THE CROWD...

--THE MASK OF THE XOCHIPECS' GOD OF DEATH... MATUCHIMA!

ISN'T THERE SOME SORT OF **CURSE**..?

ISN'T THERE **ALWAYS**? VENGEANCE FOR REMOVING IT FROM ITS **RIGHTFUL PLACE** ...LATE SHOW STUFF!

IS THE **ORIGINAL** AS GRUESOME AS THIS **REPLICA**...?

BUT NOT **ALL** SPECULATION IS ABOUT THE MASK OF MATUCHIMA...

EXCUSE ME... HAVE YOU SEEN **BRUCE WAYNE**, COMMISSIONER? HE **PROMISED** TO MEET ME HERE!

WHAT? BRUCE WAS SUPPOSED TO MEET **ME**...!

3

I'M SORRY, LADIES, I--
ACTUALLY, I THOUGHT MEETING **BOTH** OF YOU WOULD BE A FINE **COMPROMISE!**
BUT WITH THE COMMISSIONER'S **POLICE CARS** SURROUNDING THE PLACE... ONE VERY NEARLY COULDN'T GET IN AT **ALL!**
I DIDN'T REALIZE SO MANY OF YOUR MEN WERE **ART LOVERS,** GORDON...
BRUCE--!

COULDN'T JUST A **FEW** GET BACK TO FIGHTING **CRIME?** WITH ALL THE **TAXES** I PAY...
...I HATE SEEING IT LEFT **ENTIRELY** TO SOME CAPED AND COWLED **FREELANCE VIGILANTE!**
BRUCE WAYNE'S PRACTICALLY BECOME A **NEW PERSON** THESE PAST FEW MONTHS... **NOT** ONE I PARTICULARLY **CARE** FOR!

HAVING BOLSTERED MY **EFFETE SNOB** IMAGE FOR THE EVENING, MAYBE I CAN **RELAX** AND ENJOY THE--
UH-UH! WHAT'S **THIS...?**
SPIRES, WILL YOU **STOP?** YOU'RE CAUSING A **SCENE!**
YOU **BET** I AM, THAXTON! WHAT RIGHT DOES THAT FOOL **WINGATE** HAVE TAMPERING WITH **MY** EXHIBIT?!
ISN'T IT **ENOUGH** THAT HE WAITED TILL I WAS RISKING MY **LIFE** IN THE CENTRAL AMERICAN JUNGLE...
...THEN COAXED THE BOARD OF TRUSTEES INTO MAKING **HIM** MUSEUM DIRECTOR INSTEAD OF **ME?!**
YOU?! MY **FUND-RAISING** KEEPS THIS PLACE **GOING!** WINGATE WAS PROMOTED ON THE **STRENGTH** OF IT!
IF **ANYONE'S** DESERVING OF HIS JOB... **I AM!**

JUDD THAXTON AND CHIEF ARCHAEOLOGIST **AUSTIN SPIRES** ANGRILY PART, FADING INTO THE MILLING CROWD. A SHORT TIME **LATER...**
THAT'S FROM THE **XOCHIPEC EXHIBIT HALL!**
YAAAAAHHHHHHH
4

WHAT'S GOING ON HERE? WHAT--
L-LORD..! IT'S MATUCHIMA... COME TO LIFE!
WHATEVER IT IS, IT'S DONE SOMETHING TO MR. WINGATE! LOOK BEHIND THAT ALTAR THING--!
USE YOUR GUNS, MEN! USE--

BLAM
GET 'IM!

BRUCE! THAT WAS A SHOT! WHAT SHOULD WE--
BRUCE--! WHERE--??
HE'S HANDSOME, HE'S RICH... SO HE'S NOT BRAVE! TWO OUT OF THREE ISN'T BAD THESE DAYS!

THE OLD BRUCE WAYNE-- GUTSY, INVOLVED-- COULDN'T DIS-APPEAR WHEN TROUBLE POPPED UP WITHOUT CAUSING SUSPICION...
...BUT FOR THE NEW ONE... IT'S TOTALLY IN CHARACTER!
NOW TO THE CAR AND A QUICK CHANGE TO--

--THE BATMAN!
KRAASH
5

BUT, BE IT MAN OR SPIRIT OF XOCHIPEC VENGEANCE, THE EERIE FIGURE WEARING THE MASK OF MATUCHIMA IS WITHOUT AWE...
... AND POSSESSED OF STRENGTH SAVAGE AND TERRIBLE!

REFLEXES. TRAINING SINCE CHILDHOOD. THESE KEEP THE BATMAN MOVING... INTO THE BERSERK FURY OF HIS OPPONENT'S CHARGE!
USUALLY I HOLD BACK... TO AVOID CRITICALLY HURTING SOMEONE...
BUT WITH THIS GALLOPING NIGHTMARE, IT'S ALL STOPS OUT... BEFORE I AM!

THE SCARLET-CLOAKED SPECTER GRUNTS... SLOWS... BUT...
HE TOOK MY BEST...! NOW I'M WIDE OPEN!
NOTHING LEFT BUT TO TRY AND ROLL WITH IT AND--

AND A KILLING BLOW IS TURNED INTO A GLANCING ONE... STILL, THE ROOM WHIRLS, ITS FLOOR BECOMES QUICKSAND COUNTERING ALL EFFORTS TO STAND. YET THE BATMAN TRIES.

EASY, MAN! GIVE YOURSELF TIME TO RECOVER!

MY MEN ARE OUTSIDE... THEY'LL GET HIM SOON ENOUGH!

MOMENTS PASS. A THROBBING HEAD BEGINS TO CLEAR... AND AN EXAMINATION IS MADE.

SO THIS IS THE VICTIM... A FOURTH THIEF! PROBABLY WAS SCOUTING THE ROOF WHEN I SURPRISED HIS FRIENDS... THEN TRIED IT ALONE!

AND WAS BEATEN TO DEATH BY OUR ...DEMON! BUT--

COMMISSIONER! THAT THING GOT AWAY... INTO THE PARK! AN' WHEN WE WENT AFTER IT, WE FOUND...

6

...MARCUS WINGATE, THE MUSEUM'S DIRECTOR!
MUST HAVE BEEN DRAGGED HERE EARLIER BY THAT CREATURE! PERHAPS EVEN KILLED HERE...
THIS MAN WASN'T MURDERED, COMMISSIONER... HE DIED OF A HEART SEIZURE!
THE STRAIN... OR FRIGHT... OF THE ENCOUNTER COULD HAVE DONE IT!

WHAT ABOUT THIS SCRATCH...? LOOKS RECENT!
BUT SUPERFICIAL... PROBABLY FROM ONE OF THE BUSHES, BATMAN!

THAT CERTAINLY WAS NO ONE NORMAL I FOUGHT... BUT A SPIRIT? BOTH HIS MASK AND ROBE WERE ON DISPLAY ... ANYONE MIGHT HAVE DONNED THEM...
GORDON, WHERE WERE AUSTIN SPIRES AND JUDD THAXTON DURING ALL THIS?
MISSING! MANY PEOPLE FLED THE MUSEUM!
THAXTON LIVES UPTOWN, SPIRES ACROSS THE PARK! SHOULD WE--

I'LL CHECK SPIRES, YOU TAKE THAXTON, COMMISSIONER! BOTH WANTED WINGATE'S JOB...
SOME QUESTIONS ARE IN ORDER!
THE BATMAN BECOMES ONE WITH THE NIGHT, VANISHING INTO ITS ENFOLDING DARKNESS...

...TO EMERGE SOMETIME LATER!
SOMETHING I READ IN THE ADVANCE PUBLICITY ABOUT THE MASK KEEPS NAGGING AT ME... WELL, IT'LL COME...
...MEANTIME, THERE'S SPIRES' PENTHOUSE! OF THE TWO SUSPECTS, HE SEEMED MOST BITTER, MOST DESPERATE...
7

AND AT THE MOMENT... MOST IN NEED OF HELP!
MATUCHIMA!!
THAT CLEARS SPIRES, ACCORDING TO MY SUSPICIONS ...

... AND LEAVES THAXTON!
SPIRES! GET OUT OF HERE...! GET TO POLICE PROTECTION!

BUT MY SUSPICIONS DON'T EXPLAIN HOW THAXTON-- OR ANYONE ELSE--
CAN DO WHAT THIS BRUTE KEEPS DOING!

AND AS THOUGH IN RESPONSE TO THOSE THOUGHTS...

FALL RELAXED... ROLL AS YOU HIT... UP FAST! SECOND NATURE FOR THE BATMAN... BUT SEEMINGLY THE SOLE NATURE OF HIS DEATH-MASKED FOE...

...IS TO ATTACK MERCILESSLY...

...TO KILL BRUTALLY!

8

YET MANY HAVE TRIED TO KILL THE BATMAN; SOME AS MERCILESS, SOME AS BRUTAL...
...ALL HAVE FAILED.
BUT BY THE TIME AUSTIN SPIRES' APARTMENT IS REGAINED...
MATUCHIMA'S GONE! NOTHING LEFT BUT THE WRECKAGE...
...LOOKS LIKE SPIRES HAS BEEN BRINGING WORK HOME... THESE ARE XOCHIPEC PLAQUES! AND THIS NOTEBOOK...
HE'S BEEN TRANSLATING THE PLAQUES... LOT OF MATERIAL ON XOCHIPEC CULTURE... APPARENTLY LIKE OTHER INDIAN TRIBES...
THEY EXPERIMENTED WITH NARCOTICS AND--HOLD IT! HERE'S A SECTION ON THE DEATH GOD'S MASK!
"IT WAS BELIEVED TO BE A GIFT FROM MATUCHIMA... IN HIS LIKENESS, GRANTING THE USER HIS DEATH-DEALING POWERS! WARRIORS WHO WORE IT IN BATTLE ALWAYS LED THE TRIBE TO TRIUMPH...
"...AND USUALLY PERISHED SOON AFTER! A SAYING CAME INTO BEING--'WHO WEARS THE DEATHMASK CONQUERS ALL... ALL BUT THE FINAL CONQUEROR!'"
THAT'S WHAT I READ EARLIER! AND THAT--COUPLED WITH THE OTHER INFORMATION ABOUT THE DRUGS--
IS THE ANSWER TO THIS ENTIRE TERRIBLE BUSINESS!
9

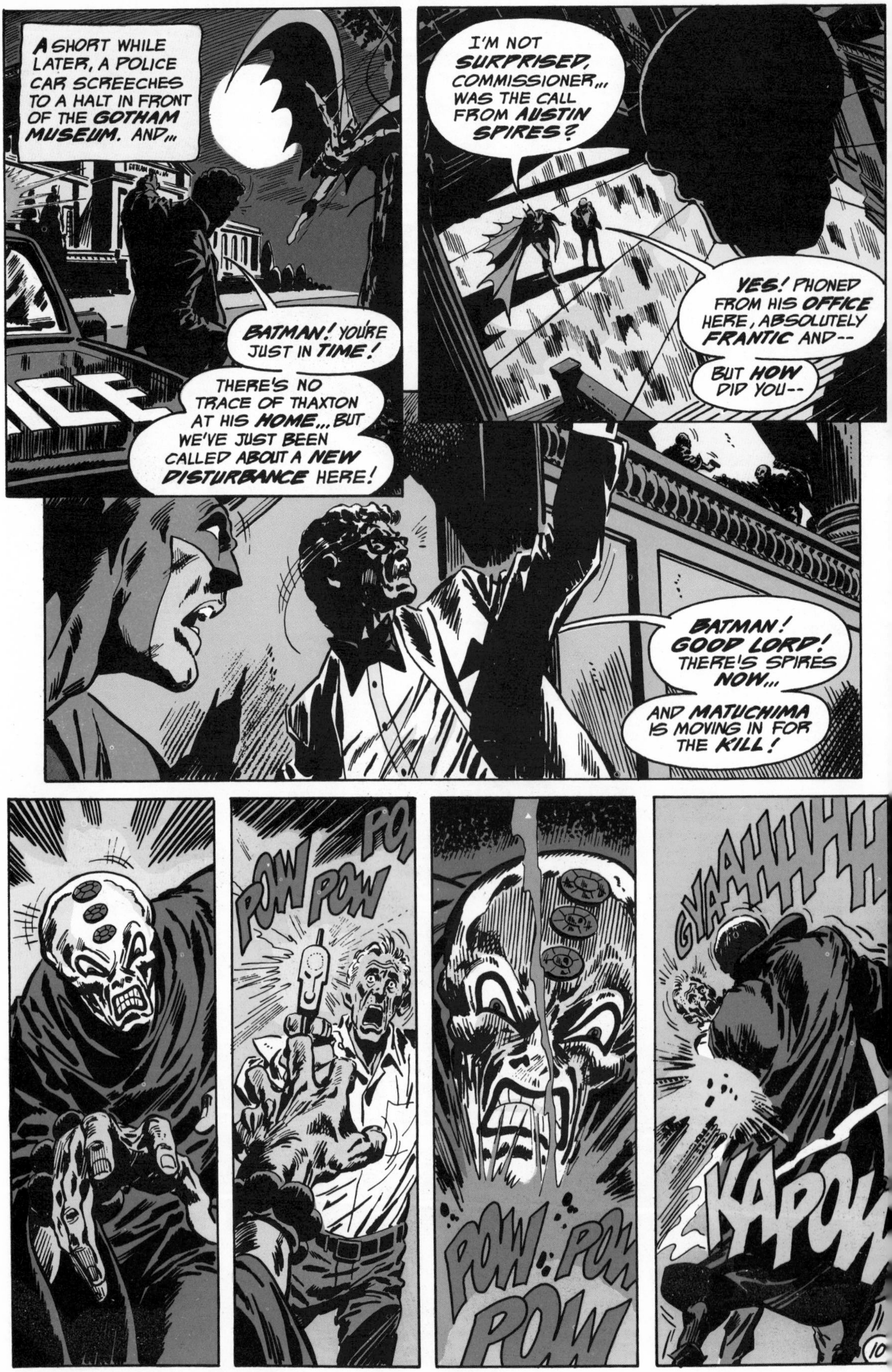

A SHORT WHILE LATER, A POLICE CAR SCREECHES TO A HALT IN FRONT OF THE **GOTHAM MUSEUM.** AND...
BATMAN! YOU'RE JUST IN **TIME!**
THERE'S NO TRACE OF THAXTON AT HIS **HOME**... BUT WE'VE JUST BEEN CALLED ABOUT A **NEW DISTURBANCE** HERE!

I'M NOT **SURPRISED,** COMMISSIONER... WAS THE CALL FROM **AUSTIN SPIRES?**
YES! PHONED FROM HIS **OFFICE** HERE, ABSOLUTELY **FRANTIC** AND--
BUT **HOW** DID YOU--

BATMAN! GOOD LORD! THERE'S SPIRES **NOW**...
AND **MATUCHIMA** IS MOVING IN FOR THE **KILL!**

GOOD LORD! IT WAS THAXTON!
SHOT AND SHOT... HE WOULDN'T FALL...!
DIDN'T GIVE ME ANY CHOICE... YOU SAW...

I SAW YOUR PLAN NEARLY BACKFIRE! JUDD THAXTON HAD A MUCH STRONGER HEART THAN WINGATE, DIDN'T HE, SPIRES?
BATMAN, WHAT...?

SPIRES FOUND MORE THAN RELICS IN THE JUNGLE... HE FOUND THE SECRET NARCOTIC XOCHIPEC PRIESTS USED TO MAKE THE MASK WORK...!

TO MAKE IT TURN THE WEARER INTO A BERSERKER... WITH MADMAN'S STRENGTH! SIMILAR TO THE MOROS IN THE PHILIPPINES WAR...
ONLY THE MASK-WEARER'S HEART BURSTS IN TIME FROM THE STRAIN!

THERE MUST BE A TINY SPUR INSIDE THE MASK THAT, ANNOINTED WITH THE NARCOTIC... SCRATCHES THE VICTIM'S NECK WHEN HE PUTS IT ON!
ALL RIGHT! YOU FOUND MY NOTES... YOU GUESSED! THAXTON AND WINGATE STOOD BETWEEN ME AND THE DIRECTOR'S JOB! MONUMENTAL EGOS LIKE THEIRS COULDN'T RESIST TRYING THE MASK OF A GOD, DEFYING A PRIMITIVE CURSE...!

WINGATE DONNED IT... KILLED THE THIEF! THAXTON, HOPING FOR THE GLORY OF RE-COVERING THE MASK, FOLLOWED HIM TO THE PARK... AND YIELDED TO THE TEMPTATION WHEN HE FOUND WINGATE DEAD!
ONLY HE HATED ME SO MUCH... I WAS THE ONE HE CAME AFTER! NOW STEP ASIDE! WITH THE MASK TO SELL, I CAN STILL--
YOU USED YOUR SEVEN SHOTS DESTROYING THE KILLER YOU CREATED! HAND ME THE MASK, SPIRES. IT'S OVER!

NOT WHILE THERE'S THIS WAY OUT!
NO, SPIRES! EVEN IF YOU CAN HANG ON--
11

--THE SUPPORT WIRES CAN'T TAKE YOUR WEIGHT!
PWEENG
PWEENG
PWEENG

NOOOOOOOOOOO

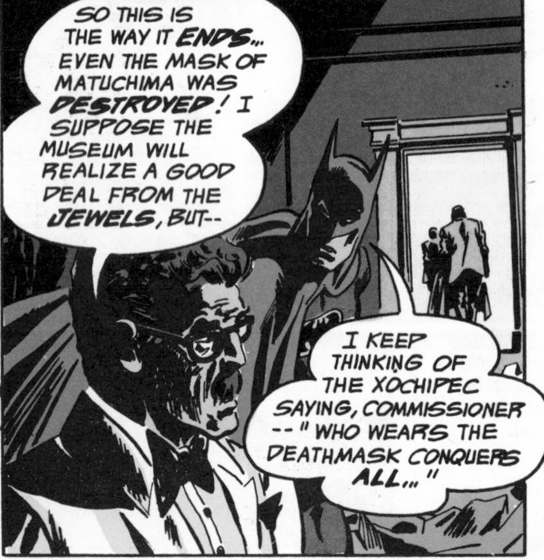
SO THIS IS THE WAY IT ENDS... EVEN THE MASK OF MATUCHIMA WAS DESTROYED! I SUPPOSE THE MUSEUM WILL REALIZE A GOOD DEAL FROM THE JEWELS, BUT--
I KEEP THINKING OF THE XOCHIPEC SAYING, COMMISSIONER --"WHO WEARS THE DEATHMASK CONQUERS ALL..."

SOMEHOW THAT TEMPTED REASONABLY INTELLIGENT MEN LIKE WINGATE AND THAXTON... EVEN KNOWING THE REST OF THE SAYING!
THERE'S STILL PLENTY OF TEMPTATION IN THE WORLD, GORDON...
I'M JUST AS HAPPY KNOWING THE DEATH-MASK WON'T BE CONTRIBUTING ITS PART!
THE END
12

BUT NEXT ISSUE, BATMAN... A MONSTER WALKS WAYNE MANOR!

Coloring by Petra Scotese

WEDNESDAY IS NAMED FOR WODEN -- OR ODIN -- THE NORSE GOD OF WISDOM!
SO I WOULDN'T BE TRUE TO MY ROLE IF I WASN'T SMART ENOUGH TO KNOW WHEN TO TAKE MY LEAVE!
SEE YOU TOMORROW, ALL!

CALENDAR MAN IS PLAYING THIS FARCE TO THE HILT!
HIS CYCLE EVEN HAS EIGHT WHEELS TO EMULATE ODIN'S EIGHT-LEGGED HORSE, SLEIPNIR!
ONCE HE ENTERS THAT UNDERPASS, I'LL NEVER NAB HIM --

-- SO I'D BETTER MAKE SURE HE DOESN'T REACH IT!
WUMP!
WUMP!

WITH UNERRING ACCURACY, THE WHIRLY-BAT'S SMOKE-BOMBS STRIKE THE STREET IN FRONT OF THE NARROW UNDERPASS --
WHOOM!
WHOOM!
-- OBSCURING IT COMPLETELY --

-- AND FORCING THE VIKING-CLAD CALENDAR MAN TO TURN ASIDE, OR RISK A SHATTERING COLLISION!
WELL DONE, BATMAN!
YOU'VE IMPROVED YOUR BAG OF TRICKS SINCE LAST WE MET!*
*WAY BACK IN DETECTIVE #259. -- PAUL

UNFORTUNATELY, SO HAVE I!
ODIN SACRIFICED AN EYE TO GAIN KNOWLEDGE --

-- BUT I SACRIFICED MINE TO GAIN POWER!!
2

CALENDAR MAN'S COVERED ALL HIS BETS! THE LASER-BLAST THAT TOTALLED THE WHIRLY-BAT MISSED ME--
--BUT I'LL STILL BE SPLATTERED ALL OVER THE SIDEWALK--
SKWA-WHOOM!

--UNLESS I CAN TURN MY CAPE INTO A MAKESHIFT GLIDER--

--AND TRY A LITTLE FANCY MANEUVERING!

MADE IT-- WITH NOTHING TO SPARE!
WELL, IT'S NICE TO KNOW SOME THINGS HAVEN'T CHANGED!
YOUR LITTLE CRIME-A-DAY SPREE IS OVER, CALENDAR MAN!
FROM NOW ON, YOU'LL BE COUNTING THE DAYS FROM BEHIND STEEL BARS!

OOOFFF!
HE CAUGHT ME OFF-BALANCE--!
WHUD!
YOU'RE STILL AS HUMORLESS AS EVER!
STILL GRINNING, THE INCREDIBLE CALENDAR MAN SUDDENLY PRESSES A SMALL BUTTON ON THE CYCLE'S HANDLEBAR--
KLIK!

--DETONATING A SERIES OF SPECIALLY-PREPARED EXPLOSIVE BOLTS--
POK!
POK!
--CUTTING FREE THE VEHICLE'S MASSIVE FRAME!

NO! THE CYCLE'S BECOME A REGULAR TWO-WHEELER-- LEAVING ME TRAPPED ON THIS RUNAWAY CHASSIS!
HAVE A NICE TRIP, BATMAN! HOPE YOU GET A BANG OUT OF IT!

CAREENING OUT OF CONTROL, THE SIX-WHEELED JUGGERNAUT ABRUPTLY VEERS TO ONE SIDE--
--AND DESTROYS ITSELF AGAINST A SOLID BRICK WALL!
3

PLAYS FOR KEEPS, DOESN'T HE?
IF THIS LAMPPOST HADN'T BEEN HERE, I'D BE CHOPPED MEAT RIGHT NOW!

THAT'S THREE CRIMES HE'S GOTTEN AWAY WITH--BUT I SWEAR IT'S THE LAST!

"CALENDAR MAN FIRST HIT TOWN ON MONDAY NIGHT, SMASHING INTO THE GOTHAM PLANETARIUM IN SUITABLY APPROPRIATE FASHION--
"--SINCE MONDAY IS NAMED FOR THE MOON!

"WHILE SOME SORT OF MAGNETIC FIELD THREW THE TWO STARTLED GUARDS INTO ORBIT AROUND HIS SHIP, THE CALENDAR MAN WENT TO WORK--

"--SNATCHING UP HANDFULS OF THE PRICELESS STAMPS WHICH HAD BEEN ON DISPLAY THERE--
"--STAMPS WHICH HAD BEEN HAND-CANCELLED BY THE ASTRONAUTS DURING ONE OF THE LUNAR VISITS!

"BEFORE THE POLICE COULD RESPOND TO THE VIOLATED BURGLAR ALARMS, CALENDAR MAN WAS GONE!
MARCH
1 2 3
8 9 10
5 6 7 14 15 16 17
12 13 21 22 23 24
20 28 29 30 31
27
"--BUT HE LEFT HIS CALLING CARD BEHIND HIM!"
4

THE FIRST TIME WE FOUGHT, CALENDAR MAN COMMITTED FOUR CRIMES, EACH ONE BASED ON A DIFFERENT SEASON--
--BUT IT LOOKS LIKE HE'S BECOME A LOT MORE AMBITIOUS SINCE THEN!
THIS TIME HE'S PLANNING SEVEN CRIMES--ONE FOR EACH DAY OF THE WEEK!

"ON TUESDAY NIGHT--NAMED FOR TIW, THE ANCIENT GOD OF WAR--CALENDAR MAN ROBBED GOTHAM'S MUSEUM OF MILITARY ANTIQUITIES--
"--STEALING ULYSSES S. GRANT'S CIVIL WAR MEDALS WITH THE AID OF AN ELECTRIFIED SWORD!

"I REACHED THE MUSEUM WITHIN MINUTES OF THE CRIME--BUT THE TRAIL WAS ALREADY STONE COLD!
MARC
"ALL I FOUND WAS ANOTHER CALENDAR PAGE--

"--WHICH WAS NOT SO MUCH A CLUE AS AN INVITATION!"
SEE YOU TOMORROW-- SOME TIME-- SOME PLACE!!

WELL, I CAME CLOSE TO THE CALENDAR MAN TONIGHT--
--JUST NOT CLOSE ENOUGH!
BUT IN ELUDING ME, HE MADE HIS FIRST BIG MISTAKE!

CALENDAR MAN HAS MANAGED TO COST ME MY NEW EXPERIMENTAL WHIRLY-BAT--
--AND THAT MAKES THIS LITTLE GAME PERSONAL!
5

THURSDAY, 8:23 PM-- AS A NIGHT-CLAD GUARDIAN STANDS VIGIL OVER THE CITY THAT HE LOVES...
I'VE WIRED EVERY SPOT IN GOTHAM THAT MIGHT BE A TARGET FOR A THURSDAY-INSPIRED CRIME!
IF CALENDAR MAN IS CRAZY ENOUGH TO STRIKE AGAIN TONIGHT--
--I'LL KNOW WHERE!

HOW'S IT GOING, BATMAN?
NOTHING YET, COMMISSIONER GORDON -- BUT IT'S ONLY A MATTER OF TIME!
WE'RE GOING TO NAIL THE CALENDAR MAN TONIGHT!

I CERTAINLY HOPE SO--BUT EVEN IF WE DON'T, WE'RE BOUND TO CATCH HIM ON SUNDAY!
THERE'S ONLY ONE THING IN TOWN WORTH STEALING ON THAT DAY--THE GOLDEN OBELISK OF THE EGYPTIAN SUN GOD RA!

WHEN CALENDAR MAN TRIES TO SNATCH IT, WE'LL BE WAITING FOR HIM WITH OPEN --
--EH?
BEEP BEEP BEEP
...
THAT'S IT, COMMISSIONER-- HE'S STRUCK!

AND WITH A RUSTLE OF VELVET AND AN UNCOILING OF STEEL-SPRING LEGS, THE BATMAN IS GONE--
--SWALLOWED BY THE DARKNESS THAT IS HIS NATURAL ELEMENT!
6

THURSDAY, 8:51 PM-- AS THE WELL-APPOINTED HALLS OF THE VAN DYKE ART GALLERY ON GOTHAM'S UPPER EAST SIDE RESOUND WITH THE ARMORED TREAD OF AN INCREDIBLY-CLAD INTRUDER...
SOFTLY WHISTLING TO HIMSELF, THE CALENDAR MAN CAREFULLY STUDIES EVERY PAINTING THAT HE PASSES--PAUSING AT LAST BEFORE A PRICELESS ABSTRACT CALLED "THE STORM KING"--

--AND WITH A FEW SWIFT STROKES OF A MINIATURE LASER BLADE--

--HE MAKES THE PAINTING HIS!

THE QUESTION NOW IS--HOW LONG CAN HE KEEP IT HIS?
IT'S ABOUT TIME, PUNK! I WAS GETTING TIRED OF WAITING OUT HERE!
WHO--?!?

DO I REALLY HAVE TO ANSWER THAT?

YOU MIGHT AS WELL, BATMAN--SINCE IT'S THE LAST THING YOU'RE EVER GOING TO SAY!
THURSDAY, YOU'LL RECALL, WAS NAMED FOR THE NORSE GOD OF THUNDER--
-- SO I'VE ARMED MYSELF WITH THE HAMMER OF THOR!

SKRAK-KOOOM!
YOU COULD ARM YOURSELF WITH A NUCLEAR WARHEAD --BUT IT STILL WOULDN'T HELP YOU!
YOU OWE A DEBT TO SOCIETY, CALENDAR MAN--
7

--AND I INTEND TO COLLECT IT!!
UUNNHH!!

SO WHO APPOINTED YOU SERVANT OF THE PEOPLE ANYWAY? YOU'RE JUST ANOTHER GUY IN A CRAZY COSTUME--
--LIKE ME!
YOU'RE WRONG, PUNK!

I'M NOTHING LIKE YOU--
POW!
-NOTHING!!

HIT A SORE SPOT, HUH? WELL, DON'T LET IT BOTHER YOU, BATMAN!
ANOTHER FEW SECONDS-- AND IT'LL ALL BE ACADEMIC!

AAWHOOOOOO
EH? HE TOUCHED HIS EAR-PHONES AND THAT STRAY DOG SUDDENLY STARTED HOWLING LIKE--
OF COURSE!

HAVE TO GET THAT HELMET OFF OF HIM BEFORE--
AARGGHH
CLOSE, HERO-- BUT A SECOND TOO LATE!

BLAST... I SHOULD'VE REALIZED... THOR WAS GOD OF THUNDER...
...SO CALENDAR MAN... IS USING ULTRASONIC THUNDER... TO DESTROY ME...
8

SIGNAL IS BEYOND THE RANGE OF HUMAN HEARING... BUT I CAN STILL FEEL IT...
IT'LL TURN MY BRAIN TO JELLY... UNLESS...
...I CAN SHUT THE SIGNAL... OFF!
SKRANG!
MY HELMET--! HE'S SHATTERED IT--!
BUT I CAN STILL FINISH THE JOB IT STARTED!
JUST LIE THERE, BATMAN! IN A FEW MORE SECONDS, YOUR SUFFERING WILL BE OVER--
--PERMANENTLY!
NO! GOTTA MOVE-- GOTTA GET UP--!
WEEEOWEEOWEEO
POLICE SIRENS--?!?
BATMAN, YOUR LUCK IS INCREDIBLE!

FRIDAY, 12:05 AM -- IN THE PENTHOUSE APARTMENT OF A BATTERED BRUCE WAYNE...
IS MASTER BRUCE ALL RIGHT, DOCTOR DUNDEE?
BETTER THAN HE SHOULD BE, ALFRED! THE ULTRASONIC DAMAGE TO HIS INNER EAR WILL HEAL--IF IT'S ALLOWED TO!
MEANING--?
MEANING YOU STAY IN BED FOR THE NEXT FEW DAYS NO MATTER WHAT--

--OR YOU MAY MAKE THAT DAMAGE PERMANENT!
ALFRED, I LEAVE HIM IN YOUR HANDS!

DUNDEE'S A GOOD MAN--BUT HE WORRIES TOO MUCH!
NOW I'D BETTER GET DOWN TO THE BAT-CAVE AND START CHECKING ON--

YOU'LL DO NOTHING OF THE KIND, SIR!
BUT THERE'S WORK TO BE DONE, ALFRED!
THEN I'M AFRAID SOMEONE ELSE WILL HAVE TO DO IT!
YOU ARE STAYING IN BED, MASTER BRUCE--IF I'M FORCED TO SIT ON YOU TO KEEP YOU THERE!

ALFRED, HAS ANYONE EVER TOLD YOU YOU'D MAKE A GREAT MOTHER?

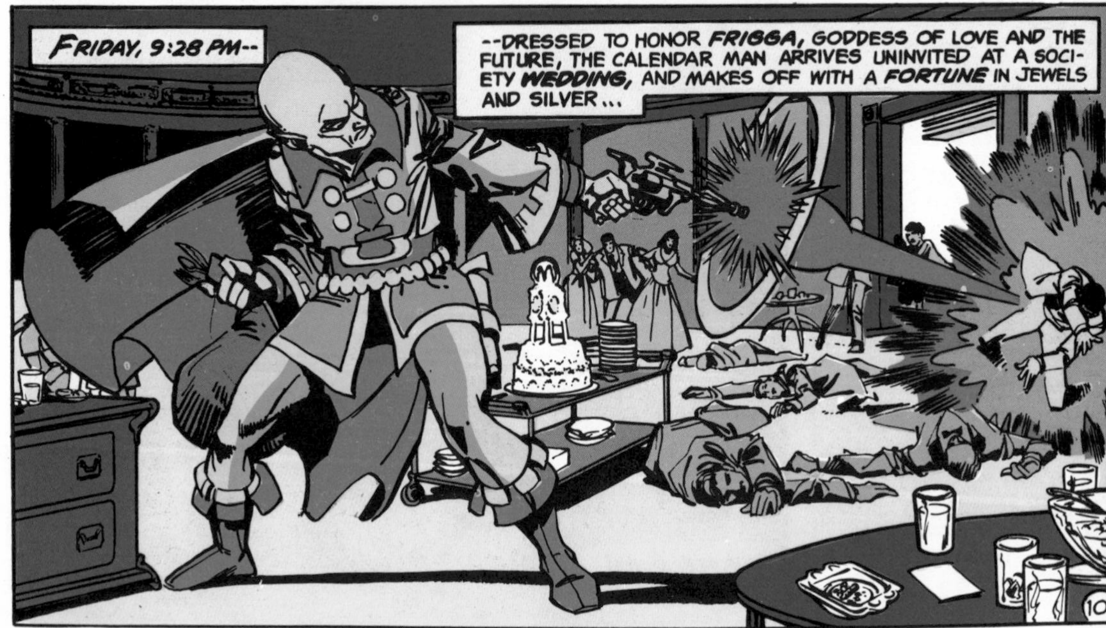
FRIDAY, 9:28 PM--
--DRESSED TO HONOR FRIGGA, GODDESS OF LOVE AND THE FUTURE, THE CALENDAR MAN ARRIVES UNINVITED AT A SOCIETY WEDDING, AND MAKES OFF WITH A FORTUNE IN JEWELS AND SILVER...
10

SATURDAY, 11:43 AM-- AS A BEDRIDDEN BRUCE WAYNE CONFERS WITH HIS FRIEND AND ASSOCIATE, LUCIUS FOX...
--AND THAT ABOUT COVERS EVERYTHING WE HAVE TO DISCUSS, BRUCE.
THE ONLY REALLY PRESSING BIT OF WAYNE ENTERPRISES BUSINESS IS THE DENNISON MERGER!
AND THAT'S LIABLE TO BE A TOUGH ONE, LUCIUS.

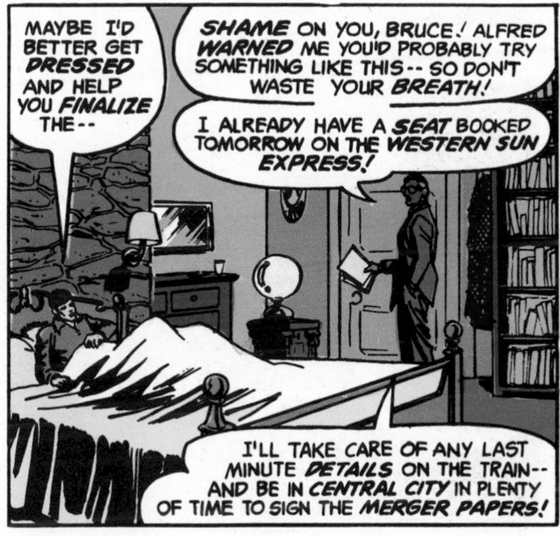
MAYBE I'D BETTER GET DRESSED AND HELP YOU FINALIZE THE--
SHAME ON YOU, BRUCE! ALFRED WARNED ME YOU'D PROBABLY TRY SOMETHING LIKE THIS-- SO DON'T WASTE YOUR BREATH!
I ALREADY HAVE A SEAT BOOKED TOMORROW ON THE WESTERN SUN EXPRESS!
I'LL TAKE CARE OF ANY LAST MINUTE DETAILS ON THE TRAIN-- AND BE IN CENTRAL CITY IN PLENTY OF TIME TO SIGN THE MERGER PAPERS!

WELL, YOU CAN'T BLAME A GUY FOR TRYING, CAN YOU?
CAN'T I?
YOU JUST STAY IN BED AND GET OVER THAT FLU, BRUCE--AND LEAVE THE BUSINESS TO ME!
THAT'S WHY YOU FIRST HIRED ME, REMEMBER?
I'LL CALL YOU FROM CENTRAL CITY AND LET YOU KNOW HOW EVERYTHING WENT!
ALFRED, YOU'D BETTER KEEP A CLOSE EYE ON YOUR BOSS--HE'S A TRICKY ONE.

BELIEVE ME, MASTER FOX-- I KNOW THAT BETTER THAN ANYONE.
YOUR CHICKEN SOUP, MASTER BRUCE!
WHOOPEE!

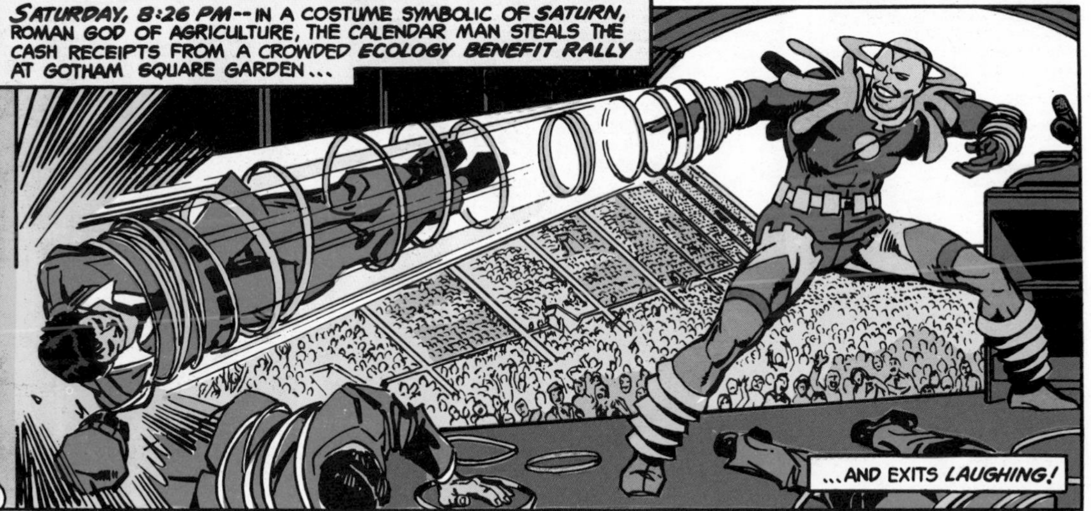
SATURDAY, 8:26 PM-- IN A COSTUME SYMBOLIC OF SATURN, ROMAN GOD OF AGRICULTURE, THE CALENDAR MAN STEALS THE CASH RECEIPTS FROM A CROWDED ECOLOGY BENEFIT RALLY AT GOTHAM SQUARE GARDEN...
...AND EXITS LAUGHING!

SUNDAY, 12:14 PM--
GET BACK IN BED THIS MINUTE, SIR!
SORRY, ALFRED--BUT I HAVE THINGS TO DO!
SUCH AS WHAT, SIR?
COMMISSIONER GORDON IS ALREADY WAITING TO APPREHEND THE CALENDAR MAN--

--AND MASTER FOX WILL BE LEAVING ON THE WESTERN SUN EXPRESS IN FIFTEEN MINUTES!
THERE'S REALLY NOTHING FOR YOU TO DO, SIR!
MAYBE YOU'RE RIGHT, ALFRED. MAYBE I--

HEY-- WAITAMINNIT!
HOW COULD WE ALL HAVE BEEN SO BLIND?

ER--AH--ALFRED, WOULD YOU MIND CALLING SELINA KYLE FOR ME?
IF I'M STAYING IN BED, I'D BETTER BREAK OUR DATE FOR TONIGHT.
WITH PLEASURE, MASTER BRUCE.
I REALIZE I MAY SEEM A TRIFLE HARSH ON YOU, SIR--

--BUT YOU KNOW I'M ONLY DOING IT FOR YOUR OWN GOOD.
MASTER BRUCE?
M-MASTER BRUCE?
OH NO!

SUNDAY, 12:23 PM--AND THE SPRAWLING RAILROAD TERMINAL THAT IS GOTHAM CENTRAL STATION BUSTLES WITH ACTIVITY...
12

ON TRACK 14, THE WESTERN SUN EXPRESS COMPLETES ITS FINAL LOADING AND PREPARES TO GET UNDER WAY--
--MUCH TO THE RELIEF OF ONE OF ITS PASSENGERS...
PLEASE BE CAREFUL WITH THAT TRUNK, PORTER. IT'S GOING A LONG WAY!
WESTERN SUN

WHICH IS A LOT MORE THAN ITS OWNER CAN SAY!
OH NO.
HOLY SMOKES, IT'S--

YOU DON'T HAVE TO TELL HIM, PORTER! I THINK HE ALREADY KNOWS!
THE BATMAN BUT HOW--?
HOW DID YOU FIND ME HERE?

WHERE ELSE WOULD YOU BE, CALENDAR MAN?
YOU'RE FAR TOO SMART TO PULL YOUR OBVIOUS SUNDAY CRIME WHEN YOU KNEW THE POLICE WOULD BE WAITING FOR YOU--
--SO THERE WAS ONLY ONE LOGICAL ALTERNATIVE!

SUNDAY IS ALSO A DAY OF REST--THE PERFECT TIME FOR YOU TO SKIP TOWN WITH WHAT YOU'D STOLEN--
--AND WHAT MORE APPROPRIATE MEANS OF TRANSPORTATION THAN THE WESTERN SUN EXPRESS?

IT WAS ALL REALLY QUITE SIMPLE-- IF ONE JUST THOUGHT ABOUT IT!
AND YOU'RE SIMPLE, BUSTER--

--IF YOU THINK FINDING ME IS THE SAME THING AS CATCHING ME!!
EH? HIS BOOK WAS RIGGED!
DOZENS OF CALENDAR PAGES SWIRLING ALL AROUND ME--LIKE A MINIATURE HURRICANE!

AND WHILE THE MASKED MANHUNTER IS MOMENTARILY OFF-BALANCE, THE MUFTI-CLAD CALENDAR MAN DISAPPEARS INTO THE DARKNESS OF A NEARBY TUNNEL...

13

...BUT THE HEAD-START IT GIVES HIM IS A SLIM ONE!
FOUND ITEMS OF CALENDAR MAN'S CLOTHING STREWN ALL ALONG THE TUNNEL--!
AND I CAN GUESS WHY!

" CALENDAR MAN ACTUALLY TOOK THE TIME TO CHANGE INTO A NEW COSTUME!"
ALL THE BETTER TO BEAT YOU WITH, BATMAN!
OR IS IT ILLEGAL THESE DAYS TO BE FASHIONABLE?
BAD TASTE IN CLOTHING IS THE LEAST OF YOUR CRIMES, MISTER --

--BUT IT'S REALLY A VERY MOOT POINT!

WHERE YOU'RE GOING, EVERYTHING YOU WEAR FROM NOW ON WILL HAVE STRIPES!
MHUUNNFF!!

FOR BOTH OUR SAKES, YOU'D BETTER SURRENDER QUICKLY, CALENDAR MAN--
--BEFORE THAT APPROACHING TRAIN TURNS US INTO HAMBURGER!

WHOK!
IN THE IMMORTAL WORDS OF TONTO--
--WHAT YOU MEAN !IS, BATMAN?

YOU WANT TO STAY AND GET SLAUGHTERED, GO RIGHT AHEAD--
--BUT I'M GETTING OUT OF HERE!
GOT TO GO AFTER HIM BEFORE--
--HUH?

I DON'T BELIEVE IT! MY FOOT IS CAUGHT BETWEEN THE TRACKS--

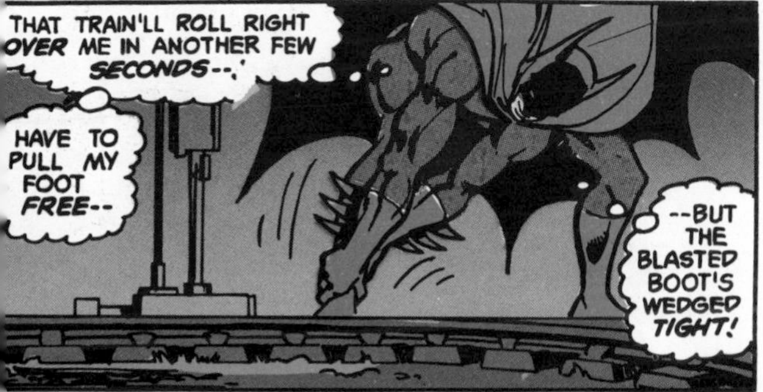
THAT TRAIN'LL ROLL RIGHT OVER ME IN ANOTHER FEW SECONDS--.'
HAVE TO PULL MY FOOT FREE--
--BUT THE BLASTED BOOT'S WEDGED TIGHT!

NO MORE TIME TO WASTE! IF THIS TRACK WANTS MY BOOT--
--IT CAN HAVE--

CHAKATACHAKATACHAKATACHAKATACHA

BLAST--! THE STUPID TRAIN MISSED THAT POINTY-EARED PEST BY A HAIR!
BUT IT STILL HELD HIM UP LONG ENOUGH FOR ME TO PUT A LOT OF DISTANCE BETWEEN US!

CALENDAR MAN IS TOO FAR AHEAD OF ME-- I'LL NEVER CATCH UP!
ONLY ONE OTHER CHANCE--!

YOU'RE SLIPPING, BATMAN!
THAT BATARANG DIDN'T EVEN COME CLOSE!

BUT PERHAPS IT WAS NOT INTENDED TO--
--FOR, WITH SNAKE-LIKE AGILITY, THE SILKEN LINE ATTACHED TO THE BATARANG COILS AROUND THE HANDLE OF A SWITCHING SIGNAL IN CALENDAR MAN'S PATH--

--AND AS THE FLEEING FELON RUSHES PAST--

--THE DARKNIGHT DETECTIVE PULLS HIS BAT-LINE TAUT!
BLANG!

CALENDAR MAN, YOU'VE HAD A BUSY WEEK-- BUT YOU'LL HAVE 20 YEARS TO LIFE TO RECOVER FROM IT!
AND THAT, DARE I SAY IT, SIGNALS THE END OF THIS CASE!
END

Coloring by Adrienne Roy

GOOD *MOVIE*, EH, MARTHA? THAT *MARLON BRANDO* SURE IS--

IT'S CALLED A *STICK-UP*, BUDDY! I'LL TAKE THAT *NECKLACE* THE *LADY'S* WEARIN'!

WHAT-- WHAT *IS* THIS--?!

YOU *HOODLUM!* DON'T YOU DARE PUT YOUR HAND ON MY *WIFE*--!

MAYBE *NOW* YOU'LL KEEP *QUIET!*

BLAM

UNNNHHH!!

THOMAS!!

HELP! POLICE-- HELP!!

CLICK!

AN' *THIS*--

--WILL SHUT *YOU* UP, LADY!

BLAM!

F-FATHER... MOTHER...

THEY'RE *DEAD!* YOU *KILLED* THEM!

S-STOP *LOOKIN'* AT ME LIKE THAT, KID! STOP *LOOKIN'* AT ME!

THE KILLER-- A MAN NAMED JOE CHILL-- FLEES. BRUCE'S *PARENTS* DO NOT *MOVE*.

THEY WILL NEVER MOVE *AGAIN*. THEY WILL NEVER *HOLD* HIM... NEVER *COMFORT* HIM AFTER A BAD *DREAM*... NEVER KNOW HOW MUCH HE REALLY *LOVED* THEM.

BRUCE STARTS TO *SCREAM*--

2

NO!!

-- AND FINISHES TWENTY YEARS LATER!

WHEW! FEEL LIKE I SPENT THE NIGHT IN A DISHWASHER! WHAT'S WRONG WITH ME, ANYWAY?

I HAVEN'T HAD THAT DREAM IN YEARS-- NOT SINCE I CAUGHT UP WITH JOE CHILL!

WHY SHOULD IT START AGAIN NOW?

WELL, I CERTAINLY CAN'T GO BACK TO SLEEP NOW!

I GUESS I'M LUCKY, IN A WAY. WHENEVER IT GETS TOO PAINFUL BEING BRUCE WAYNE--

--I CAN ALWAYS BECOME THE BATMAN!

I WONDER HOW NORMAL PEOPLE MANAGE TO COPE?

THE ANSWER TO THAT IS: SOMETIMES THEY DON'T.
PLEASE... NO...I DON'T HAVE MUCH MONEY...
HEY-- THAT'S COOL! WE DON'T NEED MUCH!
NOW-- YOU GONNA LET GO OF THAT PURSE OR DO I REMOVE IT SURGICALLY?

NONE OF THE ABOVE, FRIEND!
OH NO.
OH YES. HEADS UP, MA'AM!
THWACK

ONE DOWN-- ONE TO GO...!
CRIPES! HOW'D I GET INTO THIS?!
GOTTA GET OUTTA HERE--!!
RUNNING INTO THAT FOG BANK--? HE'S SO PANICKED HE DOESN'T REALIZE THE ALLEY DEAD-ENDS UP AHEAD!
I SHOULD HAVE THIS WRAPPED UP IN A MATTER OF--
NO! IT ISN'T POSSIBLE! WE WERE NOWHERE NEAR HERE!
HE'S RUNNING STRAIGHT INTO--
CRIME ALLEY!
MY PARENTS DIED HERE TWENTY YEARS AGO! BUT IT'S CLEAR ON THE OTHER SIDE OF TOWN! WHAT THE DEVIL--?
UH OH-- I'M LOSING HIM! BETTER POUR ON THE SPEED BEFORE HE--
SUDDENLY...
HEY! LOOK! IT'S THE GOODRICH BLIMP!
WHAT--?!
DUMMY.
GOODRICH DOESN'T HAVE A BLIMP!
THOK!
UNHH!
ROBIN!
4

DICK! WHAT ARE YOU DOING HERE? I PUT YOU ON A PLANE TO EUROPE THIS MORNING!
PLANE...? EUROPE?
YES...OF COURSE. WHAT AM I DOING HERE?!
YOU ARE HERE... BECAUSE YOU MUST BE HERE!

PHANTOM STRANGER?!
SO YOU PULLED THAT TRICK WITH THE FOG! BUT WHAT BRINGS YOU TO GOTHAM? WHAT'S WRONG?
THE WRONG, MY FRIEND, HAS YET TO BE DONE... AND, GIVEN YOUR HELP, IT MAY NEVER BE DONE.

UH, WE'VE NEVER MET BEFORE, STRANGER, BUT I TAKE IT YOU'RE HEAVILY INTO CRYPTIC.
CARE TO TRANSLATE THAT?
OF COURSE. THERE ARE WORLDS BEYOND WORLDS, DICK GRAYSON...
...HUNDREDS OF EARTHS LIKE YOUR OWN, EXISTING IN AS MANY DIFFERENT DIMENSIONS.

ON ONE SUCH EARTH, BATMAN, FORTY YEARS AGO, ANOTHER BRUCE WAYNE SAW HIS PARENTS MURDERED... AND VOWED TO AVENGE THEIR DEATHS.
TWENTY YEARS LATER, ON THIS EARTH, YOU WATCHED YOUR PARENTS DIE... AND BECAME, LIKE YOUR PREDECESSOR, THE BATMAN.

NOW-- ON STILL ANOTHER EARTH-- THE CYCLE IS ABOUT TO REPEAT ITSELF.
THOMAS AND MARTHA WAYNE WILL DIE AGAIN-- UNLESS YOU INTERVENE.
INTERVENE? YOU MEAN-- TRAVEL TO THIS OTHER EARTH AND STOP THE MURDER?
BUT-- WHY ARE YOU OFFERING ME THIS?
5

YOU'RE A BRAVE MAN, BRUCE WAYNE... BUT DESPITE ALL YOUR COURAGE, ALL THE GOOD YOU'VE DONE...
..YOU STILL FEEL YOU FAILED THE ONES YOU LOVED THE MOST.

THIS IS YOUR SECOND CHANCE, BRUCE WAYNE-- AND I OFFER IT TO YOU AS A FRIEND AND A COMRADE.
DO YOU CHOOSE TO TAKE IT?

BEHIND THE BATMAN'S MASK, BRUCE WAYNE CONSIDERS FOR LONG MOMENTS --UNTIL--
I'LL GO.
SO WILL I.
NO, DICK. I... APPRECIATE THE OFFER, BUT... I HAVE TO DO THIS ALONE.

SO BE IT.
ENTER THE FOG, BATMAN...
I DON'T LIKE THIS! BRUCE WON'T ADMIT IT, BUT WHEN IT COMES TO HIS PARENTS' DEATHS HE JUST CAN'T BE OBJECTIVE!
HE MAY NEED ME WHEREVER HE'S GOING...

...OR WHY ELSE WOULD I BE HERE?
ROBIN-- NO--!!
SAFE JOURNEY, MY FRIENDS-- AND GOOD LUCK TO YOU!

FOR A SPLIT-SECOND, THE TWO TRAVELLERS LOSE CONSCIOUSNESS AS THE FOG SWIRLS AROUND THEM...
AND WHEN IT FINALLY CLEARS, THEY FIND THEMSELVES AT--
6

GOTHAM HARBOR?! IS THIS REALLY ANOTHER WORLD--
--OR JUST ONE OF THE STRANGER'S ILLUSIONS? GOOD QUESTION. LET'S SEE IF WE CAN--
THA-BOOMM!
WHAT THE--
IT CAME FROM THE CARGO HOLD OF THAT SHIP! LET'S GO!

LOOK AT THIS STUFF! THOSE ANCIENT INCAS SURE KNEW HOW TO LIVE!
MY FENCE IS GONNA HAVE A HEART ATTACK WHEN HE SEES THIS!
THEN WE'LL JUST HAVE TO SPARE HIM THE SHOCK, WON'T WE?
WHA--?

WHAT IN THE NAME OF-- WHAT IS IT?!
SOME KINDA GIANT BAT-- SOME THING--!!
NO! IT'S COMIN' RIGHT AT ME--!!

NO! PLEASE! STAY AWAY FROM ME! STAY AWAY!!
OHHHH--
THIS IS BIZARRE! I BARELY TOUCHED HIM, AND HE FAINTED DEAD AWAY!

INCREDIBLE!
THEY PUT UP NO FIGHT AT ALL-- ACTED LIKE THEY'VE NEVER SEEN ANYTHING LIKE US!
MAYBE THEY HAVEN'T!
WHOOP WHOOP WHOOP
SIRENS! LET'S GO TOPSIDE!

HEY! WHAT'S GOING--
ALL RIGHT! HOLD IT RIGHT THERE-- WHOEVER YOU ARE!
I DON'T BELIEVE IT--!
7

--COMMISSIONER GORDON?!
LIEUTENANT GORDON--AND NOW THAT WE'VE AGREED ON WHO I AM--
--WHY DON'T WE START WITH WHO YOU ARE, AND HOW YOU BROKE INTO THIS SHIP!

UH, DON'T LOOK NOW, TOTO, BUT WE ARE DEFINITELY NOT IN KANSAS ANYMORE.
THIS CERTAINLY PROVES WE'RE ON ANOTHER EARTH! BUT SINCE WE'LL NEVER CONVINCE THE GOOD LIEU-TENANT OF THAT, WE'D BETTER--
--MOVE!

--THIS HURTS ME, OFFICER--
--ALMOST AS MUCH AS IT DOES YOU!
YOW!

FREEZE OR I'LL--
SORRY ABOUT THIS, LIEUTENANT--
OWWW!

--BUT IF WE TOLD YOU THE TRUTH--

--YOU'D HAVE US COMMITTED INSTANTLY!

MORNING IN GOTHAM-- AND TWO VISITORS WALK A FAMILIAR YET ALIEN CITY...
SO MANY SMALL DIFFERENCES! CRIME ALLEY IS STILL PARK ROW.. BASIN STREET IS BASIN AVENUE...
HOW DO WE KNOW WHERE THE WAYNES LIVE ON THIS EARTH?
WE DON'T!
WHICH IS WHY WE USE THE SOCIAL REGISTER-- IN HERE!

I CAN'T HELP FEELING EXPOSED! WE ARE WANTED CRIMINALS NOW!
WE'RE ALSO CIPHERS-- WE DON'T EXIST IN THIS WORLD, SO HOW COULD ANYONE, EVEN THE POLICE, RECOG-NIZE US?
DR. WAYNE! IS THAT YOU?
BARBARA KEAN, REMEMBER--DETEC-TIVE GORDON'S FIANCÉE? YOU ARE THOMAS WAYNE, AREN'T YOU?
UH-- YES. OF COURSE. HOW ARE YOU, MISS KEAN?
PERIODIC
I WONDER-- COULD YOU SHOW ME WHERE THE SOCIAL REGISTER IS? I SEEM TO HAVE FORGOTTEN...

WHAT A STRANGE WORLD! PLENTY OF CRIME, TERRORISM, WAR-- BUT NOT A SINGLE COSTUMED HERO!
OF COURSE, THERE WEREN'T ANY COSTUMED HEROES ON OUR EARTH TILL A FEW DECADES AGO-- BUT--
SPECIAL
GOTHAM NE
DOWNTOWN SNIPER KILLS FIVE
CONFLICT CONTINUES IN

--THERE DOESN'T SEEM TO BE ANY HEROIC MYTHOLOGY ON THIS WORLD, EITHER!
NO ROBIN HOOD-- NO CAMELOT-- NO HERCULES, ODYSSEUS, GILGAMESH--

EVEN THAT WOULDN'T BOTHER ME, THOUGH, IF IT WEREN'T FOR THIS!
ACCORDING TO THIS STAR ATLAS, THE RED STAR AROUND WHICH KRYPTON IS SUPPOSED TO ORBIT--

--DOESN'T EXIST!
IF THERE'S NO KRYPTON IN THIS DIMENSION, THEN THERE'LL BE NO SUPERMAN-- PERHAPS NO SUPER-POWERED HEROES AT ALL!
AND WITH NO LITERA-TURE TO INSPIRE THEM--
9

--THIS MIGHT BE A WORLD WITHOUT HEROES--EXCEPT FOR ITS BATMAN!
THAT'S SUPPOSITION, DICK--NOT DEDUCTION! DIDN'T I TEACH YOU BETTER THAN THAT?
COME ON--LET'S GO SEE MY PAR--UH, I MEAN THE WAYNES!

GREAT! WHENEVER BRUCE DOESN'T WANT TO HEAR WHAT I HAVE TO SAY, HE PULLS THE OLD MENTOR/PUPIL BIT!
WELL, THIS TIME I'M GOING TO HAVE TO MAKE HIM LISTEN--
--BEFORE IT'S TOO LATE!

AND, ABOARD A TRAIN THREE HOURS NORTH OF GOTHAM CITY...
OH, CRIPES! THEY BUSTED CHARLIE! I KNEW WE SHOULD'VE WASTED THAT GUARD BEFORE HE TALKED!
GOTTA STAY CALM! CHARLIE'S CONTACTS IN GOTHAM'LL TAKE CARE OF ME!
CLEVELAND FIRST NATIONAL ROBBED--TWO ARRESTED

YEAH... SURE. WITH COPS IN THREE STATES LOOKIN' FOR ME... STAY CALM.
HIS NAME IS JOE CHILL. HE'S A SMALL, SCARED, MEAN LITTLE MAN... AND HIS TROUBLES ARE JUST BEGINNING.

MEANWHILE, AT A FAMILIAR SUBURBAN MANOR HOUSE OUTSIDE GOTHAM...
NO! I DON'T WANT IT! TAKE IT BACK!

YOUR MOTHER WENT TO A LOT OF TROUBLE TO GET THAT, BRUCE! I SWEAR, I'VE HALF A MIND TO--
THOMAS, NO! IT'S JUST A PHASE HE'S GOING THROUGH!
OH, I SUPPOSE...

DEAR LORD... IT'S AS IF THEY'VE COME ALIVE AGAIN! AS IF I COULD... REACH OUT AND TOUCH THEM AGAIN...
FATHER... MOTHER... I SWEAR BY ALL THAT'S DEAR TO ME... I WON'T LET YOU DIE AGAIN!
10

THIS BRUCE WAYNE IS A SPOILED LITTLE BRAT!
I WONDER... IF WE STOP HIS PARENTS' MURDER, WILL HE GROW UP TO BECOME THE BORED PLAYBOY THAT BATMAN ONLY PRETENDS TO BE?

SHORTLY, OUTSIDE POLICE HEADQUARTERS...
I KNOW WE NEED INFORMATION ON JOE CHILL'S WHEREABOUTS, BATMAN. BUT ISN'T IT RISKY BREAKING INTO POLICE HEADQUARTERS?
POLICE
NOT "BREAK IN"--"WALK IN!" AFTER ALL, WHO'D SUSPECT ANYTHING OF--

--DETECTIVE LIEUTENANT JAMES GORDON?

AND SO, TEN MINUTES LATER...
BLAST! CHILL DOESN'T EVEN HAVE A FILE! HE MUST'VE BEEN CAGEY ENOUGH TO KEEP RELATIVELY CLEAN!
ALL I CAN DO NOW IS OPERATE ON WHAT I KNOW ABOUT THE CHILL OF MY EARTH, WHO WORKED FOR--
CRIMINAL RECORDS
LOCAL

--LEW MOXON! HE HIRED CHILL TO KILL MY FATHER FOR TESTIFYING AGAINST HIM!
I CHECKED THE FILES-- MOXON'S COUNTER-PART ON THIS EARTH RUNS A TRUCKING COMPANY ON CANAL STREET!
WELL, SINCE WE'RE SO CLOSE--

"--WHY DON'T WE JUST DROP OVER?"
WHAT IN THE--
11

WATCH CLOSELY NOW, GANG--AND TAKE NOTE THAT AT NO TIME--
--DO MY TOES EVER LEAVE MY FEET!
BLAM! BLAM! BLAM!
VROOOMM!
GOT TO MANEUEVER THIS JUST RIGHT--
--SO THEY DON'T HIT ME--
THA-BOOOMM!
--BUT THE GAS TANK!
12

WHILE THE THUGS ARE TEMPORARILY STUNNED BY THE BLAST--
GOING SOMEWHERE, MOXON?
OOF!
WHO--WHO ARE YOU?! HOW D'YOU KNOW MY NAME?

I'M ASKING THE QUESTIONS, MOXON! WHERE'S JOE CHILL-- THE THUG YOU'VE HIRED TO KILL THOMAS WAYNE?

I DUNNO WHAT YOU'RE TALKIN' ABOUT! SO HELP ME! I NEVER HEARD OF ANY CHILL!

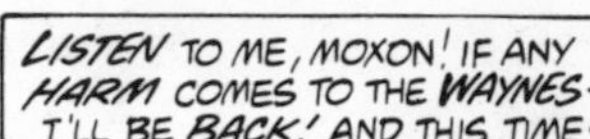
LISTEN TO ME, MOXON! IF ANY HARM COMES TO THE WAYNES-- I'LL BE BACK! AND THIS TIME--

--I'LL DO A LOT MORE THAN BLOW UP ONE OF YOUR TRUCKS!

THOSE MANIACS KNOW ABOUT MY PLANS FOR WAYNE! GONNA HAVE TO MOVE UP MY TIMETABLE... BEFORE THEY GO TO THE COPS!
GOTTA FIND SOMEBODY TO KILL THOMAS WAYNE-- AS SOON AS I CAN!

TIME'S RUNNING OUT! IT'S THE 21ST OF THE MONTH--MY PARENTS WERE KILLED ON THE 26TH!
GOTHAM CENTRAL STATION
IF WE CAN'T FIND CHILL IN FIVE DAYS-- THEN WE FOLLOW THE WAYNES' EVERY MOVE...
...AND WAIT FOR CHILL TO MAKE HIS!

WHILE, JUST A HUNDRED FEET BELOW...
MADE IT! NOW TO LOOK UP-- WHAT'S HIS NAME...?
LEW MOXON! YEAH! CHARLIE SAID MOXON'S ALWAYS GOT WORK FOR A GUY!
SHOOT, RIGHT ABOUT NOW I'D BE WILLIN' TO DO ANYTHING...
13

HOURS LATER, AT WAYNE MANOR...
BRUCE, WE DON'T BELONG HERE! WE HAVE NO RIGHT TO INTERFERE! MAYBE EVERY WORLD NEEDS A BATMAN!
AND WHAT ABOUT YOUNG BRUCE? YOU SAW YOUR PARENTS MUR-DERED TOO, DICK--
--CAN YOU PUT SOMEONE ELSE THROUGH THAT?
I AM THINKING ABOUT YOUNG BRUCE! WE COULD BE CONDEMNING HIM TO A LIFE AS A SPOILED PLAYBOY...
...AND DENYING THIS EARTH ITS ONLY HERO!
I CAN APPRECIATE YOUR CONCERNS, ROBIN... BUT I CAN'T SHARE THEM. LIVES ARE AT STAKE HERE...
...INCLUDING A LITTLE BOY'S LIFE...

... A BOY WHO'LL SEE HIS FAMILY DIE BEFORE HIS EYES.
HE'LL NEVER FORGET THAT... NEVER LOSE THE ANGER OR THE ANGUISH.
NO ONE SHOULD BE ANGRY ALL HIS LIFE, DICK. NO ONE...

I... KNOW. BUT IT SEEMS SO IMPOSSIBLE. CHILL COULD BE ANYWHERE... PHOENIX, TORONTO, MIAMI...
WHA--? OF COURSE! HOW COULD I HAVE BEEN SO BLIND?

I JUST ASSUMED THAT THIS CHILL, LIKE THE ONE ON OUR EARTH, WAS FROM GOTHAM CITY!
I DIDN'T BOTHER TO CHECK THE INTERSTATE COMPUTER RECORDS AT POLICE HQ--
--UNTIL NOW, THAT IS!
14

BUT ONLY MINUTES AFTER THE BATMAN LEAVES...
GET YOUR COAT, BRUCE-- YOUR FATHER'S TAKING US TO A MOVIE!
BUT I WAS PLAYING WITH MY TRAINS--!
YOU CAN DO THAT LATER, SON.

LEAVING FOR A MOVIE? BUT BATMAN'S PARENTS WERE KILLED COMING HOME FROM A MOVIE!
OF ALL THE TIMES FOR BATMAN TO SPLIT! SOMETHING TELLS ME I'D BETTER STICK CLOSE TO THE WAYNES--
--AND PRAY!

MEANWHILE, IN POLICE HEADQUARTERS...
BINGO! ACCORDING TO THIS, THERE'S AN INTER-STATE BULLETIN OUT ON CHILL... AND IT'S BELIEVED HE'S HEADED FOR GOTHAM!
NOW TO SEE IF I CAN--
GOOD EVENING. ENJOYING YOURSELF?

DON'T MOVE, PLEASE.
I ASSURE YOU... I'M QUITE A GOOD SHOT.

AND IN THE STREETS OF GOTHAM...
BRUCE SAID THE MURDER WASN'T SUPPOSED TO HAPPEN FOR FIVE MORE DAYS, BUT--HE MAY HAVE BEEN WRONG!
IT MAY BE UP TO ME TO STOP THIS-- AND I STILL DON'T KNOW IF I SHOULD!
BATMAN, WHERE ARE YOU?!
EMA
DIANE KEATON
NIE HALL
Patti fashions
JOH

I CAN'T EXPLAIN IT ALL, BUT I'M TRYING TO STOP A MURDERER FROM KILLING TWO INNOCENT PEOPLE!
LIEUTENANT... IN ANOTHER WORLD, ANOTHER TIME... WE'RE FRIENDS. IF YOU CAN FEEL EVEN A HINT OF THAT... TRUST ME. LET ME GO. PLEASE!

GORDON CONSIDERS... AND SOMETHING IN HIM RESPONDS TO THIS STRANGER'S VOICE. HE CAN'T SAY WHY...

...BUT HE DECIDES TO TRUST HIM.
15

MINUTES LATER, IN A HOTEL ON DUMONT STREET...
GORDON'S INFORMANTS SAID CHILL TOOK A ROOM IN THIS--
GOOD LORD!
CHILL?!

CHILL! WHAT HAPPENED? WHO DID THIS?
M-MOXON! WENT TO SEE HIM... TOLD HIM MY NAME... HE THREW ME OUT... SAID SOME MANIAC WAS AFTER ME...
I GOT BACK... AN' ONE OF HIS GOONS WAS WAITING... ON HIS WAY TO ANOTHER HIT...

ANOTHER HIT?!
YEH... SOME DOCTOR... FUNNY, AIN'T IT... ALL MY LIFE... PART OF SOMEBODY ELSE'S GANG... SOMEBODY ELSE'S ORDERS...
AN' NOW I GET OFFED... ON THE WAY TO SOMEBODY ELSE'S FUNERAL...

MONDAY
21
CHILL ISN'T THE KILLER! SOMEONE ELSE IS-- AND IT'S GOING TO HAPPEN TONIGHT!
BUT HOW? TODAY'S THE 21ST-- IT'S NOT SUPPOSED TO HAPPEN FOR FIVE--
OH NO! OF COURSE! I SHOULD HAVE REALIZED!

MY PARENTS DIED TWENTY YEARS AGO! IN THAT TIME, THERE HAVE BEEN FIVE LEAP YEARS--

--FIVE EXTRA DAYS...

...THE CALENDAR DOESN'T RECORD!

FOR ALL PURPOSES, TONIGHT IS--

--THE NIGHT OF THE 26TH--

--AND HEAVEN HELP ME... IT'S HAPPENING ALL OVER AGAIN!

AND, AT THAT MOMENT ON PARK ROW...
REAL GOOD! WE CAME ALL THE WAY INTO TOWN JUST TO FIND THE MOVIE'S BEEN SOLD OUT!
BRUCE, THERE WAS NO WAY WE COULD HAVE KNOWN...

IT'S UP TO ME NOW! SHOULD I RESPECT BRUCE'S WISHES, AND INTERFERE--
-- OR FOLLOW MY INSTINCTS, AND LET DESTINY TAKE ITS COURSE?
WHATEVER I DO-- SOMEONE WILL SUFFER!

SUDDENLY...
WHAT-- WHAT IS THIS--?!
IT'S CALLED A STICK-UP, BUDDY! I'LL TAKE THAT NECKLACE THE LADY'S WEARIN'!

YOU HOODLUM! DON'T YOU DARE PUT A HAND ON MY WIFE--!
TO BLAZES WITH DESTINY! BRUCE WAS RIGHT! I CAN'T LET INNOCENT PEOPLE DIE!
I ONLY PRAY I'M NOT TOO--
WAIT! WHAT THE--

BLAM
MAYBE THIS'LL SHUT YOU UP!
NO!!

NOT THIS TIME-- YOU HEAR ME? THIS TIME YOU'RE NOT GOING TO WIN!
17

THIS TIME...
...I DIDN'T FAIL THEM...

BRUCE! WHAT HAPPENED? THAT ISN'T CHILL.
CHILL'S DEAD. THE POLICE SHOULD'VE FOUND HIM BY NOW... AND THEY'LL FOLLOW THE TRAIL RIGHT TO MOXON. THE WAYNES ARE SAFE.
AND SO YOUR TASK IS ENDED.

YOU MUST LEAVE NOW. YOU ARE STRANGERS HERE... AS MUCH A STRANGER AS I.
WILL WE EVER KNOW WHAT'LL HAPPEN--TO YOUNG BRUCE, HIS LIFE?
PERHAPS. BUT FOR NOW, ALL YOU NEED KNOW...

..IS THAT YOU SAVED TWO LIVES... AND ALTERED FOREVER A THIRD.
AMEN TO THAT.
THE FOG STARTS TO CLOSE IN AROUND THEM...

...AND WHEN IT FINALLY CLEARS...

...THREE STRANGERS HAVE RETURNED HOME.

18

EPILOGUE

THREE WEEKS LATER:
BRUCE? HOW'D YOU LIKE TO GO SHOPPING FOR SOME NEW TRAINS?
NO THANKS, MOM! GOT SOME THINGS TO DO--COUPLA BOOKS TO READ!
'SCUSE ME!

MARTHA WAYNE LOOKS AT THE NEW BOOKS THAT LINE BRUCE'S WALLS... THE NEW INTERESTS THAT FILL HIS LIFE...
CONAN DOYLE SHERLOCK HOLMES
THE PSYCHOLOGY of CRIME
...AND DOESN'T QUITE KNOW WHAT TO MAKE OF IT ALL.

THOMAS, HAVE YOU NOTICED HOW... DIFFERENT BRUCE SEEMS SINCE THAT AWFUL ROBBERY?
IF BY DIFFERENT YOU MEAN QUIETER... MORE STUDIOUS... I THINK IT'S AN IMPROVEMENT.
MAYBE WE OUGHT TO GET MUGGED MORE OFTEN.

FOR AS LONG AS HE LIVES BRUCE WAYNE WILL REMEMBER THAT NIGHT, THREE WEEKS AGO...
...AND THE BAT-WINGED CREATURE THAT SWOOPED DOWN FROM THE SKY, SAVING THE LIVES OF HIMSELF AND HIS FAMILY.

THAT NIGHT, BRUCE WAYNE LEARNED WHAT DEATH WAS... AND HE LEARNED IT COULD BE AVERTED... AT LEAST TEMPORARILY.
YEARS FROM NOW, HE WILL MAKE A DECISION... CHOOSE A DIRECTION FOR HIS LIFE...

AND WHEN HE DOES, IT WILL NOT BE A DECISION BORN OF GRIEF, OR GUILT, OR VENGEANCE...
...BUT OF AWE... AND MYSTERY... AND GRATITUDE.
"TO KILL A LEGEND" by: ALAN BRENNERT writer DICK GIORDANO artist ADRIENNE ROY colorist JOHN COSTANZA letterer PAUL LEVITZ editor
END

Coloring by Lovern Kindzierski

...and became my wife.
The Autobiography of BRUCE WAYNE!
A VERY SPECIAL TALE OF THE GOLDEN AGE BATMAN, PRESENTED BY:
ALAN BRENNERT · writer
JOE STATON & GEORGE FREEMAN · artists
JOHN COSTANZA · letterer
LEN WEIN · editor
It was 1955, and police commissioner James Gordon was waiting-- as he had so many nights before-- on the roof of police headquarters.
I think I was more than a friend to Jim Gordon; I was his secret self, the adventurer he might have been had he not taken other paths.
He once told me he lived in dread of the night he would light the bat-signal... and no one would answer. Because the day I died, part of him would die, too.
2

That night, it all came true for him.
GOD IN HEAVEN! NO!!
RATATATATATATAT
PEDO
COMMISSIONER--NO--!
HAINER, LET ME GO! HE--HE MAY STILL BE ALIVE! HE MAY NEED HELP--!
EASY, JIM. YOU'RE THE ONE WHO NEEDS HELP.
I DON'T KNOW WHAT YOU THINK YOU SAW, COMMISSIONER, BUT IF THAT CHEMICAL ODOR IS ANY CLUE, I KNOW WHY YOU SAW IT.
IS THAT BOX YOU'RE HOLDING FOR ME, BY ANY CHANCE?
IT ARRIVED TODAY... THE POSTMARK COINCIDES WITH THE PAROLE DATE OF--
--JONATHAN CRANE, a.k.a. THE SCARECROW! OBVIOUSLY IT CONTAINED A TIMED-RELEASE GAS... DESIGNED TO CAUSE HALLUCINATIONS.
Y-YES... OF ONE'S... GREATEST FEAR...
PAROLED. THEY GO IN BAD... AND COME OUT WORSE. WHAT ARE WE DOING BUT... DETAINING THEM, TEMPORARILY?
WE DO WHAT WE'VE ALWAYS DONE, JIM-- WHAT WE HAVE TO DO.
GET SOME SLEEP. I'LL CHECK THIS IN THE BATCAVE.
3

THE YEAR'S NOT HALF OVER AND ALREADY I'VE HAD TO ROUND UP THE JOKER, THE PENGUIN, TWO-FACE... ALL EITHER PAROLED OR ESCAPED.
THIS ALL SEEMED A LOT EASIER, FIFTEEN YEARS AGO.
AND EVER SINCE THE JUSTICE SOCIETY DISBANDED...
...IT'S JUST BEEN ME, ROBIN, SUPERMAN AND WONDER WOMAN OUT HERE, TRYING TO HOLD THINGS TOGETHER.
FUNNY, THOUGH. I'M NOT NEARLY AS CONCERNED ABOUT THE SCARECROW BEING AT LARGE...
...AS I AM ABOUT ATTENDING LINDA PAGE'S WEDDING TOMORROW!
FIRST CLARK AND LOIS... THEN JAY GARRICK AND JOAN WILLIAMS...
LORD, HAS IT REALLY BEEN FIFTEEN YEARS?
It was the Batman who drove into the night...
...but, as usual, it was Bruce Wayne who had to face the DAY, at the estate of Linda's industrialist father.
WHAT THE-- BRUCE? WHAT ARE YOU DOING--
WELL, ACCORDING TO TRADITION IT'S BAD LUCK FOR THE GROOM TO SEE THE BRIDE--
-- BUT TRADITION DOESN'T SAY A THING ABOUT OLD BOYFRIENDS!
SAME OLD BRUCE. I'M SO GLAD YOU CAME. I WAS A LITTLE AFRAID YOU WOULDN'T WANT TO.
LINDA, IT'S BEEN TEN YEARS.
I KNOW, BUT THE THINGS I SAID BACK THEN...
4

...I HAD NO RIGHT TO TRY AND CHANGE YOU. I JUST COULDN'T FIGURE OUT WHY SOMEONE WITH YOUR INTELLIGENCE WOULD WANT TO SPEND HIS LIFE... PLAYING POLO.

THERE'S...NO WAY I CAN EXPLAIN MYSELF TO YOU, LINDA.

MAYBE NOT. BUT I WISH YOU'D TRIED.

I DON'T KNOW WHAT SECRET PAIN YOU'RE HIDING, BRUCE...BUT WHATEVER IT IS...

...I DO HOPE YOU MAKE YOUR PEACE WITH IT.

IS THAT... STILL HOW YOU WANT TO BE REMEMBERED, BRUCE? AS JUST ANOTHER NAME ON THE SOCIAL REGISTER?

DAMN THIS PLAYBOY POSE! I LOST JULIE MADISON BECAUSE OF IT...I LOST LINDA...

IT BEGAN AS A LARK--AMUSING TO PLAY AT BEING A RICH IDLER, WHILE PUMPING ACQUAINTANCES LIKE JIM GORDON FOR INFORMATION THE BATMAN COULD USE...

LATER, IT WAS NECESSARY TO ESTABLISH BATMAN AND WAYNE AS TWO DISTINCT PERSONALITIES, SINCE BOTH TRAVELED IN THE SAME CIRCLES...

...AND SOMEWHERE ALONG THE WAY, BRUCE WAYNE BECAME FROZEN INTO SOMEONE I'D NEVER INTENDED HIM TO BE!

LOOK AT THEM ALL. SHALLOW, STATUS-SEEKING HYPOCRITES... YET I HAVE TO PRETEND TO BE ONE OF THEM, SYMPATHIZE WITH THEM WHEN THEIR STOCKS DROP HALF A POINT!
MY ONLY REAL FRIENDS KNOW ME AS BATMAN... DICK, ALFRED, KATHY KANE...

EXCEPT...WHAT DO I DO WHEN DICK GRADUATES COLLEGE... AND ALFRED RETIRES...AND KATHY GIVES UP BEING BATWOMAN?
WHAT DO I DO... WHEN I'M FINALLY ALONE?
5

It was the first time I'd admitted to myself what I had made of my life.
The ceremony began...
And so did the nightmare.
OH MY LORD--!
EEEEEEEEE
GET IT OFF ME! PLEASE, SOMEONE, GET IT OFF--!
I'LL EXPLAIN ON THE RUN, DICK. LET'S GO.
BRUCE-- WHAT--
CRANE!
WHEW! LUCKY FOR ME I HUNG OUT WITH THE SNAKE CHARMER AT THE CIRCUS.
IT'S GOING TO BITE ME--!
BETTER FIND SOME PLACE TO SWITCH TO BATWOMAN-- TRY TO QUELL THE PANIC!
6

MY, WHAT AN IDEAL CROSS-SECTION OF HUMANITY! HARD TO FIND A CROWD IN WHICH SOMEONE DOESN'T SUFFER FROM ARACHNOPHOBIA...OPHIOPHOBIA...HELMINTHOPHOBIA...
OR, RESPECTIVELY, FEAR OF SPIDERS, SNAKES, AND WORMS!
STILL THE SCHOOLTEACHER AT HEART, EH, CRANE? ALWAYS LECTURING.
NO WONDER HE BECAME A PSYCHOPATH. PROBABLY TOO BORING TO GET TENURE.
WHAPP!
YOU'RE LATE TO CLASS, BATMAN. I THOUGHT I MIGHT DRAW YOU INTO THE OPEN AT THIS AFFAIR-- MISS PAGE IS KNOWN TO BE ONE OF YOUR FRIENDS!
CAN I CRASH THIS COURSE, TOO?
:SIGH: THAT'S RIGHT--DRIVE IT INTO THE GROUND, WHY DON'T YOU.
YOU PEOPLE DON'T KNOW WHEN TO LEAVE A GOOD METAPHOR ALONE, DO YOU?
GOOD LORD, CRANE--
--AREN'T WE BOTH GETTING A LITTLE OLD FOR--
ARGGHHH!
I thought it was just a flare-bomb designed to slow me down...
...but in the next instant I watched in horror as Robin--Dick--
--literally VANISHED into thin air!
BATMAN, ARE YOU ALL...
ROBIN!
7

For me, the nightmare had begun--

BATWOMAN, WHAT--WHAT HAPPENED? WHAT HAPPENED TO ROBIN?

ROBIN...?

But for everyone else--

ROBIN'S RIGHT HERE BESIDE ME!

BATMAN, CAN YOU HEAR--

WHAT ARE YOU TALKING ABOUT? HE JUST VANISHED INTO THIN--

OH NO--NO--NOT YOU, TOO--!

BATWOMAN! BATWOMAN!

BATMAN, ARE YOU ALL RIGHT? WHAT'S GOING ON?

LINDA, STAY BACK! YOU COULD BE--

...NEXT...!
NOOOOO...!
I DON'T UNDERSTAAA...

SCARECROW! YOU DID THIS, SOMEHOW! I'LL FIND YOU IF IT'S THE LAST THING I DO-- YOU UNDERSTAND?!
ROBIN, IT'S NO USE. HE CAN'T SEE, HEAR, EVEN FEEL US!
BATMAN, WE'RE OKAY, WE'RE HERE--
8

CRANE'S BOMB... IT MUST HAVE TRIGGERED HIS DEEPEST SUBCONSCIOUS FEAR...
THE FEAR... OF BEING ALONE...
THERE MUST BE SOMETHING WE CAN DO FOR HIM, ROBIN--
SO, BATMAN--YOUR DEMON, YOUR ROOM 101, IS AUTOPHOBIA, IS IT?
I WISH THERE WERE.
CRANE DIDN'T CREATE THE FEAR... JUST AGGRAVATED IT. ALL WE CAN HOPE...
...IS THAT HE COMES TO GRIPS WITH IT... BEFORE IT COMES TO GRIPS WITH HIM.
INTERESTING. THE MORE YOU SEARCH FOR YOUR FRIENDS, THE MORE HOPELESS IT WILL SEEM...
...AND THE DEEPER INTO DELUSION YOU WILL SINK--SO DEEP YOU SHALL NEVER ESCAPE!
I was alone, truly alone, for the first time since my parents had been killed.
I needed an ALLY-- someone, anyone, to help me find Dick and Kathy and Linda.
I went to police HQ, but Gordon was nowhere to be seen.
I went to Wayne Manor, but Alfred, too, was missing.
I called Metropolis, but at the other end of the Kents' line there was only silence.
HELLO? HELLO?
There were no FRIENDS to turn to...
9

...but what about-- an old ENEMY?

After an accident had freed her from the amnesia which plagued her for over a decade-- during which time she had first become the Catwoman--

--Selina Kyle surrendered to serve her prison term, peacefully. There had always been an attraction between us--

--but would she help me now?

IT COULD MEAN *PAROLE*, SELINA. AND YOU SEE, I...

BATMAN, I--I BARELY REMEMBER WHAT I DID AS THE CATWOMAN! I DON'T *WANT* TO. DON'T ASK ME TO PUT ON THAT DAMNED *COSTUME* AGAIN.

...I DON'T HAVE ANYONE ELSE I CAN *TURN* TO. TOO MUCH OF MY WORLD SEEMS TO BE... *SHRINKING*. DEAD ENDS AND LOCKED DOORS.

SHRINKING... YES.

I... KNOW THAT FEELING.

WILL YOU HELP ME, SELINA?

10

Two hours later...
GOTHAM UNIVERSITY? WHY WOULD CRANE BE HERE?
HE TAUGHT HERE BEFORE HE TURNED TO CRIME-- AND THAT DOLL HE SENT WAS WRAPPED IN PIECES OF THE COLLEGE NEWSPAPER.
LIKE THE JOKER, HE NEEDS TO CONFRONT ME, DELIBERATELY PROVIDING ME WITH CLUES TO FIND HIM.
E MUST BE RAZY. ALL I EVER ANTED WAS TO VOID YOU LONG NOUGH TO GET WAY WITH THE LOOT!
I KNOW. AFTER PSYCHOTICS LIKE THE JOKER AND THE SCARECROW, YOU HAVE NO IDEA HOW REFRESHING IT WAS TO DEAL WITH SOMEONE WHO WAS JUST IN IT FOR THE MONEY.
I'LL TAKE THAT AS A--
ROARRR
BATMAN!
SNAPP
NO TIME TO USE MY CAT-NIP-- I HAVE TO DRAW ITS ATTENTION!
SORRY, LEO. IT ONLY HURTS FOR A SECOND.
CAN'T BLAME YOU FOR BEING ANGRY, LEO--I'D BE, TOO, IF SOMEONE PAINTED ME WHITE!
STILL--
11

--I HOPE YOU DON'T MIND A LITTLE TRANQUILIZING POWDER IN YOUR FACE!

OF ALL THE INHUMAN--! CRANE MUST'VE DRUGGED HIM, RENDERING HIM RELATIVELY IMMOBILE ON THAT PEDESTAL--

--THEN ACTIVATED THIS ELECTRIC SHOCK STIMULUS BY REMOTE CONTROL, SENDING THE POOR THING INTO A RAGE JUST AS WE APPROACHED!

YOU REALLY LOVE THOSE ANIMALS, DON'T YOU?

THEY'RE BETTER THAN MOST PEOPLE.

I'LL REMOVE SOME OF THIS GREASEPAINT SO HE WON'T SUFFOCATE...

...AND WHEN I GET MY HANDS ON THE MANIAC WHO DID THIS, I'LL PLUCK THE STRAW OFF HIM WITH MY CAT-O'-NINE-TAILS!

NICE OF HIM TO LEAVE US A ROAD SIGN.
WE'D BE CRAZY TO FOLLOW IT.
WE DON'T HAVE MUCH CHOICE. YOU TAKE THE REAR ENTRANCE, I'LL TACKLE THE FRONT.

ODD. SELINA HAD AMNESIA DURING HER CATWOMAN YEARS--
--YET SHE SEEMS TO RECALL MUCH OF IT VERY CLEARLY INDEED! COULD SHE HAVE REGAINED HER MEMORY--AS WELL AS HER CATWOMAN PERSONALITY?
CAN I REALLY TRUST HER?
BILFINGER HALL PHYSICAL SCIENCES

GOD HELP ME, IT FEELS GOOD TO BE BACK IN ACTION... BUT...
BATMAN'S ACTING SO STRANGE, SO OBSESSED... IS THERE SOMETHING WRONG WITH HIM...
...OR AM I JUST LETTING MY FEELINGS FOR HIM MAKE ME WORRY TOO MUCH?
12

Entering the main hall, we found...
...TODAY'S CLASS WILL FOCUS ON SOME OF THE MORE ESOTERIC PHOBIAS HUMAN BEINGS ARE PREY TO...
...I'M SPEAKING, OF COURSE, OF THE FEAR OF NATURAL PHENOMENA... THINGS OVER WHICH WE HAVE NO CONTROL...
FEARS SUCH AS HELIOPHOBIA, OR AN ABNORMAL DREAD OF THE SUN...
...SIDEROPHOBIA, A FEAR OF STARS...
...EVEN COMETOPHOBIA, WHICH IS, I SHOULD THINK, RATHER SELF-EXPLANATORY!
13

MORE COMMON IS ASTRAPHOBIA, FEAR OF LIGHTNING...
Van der Graaf generator

...AND PYROPHOBIA, THE TERROR, OF COURSE, OF--
SELINA!!
CROSSBOW
ANEROMETER

--FIRE!
AAAAGHHHH!
BATMAN!

LOST SEVERAL SECONDS GETTING MY CAPE OFF... DEAR GOD, LET HIM BE ALL--
...A RELATED PHOBIA...
THAT CAN'T BE THE SAME RECORDER! WHERE--
RADIO

...IS KNOWN AS--
SQUAWWK
OH, SHUT UP!
MY GOD, WAS I THE ONLY ARCH-CRIMINAL AROUND WHO DIDN'T DELIVER LECTURES?
14

SHORTLY, IN THE CAMPUS MEDICAL CENTER...
I THOUGHT THAT OUTFIT OF YOURS WAS FLAME-RETARDANT.
RETARDANT, YES; INDESTRUCTIBLE, NO.
IF YOU HADN'T SMOTHERED THE FLAMES IN TIME--

WELL, YOU SAVED ME FROM THAT HAIL OF--
GOOD... LORD...
BAD BURN?
NO, IT'S JUST... ALL THIS... SCAR TISSUE ON YOUR BACK...

OH. THAT. OCCUPATIONAL HAZARD. FIFTEEN YEARS OF FIGHTING WILL DO THAT TO A PERSON.
DOES IT... HURT?
SOMETIMES. YOU LEARN TO LIVE WITH IT.

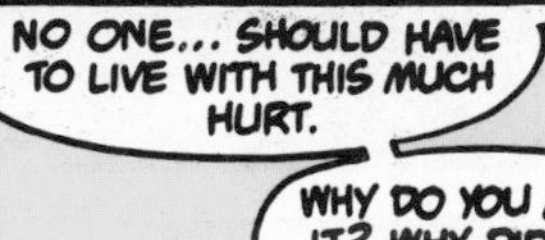
NO ONE... SHOULD HAVE TO LIVE WITH THIS MUCH HURT.
WHY DO YOU DO IT? WHY DID YOU START?
I don't know why I answered-- but I did.

MY... PARENTS... WERE KILLED BY A PETTY THIEF. WHEN I WAS TEN.
FOR SOME, THE MEMORY OF THAT WOULD FADE IN TIME. FOR ME, IT JUST GOT MORE VIVID.
I HAD TO DO SOMETHING... TO MAKE LIVING WITH IT EASIER. TO GET THE ANGER OUT.

ANGER... MAKES YOU DO STRANGE THINGS, DOESN'T IT?
SO YOU BECAME THE BATMAN... AND YOU'VE SPENT YOUR LIFE... AVENGING THEIR DEATHS?

YES. AND I WON'T LOSE ROBIN AND THE OTHERS... THE WAY I LOST MY PARENTS.
I'LL FIND THEM... IF IT TAKES MY LIFE TO DO IT!
15

And, unknown to us at the time...
TIME TO MOVE ON TO ADVANCED STUDIES, BATMAN! HA HA
MY FIRST GAS-BOMB AWAKENED YOUR SUBCONSCIOUS FEARS...
...BUT THESE CAN TRIGGER SPECIFIC PHOBIAS OF MY CHOOSING!
THE GAS HAS THE SAME RELATIVE DENSITY AS AIR ITSELF, SO IT WILL LINGER... CREATING POCKETS OF FEAR ALL OVER THE CAMPUS!
YOU'RE BOUND TO PASS THROUGH A FEW OF THEM IN YOUR SEARCH.
OF COURSE, THE EFFECTS ARE ONLY TEMPORARY...BUT COMBINED WITH YOUR ANXIETY OVER YOUR "MISSING" FRIENDS...
...I THINK WE CAN LOOK FORWARD TO A COMPLETE EMOTIONAL BREAKDOWN BEFORE THE NIGHT IS DONE!
YOU KNOW, BATMAN... IF THE SCARECROW MADE GORDON SEE WHAT HE DID LAST NIGHT... PERHAPS YOUR FRIENDS' DIS-APPEARANCE WAS ALSO SOME KIND OF--
ILLUSION? I THOUGHT OF THAT. AND DISMISSED IT. IT WAS REAL, SELINA. REAL AS THIS ROPE I'M HOLDING!
EMOTIONALLY REAL, PERHAPS, BUT--
I'M TELLING YOU, IT WAS NO TRICK! I KNOW REALITY FROM ILLUSION!
THE SUBJECT IS CLOSED!
;WHEW; THAT CUTS IT. HE'S DEFINITELY NOT HIMSELF... UNDER SOME KIND OF SPELL.
EXCEPT HOW DO I CONVINCE HIM OF--
16

OH MY...LORD... WHAT...
SELINA! WHAT'S WRONG?
SO...HIGH UP! WHAT AM I...DOING UP HERE?
OH GOD, THE GROUND, IT'S SO FAR AWAY! HOW--HOW DO I GET DOWN?
HOW DO I--
NO!!
SELINA!
EASY. I'VE GOT YOU!
THIS IS...ABSURD! I'VE NEVER BEEN AFRAID OF... HEIGHTS BEFORE...!
IT'S GONE NOW. THE SCARECROW... HE MUST BE--
SELINA! DO YOU--DO YOU FEEL IT? THE DARKNESS? CLOSING IN?
IT'S GOING TO CRUSH US... KILL US, IF WE DON'T--
NO...NOT THE DARKNESS...
LOOK WHERE WE ARE, BATMAN! LOOK AROUND US!
Sudden AGORAPHOBIA sent us running to the nearest building--
SO MUCH OPEN SPACE! WHAT FOOLS WE ARE--CRANE COULD PICK US OFF LIKE FLIES!
YOU'RE RIGHT! WE--WE'VE GOT TO FIND COVER!
17

-- THE UNIVERSITY LIBRARY!
I FEEL LIKE A FOOL! RUNNING LIKE A--
I HATE FEELING SO-- SO HELPLESS! I BECAME THE CATWOMAN SO I'D NEVER HAVE TO BE AT ANYONE'S MERCY EVER AGAIN, AND NOW LOOK AT ME!
"BECAME THE..."?

I THOUGHT AS MUCH.
THAT STORY YOU TOLD ME, SELINA... HOW A PLANE CRASH GAVE YOU AMNESIA...
IT WAS ALL A LIE, WASN'T IT?

DAMN.
I'M SORRY, BATMAN. I DIDN'T WANT TO LIE TO YOU, BUT... I JUST DIDN'T SEE ANY OTHER WAY OUT.
OUT? OUT OF WHAT?
YOU FIRST KNEW ME AS A JEWEL THIEF CALLED THE CAT. LORD, IT SEEMS A MILLION YEARS AWAY, DOESN'T IT?

WHAT YOU DIDN'T KNOW... WAS THAT I HAD BEEN THE CAT FOR OVER TWO YEARS... SINCE THE END OF MY... MARRIAGE.

YOUR--?

I'D BEEN VERY YOUNG-- IT WAS A MISTAKE, A BAD ONE. MY HUSBAND WAS VERY WEALTHY.

HE ALSO LIKED TO BEAT ME.

WHEN I DIVORCED HIM, HE RESPONDED... BY USING HIS CONNECTIONS TO TRY AND RUIN ME FINANCIALLY, PROFESSIONALLY, EMOTIONALLY!

I HATED HIM, WANTED TO GET BACK AT HIM. BUT THE ONLY LOSS HE UNDERSTOOD WAS MATERIAL LOSS, SO...
ONE NIGHT, WHEN HE WAS OUT OF TOWN, I SNEAKED ONTO HIS ESTATE... RANSACKED HIS OFFICE, HIS SAFE, THE JEWELS HE'D BOUGHT ME AND THEN KEPT...
IT FELT SO GOOD! TOO GOOD. IT WAS SO EASY TO CONTINUE... TO CONVINCE MYSELF THAT I DESERVED THE THINGS I STOLE, BECAUSE OF ALL THE PAIN I'D BEEN THROUGH!
"BUT... WHY THE CHARADE, THE AMNESIA--?"
BECAUSE I WAS TRAPPED! I WASN'T SELINA KYLE ANYMORE, I WAS THE CATWOMAN! BECAUSE I WAS THIRTY YEARS OLD AND I DIDN'T WANT TO DIE WITHOUT LOVE, WITHOUT CHILDREN--
I WANTED TO START OVER AGAIN. IS THERE SOMETHING WRONG WITH THAT?
NO.
FUNNY. WE BOTH CHOSE OUR PATHS OUT OF ANGER...AND WE BOTH FOUND OURSELVES TRAPPED. YOU LOST SELINA KYLE, AND I LOST... SOMEONE ELSE.
BUT YOU FOUND A WAY OUT, AND I... I DON'T KNOW HOW TO GET OUT.
DON'T YOU?
19

I never wanted to hold on to someone as much in my life...but...

SELINA, THIS ISN'T RIGHT. NOT WHILE ROBIN AND THE OTHERS ARE STILL MISSING. WE HAVE TO FIND THEM!

BATMAN, LISTEN TO ME--

--THE SCARECROW, HE'S AFFECTED YOUR MIND-- THEY'RE NOT REALLY--

LOOK! THERE HE IS! COME ON!

IF THEY WERE GONE, WOULDN'T IT BE IN THE PAPERS? WOULDN'T THE POLICE BE HERE? WOULDN'T--

CRANE! CRANE! YOU DEMENTED JACKAL, WHERE ARE THEY?!

OH GOD--HE'S GOING OVER THE EDGE...

BLAST YOU, CRANE, WHERE ARE--
WHAT--NO! NO! IT CAN'T-- YOU CAN'T--

BLAST YOU! BLAST YOU, WHERE ARE THEY?!
ROBIN! KATHY! LINDA!--
BATMAN, PLEASE--
I turned to face her...
20

...and was filled with a sudden fear!
NO... GO AWAY... I CAN'T... STAND... CATS...
OH NO... CRANE'S GIVEN HIM AILUROPHOBIA NOW... FEAR OF FELINES...
AND I... I FEEL SOMETHING HAPPENING TO ME, TOO...
OH GOD, NOW HE'S GOT ME, TOO! CHIROPTOPHOBIA... FEAR OF... BATS...!
B-BATMAN, WE'VE GOT... TO FIGHT THIS! AND YOU'VE GOT TO FIGHT THE DELUSION CRANE'S FED YOU!
S-SELINA... PLEASE... STAY AWAY...!
DON'T YOU SEE? ALL YOUR LIFE YOU'VE BEEN TERRIFIED OF LOSING ANYONE ELSE THE WAY YOU LOST YOUR PARENTS! SO YOU CREATED A WORLD FOR YOURSELF-- A WORLD OF CONFLICT AND CONFRONTATION--
--A WORLD WHERE NO ONE COULD EVER GET THAT CLOSE AGAIN! CRANE'S USING THAT FEAR, CAN'T YOU SEE?
THEN ALL I HAVE TO DO... IS CATCH CRANE... AND IT'LL BE ALL RIGHT...
NO! YOU'VE SPENT FIFTEEN YEARS CATCHING THE ENEMY--FIGHTING, CHASING, CAPTURING--
BUT THIS TIME THE ENEMY IS YOU! THROWING PUNCHES, SOLVING FANCY PUZZLES, THAT WON'T HELP, NOT THIS TIME!
MAYBE... MAYBE YOU'RE--
NO! YOU'RE STARTING TO FADE-- LIKE THE OTHERS--!
GOOD LORD! SELINA...?!
THEN THERE'S ONLY ONE WAY, MY DARLING. ONLY ONE WAY...
21

LOOK! THE CAT IS GONE. THERE'S NOTHING TO BE AFRAID OF ANYMORE.
NOW...IT'S YOUR TURN, MY DARLING. TO TAKE AWAY MY FEAR...
I knew what had to be done...but a lifetime of inhibition stayed my hand.
I couldn't--

I COULDN'T--

I HAD TO.

SELINA! OH GOD, SELINA, I ALMOST LOST YOU...!
BUT CRANE... HE'S STILL OUT THERE... I SHOULD CATCH HIM--
DON'T YOU ALWAYS? IT CAN WAIT.

YES...I SUPPOSE IT CAN.
22

I found and captured the scarecrow, of course... but more important... that night I found Bruce Wayne.
And I found the woman who would share my life for the next twenty years.

She's been gone, now, for many months, but it still seems impossible to me.
Her death was pointless, tragic...

...but I have long since given up trying to find meaning in death.
The meaning is in life, not death...

...and Selina's life was as full of meaning as it was of love, and spirit, and courage.

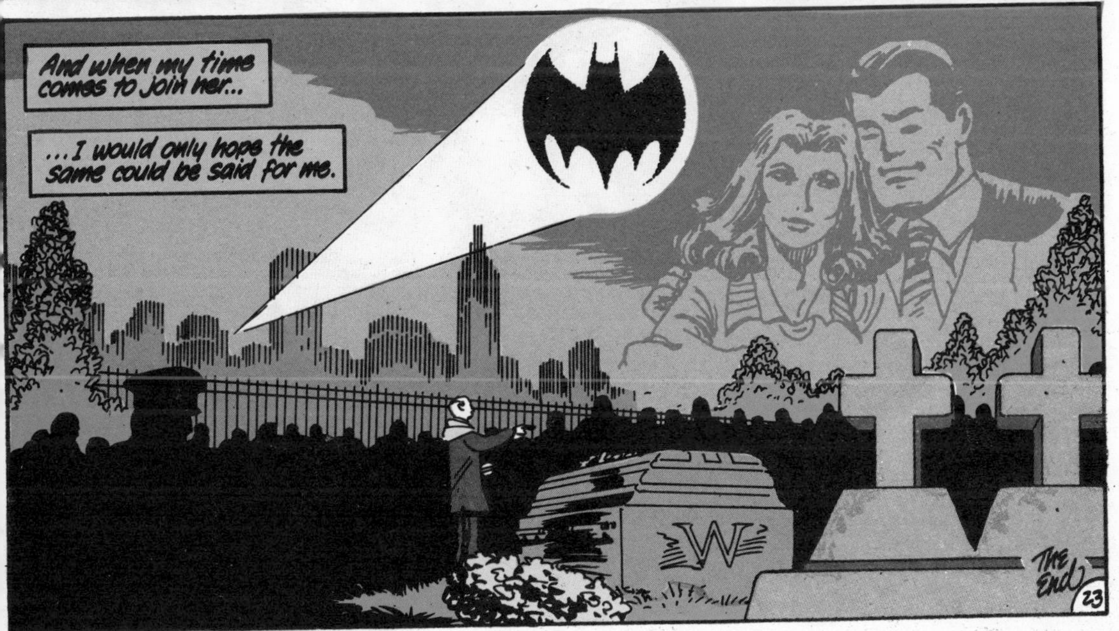
And when my time comes to join her...
...I would only hope the same could be said for me.
W
The End
23

BATMAN
SON OF THE DEMON

MIKE W. BARR
WRITER

JERRY BINGHAM
ILLUSTRATOR

JOHN COSTANZA
LETTERER

BATMAN CREATED BY
BOB KANE

THEN:
THE EARTH SCREAMS, LIKE A WOMAN GIVING BIRTH...
...AND THE OLD/NEWBORN STALKS OFF, HIS SHOULDERS HUNCHED...
...AS IF AGAINST THE ONSLAUGHT OF SOME COMING STORM.
NOW:
"SWAT-3 TO GOTHAM-1, WE HAVE SECURED POSITION AT THE BACK OF THE GOTHAM CHEMICAL PLANT. WILL WE CHARGE THE PLANT, REPEAT, WILL WE--"
GOTHAM-1 TO SWAT-3, NEGATIVE. UNDER NO CONDITIONS ARE YOU TO ASSAULT THE PLANT...

"...THE INSURGENTS HAVE HOSTAGES, AND ACCESS TO DEADLY CHEMICALS. WE ARE AWAITING ARRIVAL OF NEGOTIATING TEAMS. TAKE NO ACTION, REPEAT, NO ACTION."
LOOKS LIKE THEY BELIEVE US, THEY'RE STAYING AWAY.
THEY'D BETTER. IF IT RAINS, AND WE RELEASE THAT TOXIC GUNK INTO THE WATER SUPPLY... WELL, THAT'S ALL SHE WROTE.
BACK IN LINE, YOU! NOW!
ANY WORD ON THE SEARCH PARTY? THEY HAVING ANY LUCK BACK IN THE WAREHOUSE?
NO WORD FROM THEM YET. WE MAY NEED TO BUY A LITTLE MORE TIME.
YOU. C'MERE, BITCH!
P-PLEASE, DON'T...!
MARK, WHAT ARE WE GOING TO DO...?
DON'T WORRY ABOUT THAT, NANCY, KEEP CALM. THINK OF THE BABY--
LISTEN UP, COPS! I GOTTA FAT LADY HERE! YOU TRY ANYTHING, SHE BUYS IT! YOU FOLLOW?
WELL?
PLEASE, THERE IS NO NEED TO HARM THE HOSTAGES! PROFESSIONAL NEGOTIATORS ARE ON THEIR WAY!
"SCREW YOUR 'NEGOTIATORS,' MAN!"

HAVE IT YOUR WAY, JUNIOR...
...BUT I GUARANTEE, YOU WON'T LIKE THE ALTERNATIVE...!
HURT HER? YOU KIDDIN'? I LIKE HER...
ARE YOU ALL RIGHT, NANCY? DID HE HURT YOU?
E HER SO MUCH, ONNA GIVE HER THING SHE HASN'T FOR A WHILE, RIGHT...?
GASP
DON'T WORRY, YOU'RE GONNA LIKE IT, TOO... I PROMISE...
N-NO... SOB
DAMN IT, YOU CAN'T--
I CAN DO ANYTHING I WANT, PAL-- MY PIECE SAYS SO...
MARK!
WHAKT
...AND WHAT I WANT MOST...
SNIK

"...IS TO BRAND THIS BITCH... PUT HIS MARK ON HER..."
CLUD
...MAKE HER ONE OF-- UNNNGH!
WHO DID THAT? WHO?
BRRRRRT
THERE! IN THE SHADOWS! GET HIM!
HSSSST
LOOK OUT, HE'S THROWING SOMETHING--!
GAS! ;KA GET TH MASKS... ON THE WA
NO! SOMEBODY'S ;KAFF; CUT 'EM!
TELL THE SEARCH PARTY... SOMEONE'S AFTER ;KAFF; AFTER USSSS...

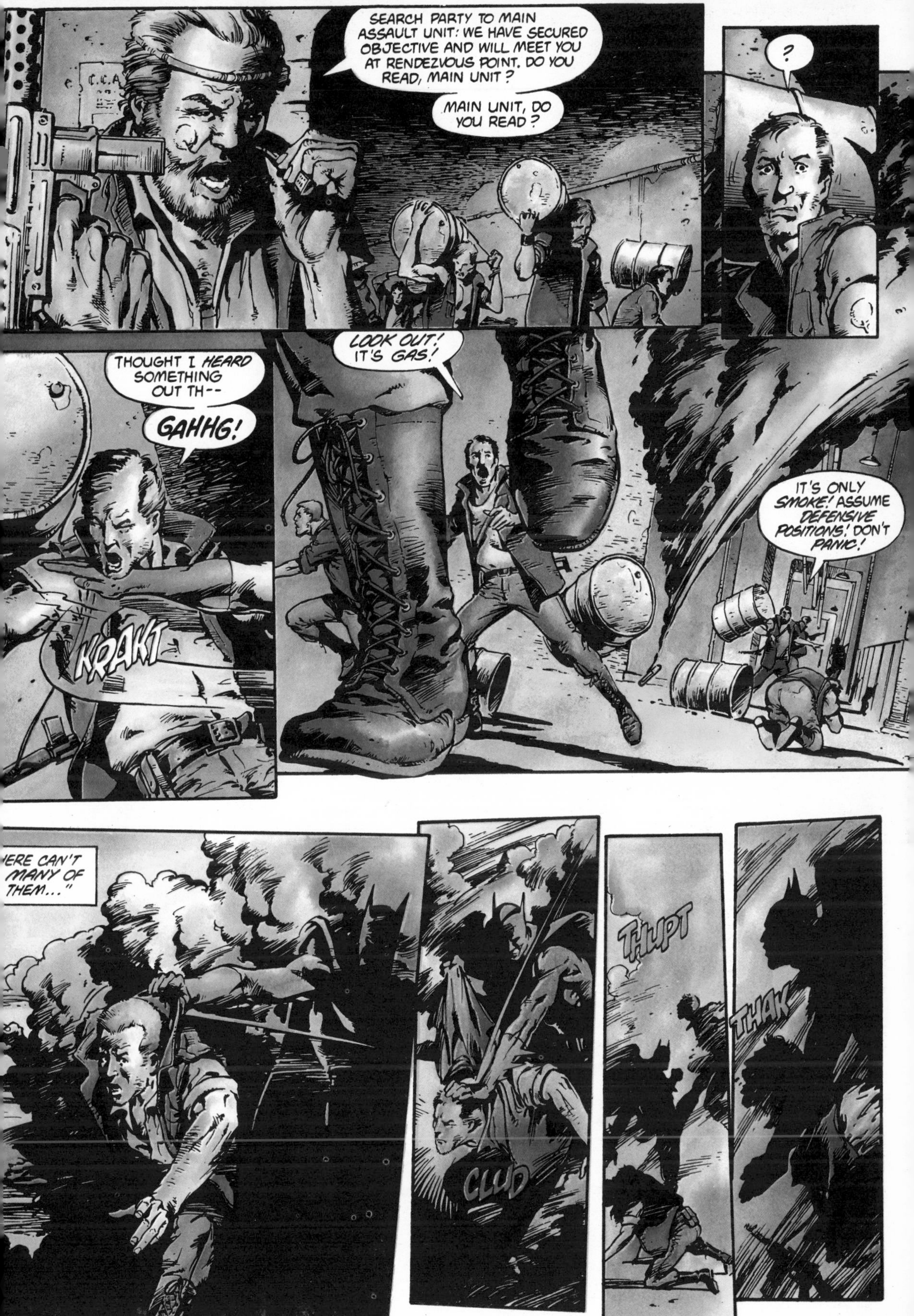

SEARCH PARTY TO MAIN ASSAULT UNIT: WE HAVE SECURED OBJECTIVE AND WILL MEET YOU AT RENDEZVOUS POINT. DO YOU READ, MAIN UNIT?

MAIN UNIT, DO YOU READ?

?

THOUGHT I *HEARD* SOMETHING OUT TH--

GAHHG!

KRAKT

LOOK OUT! IT'S GAS!

IT'S ONLY *SMOKE!* ASSUME *DEFENSIVE POSITIONS!* DON'T *PANIC!*

"...IT'S PROBABLY JUST ONE MAN...
"...WE CAN HANDLE HIM! STAY CALM...
"REMEMBER YOUR PARTNER...
BRRRRRT
"...ALWAYS KEEP HIM IN VIEW!"
HE'S ONE MAN, ONLY--
JESUS...!

THE HOSTAGES--!

LISTEN TO ME, WHOEVER YOU ARE! YOU'VE GOT FIVE SECONDS TO SHOW YOURSELF...
...OR THIS WOMAN BUYS IT! CLEAR?
FIVE...

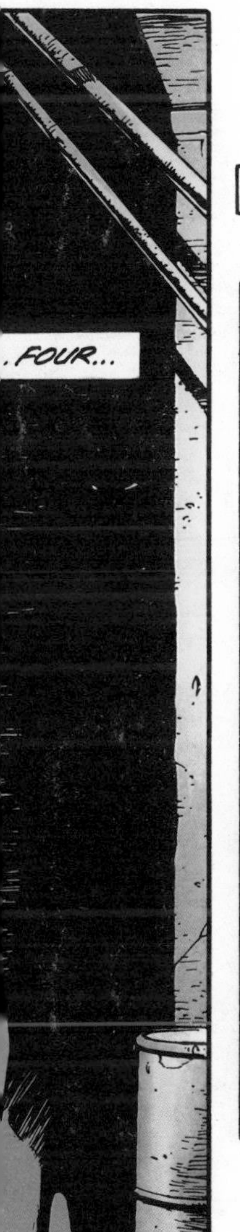
.FOUR...

"...THREE...

"...TWO...
"...ONE."
TIME'S UP.

YEAH... FOR YOU!
BRRRRT
UNH
NOOOO--!
FSSSST
AIEEEEEEE
GOD DAMN YOU...!
TOXIC: CONTENTS UNDER PRESSURE
LOOKS LIKE HE GOT YOU FIRST.
KLIK SEARCH PARTY AND MAIN UNIT, DO YOU READ...?

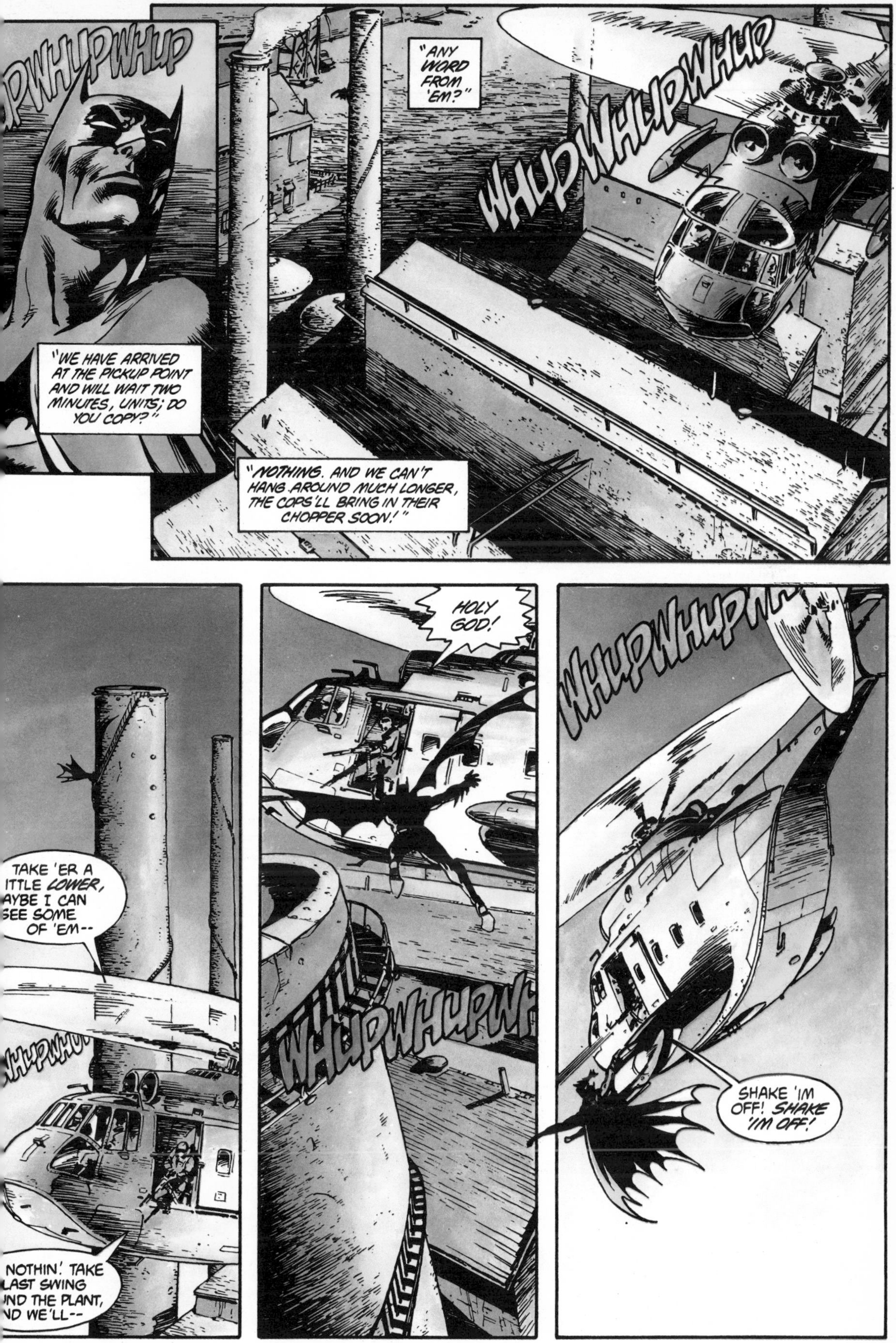

PWHUPWHUP

"ANY WORD FROM 'EM?"

WHUPWHUPWHUP

"WE HAVE ARRIVED AT THE PICKUP POINT AND WILL WAIT TWO MINUTES, UNITS; DO YOU COPY?"

"NOTHING. AND WE CAN'T HANG AROUND MUCH LONGER, THE COPS'LL BRING IN THEIR CHOPPER SOON!"

WHAT'RE YOU, BLIND? CAN'T YOU HIT ANYTHING WITH THAT?
STOP IT, YOU TWO! SAVE THAT FOR--
THERE! GET HIM BEFORE HE--
YOU WANNA COME BACK HERE AND TRY?

HE'S HERE! HE'S--
UNNNGH

HELP ME! GET HIM OFF ME!
NO! YOU'RE NOT TAKING ME...

YOU'RE NOT-- UNNNH!
BRRRRT

WHUPWHUPWHUP
WOOOSH
DAMN IT, WHERE'S OUR CHOPPER? THEIR FUEL TANK'S GONE UP! FORGET ABOUT PRISONERS, BATMAN--
"--GET OUT OF THERE, BEFORE..."
WHUPWHUPWHUP
SERGEANT--
"YESSIR?"
WHUPWHUPWHUP WHOOOM
CANCEL THE CALL FOR THE AIR BACKUP... TELL THE HARBOR PATROL TO START DRAGGING THE RIVER, INSTEAD.
YESSIR.

"WAIT! SOMETHING'S MOVING--!
"STEP ON THAT HARBOR PATROL BOAT, SERGEANT--AND WAIT FOR ME!"
"YESSIR!"
HOW GASP HOW ARE THE HOSTAGES, COMMISSIONER?
"FINE, BATMAN... GOOD WORK."
"NOT GOOD ENOUGH, OR I WOULD HAVE FOUND THEIR FLIGHT PLANS. LET'S GET BACK, I WANT A CRACK AT THOSE PRISONERS."
G.C.P.D.
AND WHAT SEEMS TO BE THE TROUBLE WITH YOU?
I'M SHOT. I'M BLEEDING.
WELL, LET'S HAVE A LOOK AND SEE WHAT WE--
"THAT MAN CAN WAIT, DOCTOR."
I BEG YOUR--
I SAID, HE CAN WAIT--
HE--HE HAS SOME RIGHTS, YOU KNOW.
"THAT WOMAN HAS MORE."
NO NEED TO BE SO SNOTTY.

E TWO
ALL
MA'AM?
WHY... ER... YES... THANK YOU FOR ALL YOUR... YOUR HELP, BATMAN...
AND YOUR CHILD?
I... I THINK HE'S FINE... THANK YOU...
GOOD.
...A CHILD NEEDS HIS PARENTS... IT'S A TERRIBLE THING FOR A CHILD TO HAVE TO GROW UP ALONE.
COMMISSIONER, I'LL LET YOUR MEN HANDLE THE INITIAL INTERROGATION. I'LL STOP BY LATER.
BATMAN, YOU'D BETTER HAVE THAT WOUND LOOKED AT, BEFORE--
I'LL STOP BY LATER.
NOT SMART, DIVING INTO THE GOTHAM RIVER WITH AN OPEN WOUND. THAT RIVER'S A SEWER, HAS BEEN FOR YEARS.
A GRANT FROM THE WAYNE FOUNDATION MAY BE JUST WHAT THE CITY'S ENVIRONMENTAL PROTECTION BOARD NEEDS...

... BUT WHAT I NEED IS ABOUT THIRTY STITCHES AND A MILE OF GAUZE. THAT WILL HAVE TO WAIT UNTIL I GET HOME... MAYBE I'LL WALK FOR AWHILE... TAKE IT EASY...
... OR MAYBE I'LL CALL ALFRED...
... HAVE HIM COME AND PICK ME...
... UNHHH...
HIS EYES CLOSE...
... AND EVERY TIME HIS EYES CLOSE, HE WATCHES HIS PARENTS DIE.
DAD? MOM?
THIS'LL SHUT YOU UP!
BANG
WAYNE
I SWEAR -SNIF- I'LL SPEND MY LIFE MAKING SURE NO ONE HAS TO SUFFER LIKE YOU DID...
... OR LIKE HE SUFFERED... GROWING UP ALONE...

DENIED A NORMAL LIFE
FAMILY AND FRIENDS...
IVEN BY A FORCE
EATER THAN HIMSELF...
I HAVE CHOSEN YOU, BRUCE WAYNE...
"...YOU ARE MINE, AND YOU WILL BECOME ME... I AM YOUR TRUE FATHER... AND YOU ARE MY SON."
FATHER? NO, I--
--I...
? THE BATCAVE. BUT HOW--?
ALFRED? ALFRED, ARE YOU--
YOUR MANSERVANT IS UPSTAIRS, BELOVED, LEAVING YOU TO MY TENDER MERCIES -- AND MY MEDICAL TRAINING.
TALIA?
YES.
I FOLLOWED YOU FROM THE FACTORY, BELOVED... I KNEW YOU WOULD NEED ASSISTANCE, EVEN THOUGH YOU WOULD NOT ADMIT IT YOURSELF.

BUT WHAT WERE YOU DOING AT THE FACTORY? THOSE WEREN'T YOUR FATHER'S MEN, OR I WOULD HAVE--
NO. I HAVE, HOWEVER, AN INTEREST IN THEIR LEADER.
THEIR LEADER? THEN YOU KNOW WHO HE--
HELLO, ALFRED.
AH, MASTER BRUCE, YOU HAVE AWAKENED.
KEEP IT HOT, ALFRED, I'VE GOT WORK TO DO.
BELOVED, YOU CANNOT MOVE IN YOUR CONDITION. YOUR WOUND--
I AM FORCED TO AGREE WITH MISS TALIA, SIR. I FORBID--
I DON'T RECALL ASKING FOR A VOTE.
:SIGH: YOU CAN BE MOST EXASPERATING AT TIMES.
INDEED.
PLEASE, MISS TALIA... TAKE CARE OF HIM.
I WILL, ALFRED.
"WE'VE JUST GOTTEN SOME INFORMATION FROM INTERPOL THAT PUTS THE WHOLE THING IN PERSPECTIVE, BATMAN..."
...IF YOU'RE SURE WE CAN TALK FREELY IN FRONT OF...ER...
WOULD YOU PREFER I LEAVE, COMMISSIONER GORDON?
SHE'S STAYING, GORDON.

"Y WELL. ALL THE TERRORISTS CAPTURED
E THE SAME MARK-- THE LETTER "Q"
VED INTO THEIR FLESH. WE THINK THEY
RK FOR A MAN NAMED QAYIN--"
A TERRORIST AND MURDERER... LIKE HIS NAMESAKE, CAIN.
"YES. QAYIN IS A REAL MYSTERY MAN, HE'S NEVER BEEN CAPTURED, NOT EVEN PHOTOGRAPHED. INTERPOL HAS LINKED QAYIN WITH THIS MAN--"
GENERAL YOSSID OF GOLATIA. HE RECENTLY SIGNED A PACT WITH AMERICA AFTER YEARS OF COURTING BOTH THE USA AND THE USSR. DO YOU THINK HE AND QAYIN ARE ALLIES?
LAKE SEVAN
KARASU
ARAS
MTS.
KARAKÖSE
IGDIR
ARARAT
HAMUR
TUTAK
HINIS
U.S. ARMY BASE
MAKU
ARAKS
ERCIS
GOLATIA
SUPHAN DAG
LAKE VAN
L. ERCEK
IRA
VAN
SALMAS
TARVAN
BITLIS
GEVAS
GURPINAR
IF THEY ARE, THEY'RE BIRDS OF A FEATHER. YOSSID TOOK OVER GOLATIA TEN YEARS AGO, IN A BLOODY COUP, AND HAS REMAINED RULER EVER SINCE.
QAYIN MAY HAVE A BASE SOMEWHERE IN GOLATIA, WITH YOSSID'S BLESSING.
SOMEONE'S GOING TO HAVE TO FIND HIM AND STOP HIM.
I KNOW.
WHAT'S THE WORD ON THOSE BARRELS QAYIN'S MEN WERE TRYING TO HEIST, COMMISSIONER? WHAT WAS IN THEM?

NOT WHAT YOU'D EXPECT THEM TO MAKE A GRAB FOR... NOT EXPLOSIVES, OR POISON, NOTHING LIKE THAT.
IT WAS AN EXPERIMENTAL PREPARATION, TO BE USED IN-- BLAST IT, WHERE IS THAT REPORT...?

HERE WE ARE. PLUVICULTURE, THAT'S WHAT THE CHEMICAL WAS TO BE USED FOR... WHATEVER THAT IS.
I SEE.
YOU DO?

PLUVICULTURE IS THE SCIENC OF RAINMAKIN COMMISSIONE AND WHAT I D KNOW, I CAN LOOK UP.

"BLAINE-PEARSON RESEARCH. BELOVED, IS THAT DR. HARRIS BLAINE?"

"THAT'S RIGHT, TALIA. YOU WAIT HERE, I WON'T BE LONG."

BLAINE-PEARSON RESEARCH FACILITY

EXCELLENT SECURITY SYSTEM, IT TOOK ME ALMOST 30 SECONDS TO BYPASS IT. AS I RECALL, THIS IS DR. BLAINE'S OFFICE--

DR. BLAINE?

DEAD. BUT ONLY SECONDS AGO. THE KILLER MAY STILL BE AROUND...

THE WEAPON STILL IS.
TTER TASTE, BUT SUGAR
THE COFFEE WOULD HIDE
AT... IN SECONDS, IT
WOULD BE OVER.

POISON
STRYC

"YES, COFFEE FROM THAT PERCOLATOR IN THE CORNER. SOMEONE SPIKED IT AND LEFT. BLAINE SAT DOWN, TOOK A GULP... AND THAT WAS IT.

"... BUT WHO RIPPED A PAGE FROM THIS ASTRONOMY TEXT? THE KILLER? NO, HE WOULD HAVE JUST TAKEN THE BOOK WITH HIM, RATHER THAN CALL ATTENTION TO IT...

"... BUT BLAINE WOULD HAVE HAD TIME TO RIP IT OUT BEFORE THE POISON TOOK FULL EFFECT..."

... AND THERE'S ONLY ONE REASON WHY A DYING MAN WOULD TEAR A PAGE FROM A BOOK.

WITH NO WRITING IMPLEMENTS AROUND, IT WAS THE ONLY WAY HE COULD NAME HIS KILLER!

"? A STAR CHART... OF THE CONSTELLATION PERSEUS... FOCUSING ON THE BINARY STAR...

"DR. BLAINE? DR. BLAINE!"

"... ALGOL?"

ALGOL

DR. BLAINE, ARE YOU ALL--OH!
SLAM
CALL COMMISSIONER GORDON OF THE GOTHAM POLICE.
I...
GO.

DAD?
OH, MY GOD. HE FINALLY DID IT!
HE... HE'S DEAD?
BLAINE

"WHO ARE YOU?"
PEARSON, JOHN PEARSON. I'M HARRIS' PARTNER. HE HANDLES THE LAB SCIENCE, AND I HANDLE THE COMPUTER PROGRAMMING.

"YOU'RE BLAINE'S SON."
HARRIS BLAINE, JR....I-I WAS DAD'S ASSISTANT, HE WAS TRAINING ME TO TAKE HIS PLACE SOME... SOMEDAY...
OH, DAD...
"AND YOU?"
PROFESSOR MARGARET TRASK. I DON'T REALLY THINK WE SHOULD BE ANSWERING QUESTIONS WITHOUT A LAWYER--
PROBABLY NOT. WHAT WERE YOU WORKING ON, PROFESSOR?
I WAS WORKING DR. BLAINE -- S ON HIS PLUVICU EXPERIMENTS
HAS ANYTHING IN HERE BEEN DISTURBED? ARE HIS NOTES STILL HERE?
LET ME CHECK...

"...YES, HER THEY ARE.

PLUVICULTURE

"THEN HIS KILL DIDN'T TAKE THEM."

KILLER? HE WASN'T MURDERED. HIS OFFICE WAS LOCKED FROM THE INSIDE. HE MUST HAVE... MUST HAVE...

NO! MY FATHER NEVER WOULD HAVE KILLED HIMSELF!

BUSINESS HAS BEEN BADLY FOR US, HARR YOUR FATHER WAS TA THAT VERY HARD.

THE KILLER WANTED HIS CRIME TO LOOK LIKE A SUICIDE, BUT YOUR FATHER WAS MURDERED, MR. BLAINE...

...MURDERED BY A
AN WHOSE PATH BOTH
UR FATHER AND I
AVE CROSSED BEFORE.
I'M SORRY. BUT IF IT MEANS ANYTHING TO YOU...
JUSTICE WILL BE DONE. I PROMISE.
"WHAT DO YOU STUDY SO INTENTLY, BELOVED? IT IS A CLUE OF SOME SORT?"
"IT IS, TALIA..."
GOL" IS A STAR
SE NAME LITERALLY
S "THE GHOUL,"
THE DEMON."
"BELOVED, YOU DO NOT SUSPECT--"
YES. HE'S ALIVE, ISN'T HE, TALIA?
EVEN IF HE IS, MY FATHER DID NOT TAKE THE LIFE OF HARRIS BLAINE.
PROVE IT TO ME, TALIA. TELL ME WHAT YOUR INTEREST IS IN THIS WHOLE AFFAIR...AND IN QAYIN.
I... I CAN SAY NO MORE.

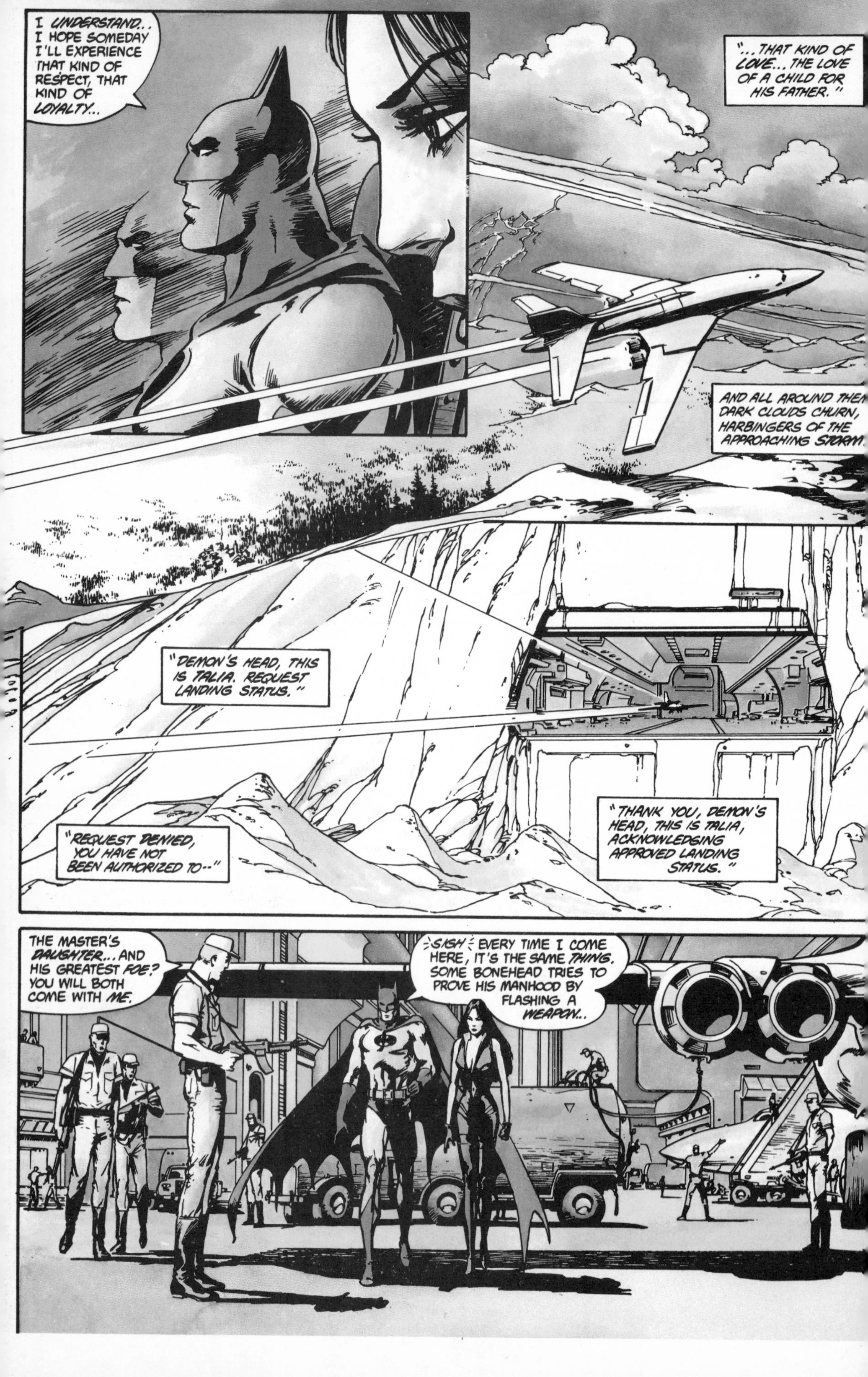
I UNDERSTAND... I HOPE SOMEDAY I'LL EXPERIENCE THAT KIND OF RESPECT, THAT KIND OF LOYALTY...
"...THAT KIND OF LOVE... THE LOVE OF A CHILD FOR HIS FATHER."
AND ALL AROUND THEM DARK CLOUDS CHURN, HARBINGERS OF THE APPROACHING STORM
"DEMON'S HEAD, THIS IS TALIA. REQUEST LANDING STATUS."
"REQUEST DENIED, YOU HAVE NOT BEEN AUTHORIZED TO--"
"THANK YOU, DEMON'S HEAD, THIS IS TALIA, ACKNOWLEDGING APPROVED LANDING STATUS."
THE MASTER'S DAUGHTER... AND HIS GREATEST FOE? YOU WILL BOTH COME WITH ME.
SIGH EVERY TIME I COME HERE, IT'S THE SAME THING. SOME BONEHEAD TRIES TO PROVE HIS MANHOOD BY FLASHING A WEAPON...

ND I PROVE MINE, BY TAKING IT AWAY FROM HIM.
GAAAK--!
SOMEDAY, YOU BOYS WILL LEARN.
THERE IS GRIND, MY FATHER'S BODYGUARD... HE CANNOT BE FAR A--
HUSH, TALIA... LISTEN...
"LET US BEGIN THE FINAL REACTIVATION PHASE, DR. WELTMANN."
THAT VOICE... I KNEW HE WAS STILL ALIVE...
...BUT I DIDN'T LET MYSELF BELIEVE IT...
"...UNTIL NOW."
TAKE CARE H THOSE CHEMICALS THEY ARE SPILLED, J SHALL BATHE IN THEM!
DO NOT WORRY, MASTER; SOON THE LAZARUS PIT WILL SERVE YOU AS IT HAS SO MANY TIMES BEFORE.
EXCELLENT, DR. WELTMANN. YOU HAVE DONE WELL.

"RA'S."
WHO--?
AH, THE DETECTIVE...
...I MIGHT HAVE KNOWN YOU WOULD INTRUDE, EVEN AS I PREPARE MY GREATEST CAMPAIGN.
AND WHO ACCOMPANIES YOU?
HELLO, FATHER.
IS IT YOUR INTENTION TO BETRAY ME AGAIN, AS YOU DID THE LAST TIME WE MET?
I WOULD NOT HOPE TO... BUT I DO WHAT I MUST, FATHER, AS DO YOU.
CLAP CLAP
SPOKEN LIKE FLESH OF MY FLESH! YOU WILL DINE WITH ME.
GRIND! ALERT THE SERVANTS.
FILTHY AMERICAN!
YOU DON'T LOOK LIKE YOU'RE GETTING ENOUGH RED MEAT, GRIND-- I'LL TRY TO SAVE YOU A BONE.

YOU DO NOT EAT, DETECTIVE. IS THE MEAL DISTASTEFUL TO YOU?
I CAN'T ACCEPT A MAN'S HOSPITALITY UNDER FALSE PRETENSES, RA'S. YOU MENTIONED "YOUR GREATEST CAMPAIGN." I HAVE TO KNOW WHAT THAT IS.
I SEE. IT MAY BE A MISSION IN WHICH THE THREE OF US FIND OURSELVES AS ALLIES... AND IT MAY BE MY LAST MISSION, FOR SHOULD I PERISH IN THIS ENDEAVOR, THE LAZARUS PIT MAY NO LONGER BE ABLE TO RESTORE ME.
"AND SHOULD THAT BE THE CASE, ARE YOU SEEING THAT ALL YOUR OLD ENEMIES PRECEDE YOU?"
"YOU MAY SPEAK MORE CLEARLY THAN THAT, DETECTIVE."
"LIKE DR. HARRIS BLAINE."
"BLAINE. HE ONCE HAD THE PRESUMPTION TO JOIN YOUR FORCES AGAINST ME, DID HE NOT?"
HE DID. HE'S BEEN MURDERED, AND I HAVE REASON TO BELIEVE YOU WERE BEHIND IT.
I ASSURE YOU, DETECTIVE, I WAS IN NO WAY INVOLVED IN BLAINE'S DEATH. INDEED, THE RENDERING USELESS OF SUCH AN INTELLECT IS DISTASTEFUL TO ME."
YOU'LL UNDERSTAND IF I NEED TO BE CONVINCED.

I HAVE TO BE CERTAIN ABOUT THIS, RA'S. WITH YOUR RESOURCES, YOU CAN DO NEARLY ANYTHING YOU SET YOUR MIND TO. I'D SUSPECT TALIA, IF I HAD A LOGICAL REASON...
...BUT SHE WAS WITH ME WHEN BLAINE TOOK THE POISON THAT KILLED HIM. AND BESIDES, THERE'S A THIRD PARTY INVOLVED IN THIS...
...TELL ME, RA'S, HAVE YOU EVER HAD ANY DEALINGS WITH A MAN NAMED QAYIN?
QAYIN? YOU DARE MENTION HIS NAME TO ME?
THEN THERE IS A CONNECTION?
"FATHER, HE DOESN'T KNOW..."
MOST ASSUREDLY, DETECTIVE. QAYIN IS THE MURDERER OF MY WIFE.
YOUR WIFE?
MY MOTHER. I BARELY REMEMBER HER...

SHE WAS
EAUTIFUL..."
SHE REMAINS SO, IN OUR HEARTS, DAUGHTER. NEVER FORGET THAT.
"PUT BRIEFLY, DETECTIVE, DURING THE LAST WORLD WAR, I HAD AN ORGANIZATION OF MY OWN, WHICH I OFTEN USED TO COMBAT THE AXIS POWERS.
"WE HAD MUCH TO FIGHT FOR IN THOSE DAYS. YEARS EARLIER, MY TRUSTED LIEUTENANT, LANDOR, HAD BEEN BLESSED WITH A SON, AND I HAD BEEN MADE HIS GODFATHER. I CARED FOR HIM WHEN HIS PARENTS WERE OFF ON MISSIONS...
"...SUCH AS THE MISSION I SENT THEM ON TO THE JAPANESE CITY OF HIROSHIMA...
"...ON AUGUST 6, 1945."
A DATE OF SOME HISTORICAL SIGNIFICANCE, I THINK YOU WILL RECALL, DETECTIVE.
"YOUNG QUINLAN HAD COME WITH ME TO MEET HIS PARENTS, AND I HAD TO PHYSICALLY RESTRAIN HIM FROM JOINING THEM.

"I THOUGHT THE BOY'S HEART WOULD BREAK. WORSE, IT HARDENED...
"...FROM THAT DAY FORWARD, HE BEC MOODY, FATALISTIC, OBSESSED WITH SUBJECT OF DEATH. HE DEMANDED CALL HIM QAYIN, AFTER A VARIATION THE NAME OF THE FIRST MURDERER.
"MY BELOVED WIFE, MELISANDE, AND I COULD DO NOTHING TO RELIEVE HIS MELANCHOLY. MELISANDE, WHO WAS, AT THAT TIME, CARRYING TALIA, BEGGED ME TO EXPEL HIM FROM OUR HOUSEHOLD.
BIBLE
"I FELT THAT I COULD NOT. WOUL THAT I HAD.
"ONE NIGHT, WHEN TALIA WAS ONLY A CHILD, MELISANDE CAUGHT QAYIN PROWLING ABOUT THE SECRET ROOM WHERE I KEPT AN EARLIER VERSION OF THE PIT.
"AND TALIA SAW IT?"
YES...
"HORRIFIED--FOR THAT ROOM WAS FORBIDDEN TO ALL, SAVE ME--QAYIN FLED... AND IN DOING SO, PUSHED MY BELOVED INTO THE PIT.
"HER DEATH WAS INSTANTANEOUS..."

BUT QAYIN ESCAPED THAT
T, AND VIRTUALLY DISAPPEARED.
YEARS WE COULD FIND NO
ACE OF HIM. BUT NOW HE
IS BACK...
...AND I WISH TO KILL HIM. NOT ONLY TO AVENGE MY MOTHER...
...BUT TO ALSO PROVE TO MY FATHER THAT I STILL LOVE HIM.
HERE IS NO NEED TO PROVE
AT I ALREADY KNOW, TALIA.
FORGIVE YOU YOUR PAST
DISOBEDIENCES.
HOWEVER, WITH THE THREAT
F QAYIN LOOMING ON THE
ORIZON, PERHAPS IT IS TIME
TOOK AN ALLY TO DEFEAT
HIM-- YOU, DETECTIVE.
AYIN MENACES YOUR
RLD AS WELL AS MINE,
ECTIVE. I FEEL IT WILL
QUIRE ALL OUR SKILLS
O OVERCOME HIM...
...AND THERE IS NO GUARANTEE THAT WE WILL NOT MEET DEATH IN THE BARGAIN.
OU ACCEPT
OFFER?
YES.
...AND WITH THIS POSITION COMES THE HAND OF MY DAUGHTER. TO ACCEPT THE FIRST IS TO ACCEPT THE SECOND, THERE IS NO MIDDLE GROUND.
DO YOU STILL ACCEPT MY OFFER, DETECTIVE?
"I DO."
YOU DO? I SUPPOSE
HOULD BE FLATTERED
T YOU DEIGN TO
MEMBER ME
ER ALL THIS
IME?
THERE'S NEVER BEEN ANY ROOM IN MY LIFE FOR A WOMAN... THAT'S WHAT I TOLD MYSELF, AFTER EVERY LIAISON I'VE EVER KNOWN SHATTERED...
..., MAYBE THAT'S JUST WHAT I WANTED TO BELIEVE. I'VE TRIED TO FORGET YOU, GOD KNOWS...

...BUT I CAN'T. I NEVER COULD.
I NEVER WILL.
I ACCEPT YOUR APOLOGY...
"...MY BELOVED."
THIS IS OUR CHAMBER, OURS ALONE. I HAVE BEEN SAVING IT FOR YOU.
TALIA, YOUR FATHER IS A VERY PROPER MAN, IN HIS OWN WAY. SHOULDN'T THERE BE A CEREMONY OF SOME SORT?
:SIGH: BELOVED, HAVE YOU SO QUICKLY FORGOTTEN? THERE ALREADY HAS BEEN...
"...MY FATHER ONCE MARRIED US, IN AN ATTEMPT TO KEEP YOU FROM INTERFERING WITH HIS PLANS.
"IN HIS COUNTRY, ONLY THE CONSENT OF THE BRIDE IS REQUIRED FOR A MARRIAGE..."

I
I REMEMBER, BUT IT'S HARD FOR ME TO CONSIDER THAT MARRIAGE REAL.
BELOVED, YOU GIVE TOO MUCH THOUGHT TO WHAT IS "REAL," AND WHAT IS NOT, TO WHAT IS "TRUE," AND WHAT IS "FALSE..."
I REALIZE THAT IS YOUR WAY, BUT JUST THIS ONCE, ACCEPT THINGS AS THEY ARE...
FOREGO CONTROL, DISCIPLINE...
...JUST ONCE, LET YOURSELF GO...
"...AND TAKE ME WITH YOU."

HIGH OVER THE MOUNTAINS, THERE IS A LOW MOAN OF THUNDER...
... AS EBON CLOUDS GATHER...
... FORETOKENING THE COMING STORM.
ATTENTION, ALL OF YOU. FROM THIS DAY FORTH, I HEREBY DESIGNATE THE BATMAN AS MY SECOND-IN-COMMAND... MY SON. OBEY HIM AS YOU WOULD ME.
AND THEY DO...
... AS IN THE FOLLOWING WEEKS, THE WORLD'S MOST SKILLED COMBATANT TEACHES RA'S AL GHUL'S ASSASSINS TECHNIQUES IN NON-LETHAL WARFARE OF WHICH EVEN THEY ARE IGNORANT...
... WHILE STILL FINDING TIME TO BE A NEWLYWED, A ROLE IN WHICH HE IS QUITE UNSKILLED...
... BUT--T
DELIGH
QUICKL
LEAR

OLATIA, A SMALL MEDITERRANEAN
OUNTRY, HAS ONLY TWO FEATURES
F NOTE: A STRATEGIC POSITION,
UST SOUTH OF THE SOVIET UNION...

WE HAVE *ARRIVED*, GENERAL YOSSID.

...AND ITS NAME, TAKEN FROM THE BIBLICAL GIANT. IT RESEMBLES THE HISTORIC GOLIATH IN NEITHER STRENGTH NOR *SIZE*, BUT WHERE THERE'S A *WILL*, THERE'S A *WAY*...

...AND THIS MAN IS GOLATIA'S WILL.

VERY GOOD.

HELP ME, PLEASE...
KILL ME... PLEASE...

HERE YOU ARE, GENERAL YOSSID.
"WELCOME, GENERAL YOSSID..."
QAYIN? ARE YOU THERE? THIS DAMNED DARKNESS...

I RATHER LIKE IT, MYSELF...
...IT TENDS TO MAKE THE PRISONERS MORE TRACTABLE.

"YOU LOOK A LITTLE PEAKED, GENERAL. DON'T TELL ME THE SCREAMS DISTURB YOU?"
IT IS NOT THE SCREAMS, QAYIN, IT IS THE CHANCE THAT THE AMERICANS WILL FIND OUT YOU AND I ARE ALLIED. THEY HAVE A RATHER NAIVE VIEW OF HUMAN RIGHTS.

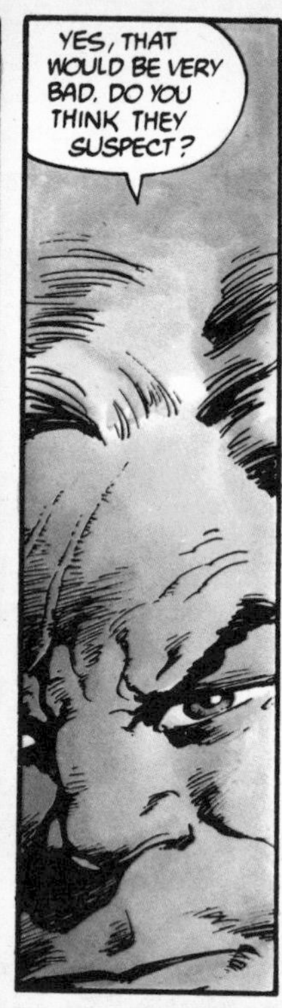
YES, THAT WOULD BE VERY BAD. DO YOU THINK THEY SUSPECT?

IF THEY DO, THEY VALUE GOLATIA'S STRATEGIC POSITION MORE. BUT I THINK WE HAVE NO REASON TO FEAR; THE LAUNCH IS SCHEDULED FOR TWO DAYS.
EXCELLENT. IT GOES WELL, THEN.

...BUT YOU ARE OVERSTEPPING YOUR BOUNDS, QAYIN, I DID NOT AUTHORIZE THE MURDER OF THE AMERICAN...WHAT WAS HIS NAME...?
BLAINE. BUT MY AGENT FELT IT WAS NECESSARY, GENERAL... AND I CONCURRED. DO NOT WORRY, YOUR TIME -- GOLATIA'S TIME -- IS ALMOST AT HAND.
SOON YOU WILL NO LONGER HAVE TO CURRY THE AMERICANS' FAVOR FOR PROTECTION FROM THE SOVIETS...

...SOON YOU WILL HAVE POWER OF YOUR OWN!
TO OUR MUTUAL STRENGTH, MY FRIEND.
OUR MUTUAL SUPERIORITY, GENERAL.

YOU FOOL.

MR. QAYIN? MR. QAYIN, I HAVE NEWS FOR YOU.
WHAT IS IT, HALLAM? IF IT IS ABOUT THE SATELLITE--
NO, MR. QAYIN, I HAVE THE TEST RESULTS.

WELL?
RIGHT HERE, MR. QAYIN...
"I'M AFRAID THE PROGNOSIS IS NOT GOOD, YOU--"
I'M DYING, AM I NOT?
"YES."
HOW LONG?
A MATTER OF WEEKS. EIGHT, PERHAPS... MORE LIKELY, SIX.
THAT WILL BE ENOUGH TIME...
ENOUGH TIME TO
HER SAVE MYSELF,
TO TAKE THE WORLD
WITH ME."
"IT HAS BEEN A LONG TIME SINCE I HAD A WORTHY OPPONENT AT CHESS, DETECTIVE."
AND THE THUNDER MIGHT
E TAKEN FOR A FUSILLADE
OF CANNON, GROWING
EVER NEARER, EVER LOUDER...
"I HOPE THAT'S ALL YOU AND I WILL BE OPPONENTS OVER, RA'S."

YOUR KNIGHT IS IN DANGER.
YOU HAVE TAKEN TO SPEAKING IN *RIDDLES* OF LATE, DETECTIVE. I DO NOT UNDERSTAND YOU.
I SEE IT.
I THINK YOU UNDERSTAND ME VERY *CLEARLY,* RA'S. I KNOW NOW THAT YOU HAD NOTHING TO DO WITH BLAINE'S MURDER--
--AND I KNOW WHO *DID*--
"--BUT IT WOULD BE A SHAME IF YOU AND I HAD TO BECOME FOES ONCE MORE, AFTER WE'VE TAKEN CARE OF QAYIN.
"BY THE WAY, YOU'RE IN CHECK."
SO I AM.
DETECTIVE, AS YOU KNOW, I AM CURSED WITH A LOVE FOR EMPTINESS... DESOLATION. IT IS A BEAUTY TO WHICH MY SOUL RESPONDS... AS PURE, AS UNTAINTED AS THE DESERTS OF MY BIRTH.
I DEEM IT MY MISSION TO *PURIFY* THIS PLANET, TO RESTORE IT TO ITS FORMER BEAUTY...
...A MISSION I WILL BROOK NO INTERFERENCE IN...
...BUT FOR NO *ARE* ALLIES... AI HOPE THAT STAT CONTINUE
HMMM... BY REMOVING MY KING FROM CHECK, I FIND WE HAVE ACHIEVED A *STALEMATE.*
I FIND THAT QUIT FITTING.
I PLAY TO *WIN.*

"GOLATIA BASE TO CANAVERAL; LIFT OFF IS ZERO MINUS THIRTY MINUTES, DO YOU COPY?"
"CANAVERAL TO GOLATIA; WE READ YOU LOUD AND CLEAR, OVER."
WE'RE QUITE PROUD OF THE FACILITIES WE'VE BUILT HERE, GENERAL. THE PRESIDENT WANTED ME TO ASSURE YOU HOW GRATEFUL HE WAS FOR YOUR COOPERATION.
NONSENSE, GENERAL CONNORS, WE OF GOLATIA ARE PROUD TO ALLY OURSELVES WITH YOU AMERICANS.
EASY WITH THAT ACID SPRAY, DONAL; IT'LL TAKE THE SKIN RIGHT OFF YOU.
ALMOST THROUGH, SIR. ANOTHER FEW SECONDS...
E INSIDE NOW. ALL CONVERSATION MINIMUM, STAY AND QUIET.
YOU SEEM SOMEWHAT DISTRAUGHT, BELOVED.
I'M NOT USED TO BREAKING INTO MY OWN COUNTRY'S FACILITIES, TALIA. BUT IF THIS WEATHER SATELLITE IS LAUNCHED, I'M CERTAIN QAYIN WILL USE IT AGAINST MANKIND...
"...AND I CAN'T PERMIT THAT."
HSSST.
A GUARD APPROACHES. BE STILL.

"ONLY ONE MAN."
"GRIND, HE'S YOURS."
NO, GRIND, DON'T KILL HIM. KNOCK HIM OUT, LIKE I SHOWED YOU.
BAH. YOU MAKE US SOFT.
"MAYBE SO... BUT WHILE I'M FIELD COMMANDER, YOU'LL DO THINGS MY WAY!"
?
NOW, ASSEMBLE THE BOMB.
WE HAVE ALREADY BEGUN, BELOVED.

GOOD WORK. QUICKLY NOW, WE HAVEN'T MUCH TIME.

?
GRRRR

SECURITY, HAVE INTR REPEAT, UN AUTHORIZE PERSONNEL BREACHED BASE.

GENERAL, WE HAVE UNAUTHORIZED PERSONNEL ON THE BASE. THEY MAY BE PLANNING TO SABOATAGE THE LAUNCH.
DEPLOY THE SECURITY FORCE.
QAYIN, YOUR PRESENCE MAY HAVE BEEN DISCOVERED..
"...FINISH MODIFYING THE SATELLITE AS QUICKLY AS POSSIBLE; NOTHING MUST DELAY THIS LAUNCH."
HALT, ALL OF YOU! HANDS OVER YOUR HEADS!
DAMN.
YOU DRAW HIS ATTENTION, I WILL DISARM HIM.
NOT THAT WAY, DONAL...
BRRRRT
THIS WAY.

A-OOGAH
A-OOGAH
THEY KNOW WE'RE *HERE*. TALIA, DISPERSE THE MEN AND DIVERT THE *GUARDS*...
... I'LL FINISH ASSEMBLING THE DETONATOR.
A-OOGAH
HELP M *PLEASE!* MAN *KIDN* ME... BRO ME *HER*
A-OOGA
... DON'T *MOVE*--?
HI-YAHHHH
? JUST STAND *STILL*, MISS...
HALT, YOU!
CAREFUL NOW, DONAL... ALLOW THEM TO GET YOUR *SCENT*, FOLLOW YOU FAR AWAY FROM THE *BATMAN*...
... THEN, A SUDDEN *DODGE*...
QUIET, SOMEONE'S *COMING!*
... AND I AM *FREE*, I--?
"*YES... A PRISONER FOR QAYIN!*"

DONE! I'VE GOT JUST ENOUGH TIME TO GET OUT OF HERE...
"...BEFORE SOMETHING ELSE HAPPENS."
HAT'S GOT TO QAYIN! AS I OUGHT, HE HAS S OWN MISSION HERE...
UNNNH!
...BUT I CAN'T LET HIM STOP ME! GOT TO KEEP HIS ATTENTION ON ME, UNTIL IT'S--
?
--TOO LATE!
UMMPH

ZNNG SPWEEE
BELOVED--?
THERE! BY THE GANTRY! TELL THE BASE WE'VE GOT 'EM!
"RESUMING COUNTDOWN: 10-9-8--"
SHOULD BE JUST FIVE SECONDS MORE...!
"--7-6-5--"
"NO--!"
SHPPPT
"LIFTOFF."
NOTHING MORE I CAN DO! BUT IF I LET QAYIN THINK HE'S WON...
...THE ROCKET MAY DO PART OF MY JOB FOR ME!
FWOOOOOM

K-A-ROOOOM
"WHAT DO YOU LOOK FOR, BELOVED? DID WE NOT FAIL?"
"WE FAILED TO ATTACH THE BOMB, IN CASE QAYIN DOES TRY TO USURP THE WEATHER CONTROL SATELLITE FOR HIS OWN ENDS--I THOUGHT HE MIGHT WANT IT WHEN I LEARNED OF HIS INTEREST IN RAINMAKING, AND THE FACT IT WAS BEING LAUNCHED FROM GOLATIA WAS ANOTHER CLUE..."
...BUT I WAS HOPING THE BACKWASH WOULD AT LEAST TAKE CARE OF QAYIN FOR ME--NO SUCH LUCK.
THERE WILL BE ANOTHER TIME, BELOVED... THEN WE WILL "TAKE CARE" OF HIM--PERMANENTLY.

MISS TALIA, A WORD...?
WHY SO HAPPY, RA'S? WE FAILED, AND WE LOST DONAL.
WE HAVE AT LEAST ESTABLIS LINK BETWEEN Q AND THE NATION GOLATIA, DETEC QAYIN'S BASE MUST BE--
BELOVED, A WORD...?
CAN'T IT WAIT, TALIA?
IT CANNOT.
GO, DETECTIVE, WE SHALL SPEAK OF THIS LATER.
NOW, TALIA, WHAT'S SO IMPOR--
BELOVED, I AM WITH CHILD.
WITH CHI--
I AM PREGNANT.
YOU'RE...
...PREGNANT?
THAT'S WONDERFUL!
ISN'T IT?
DETECTIVE, DR. WELTMANN COULD NOT KEEP THIS FROM ME. MY CONGRATULATIONS.
ARE YOU SO HAPPY TO BE A GRAND-FATHER, FATHER?
I AM...
...IF IT MEANS YOUR HAPPINESS.
IT DOES.
"A CHILD. WE'LL NAME IT THOMAS... OR MARTHA, IF IT'S A GIRL.
"IT'LL BE THE HAPPIEST BABY IN THE WORLD."

DRINK, ALL OF YOU! EAT TILL YOU CAN HOLD NO MORE! MY DAUGHTER IS GIVING ME A GRANDSON!
YAYYYYYY
HEY ARE
OD MEN,
TECTIVE...
ARE YOU.
YOU KNOW, WE SPENT MUCH TIME IN OPPOSITION, WHEN WE REALLY MAKE BETTER ALLIES.
MAY WE REMAIN SO, RA'S.
HE SEEMS READY TO TALK, QAYIN. I TOLD YOU OUR METHODS WOULD FREE HIS TONGUE.
SO SOON? AL GHUL'S MEN ARE NOT WHAT THEY ONCE WERE...

...BUT ANY OLD PORT IN A STORM, I SUPPOSE.

RELEASE HIS GAG--LET HIM *SPEAK*.

YES, QAYIN.

"*HA!* A
SUSPEC

...HIS ACQUIESCENCE WAS MERELY A *SHAM*...

MRRRG!

...SO YOU WOULD REMOVE HIS *GAG*...

"... AND HE COULD RELEAS
POISON IN THIS *FALSE* TOO

...THUS DEPRIVING *ME* OF DESIRED *INFORMATION*... AND YOU OF NO LITTLE *PLEASURE*, DR. HALLAM.
MOST DISCOURTEOUS.

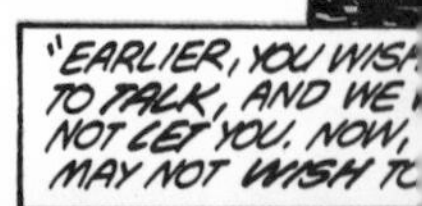

"EARLIER, YOU WIS
TO *TALK*, AND WE
NOT *LET* YOU. NOW,
MAY NOT *WISH* T

"BUT YOU
TALK."
PLEASE...!
AIEEEEE
...YOU SAID YOU
WOULD KILL ME
WITH NO PAIN IF
I TOLD YOU
WHERE AL GHUL
IS.
SO I DID.
I HAVE
TOLD YOU...
YOU
VE...
"...AND SO I
WILL."
WHAT ARE
YOU--NO!
I AM
KEEPING MY
PROMISE.
DON'T--
PLEASE--NO--
AGHHHHHHHHHH
WELL, I KEPT
HALF MY
PROMISE.

ALERT THE TROOPS, DR. HALLAM, TELL THEM WE WILL BE--
QAYIN? QAYIN, WOULD YOU KEEP ME WAITING?
GENERAL, I AM SO SORRY, I WAS OCCUPIED. THIS WAY, PLEASE.
...AND HERE IS OUR LITTLE NERVE CENTER, GENERAL-- FULLY READY.
MOST IMPRESSIVE.
YES. WE WAIT ONLY FOR THE AMERICANS TO ACTIVATE THE SATELLITE, WHICH SHOULD BE A MATTER OF DAYS.
YOU HAVE DONE WELL, QAYIN. I WILL BE IN--
TRANSPORT? QAYIN, THE AMERICANS ARE ALREADY SUSPICIOUS OVER THE LAUNCHING. TO SUPPLY YOU VEHICLES WOULD--
I WAS NOT MAKING A REQUEST, GENERAL.
I SEE.
VERY WELL.

"BELOVED, I HAVE NEVER BEEN SO HAPPY."
WHUPWHUPWHUP
"NEITHER HAVE I.."
WHUPWHUP
AS A MATTER OF FACT, I'VE NEVER BEEN HAPPY AT ALL.
I LIKE IT.
I'M GLAD.
HERE, I BROUGHT YOU THIS.
AND WHAT IS IN IT?
LOOK AND SEE.
"=GASP= BELOVED, IT IS BEAUTIFUL."
WHENEVER I WEAR IT, I SHALL THINK OF YOU...

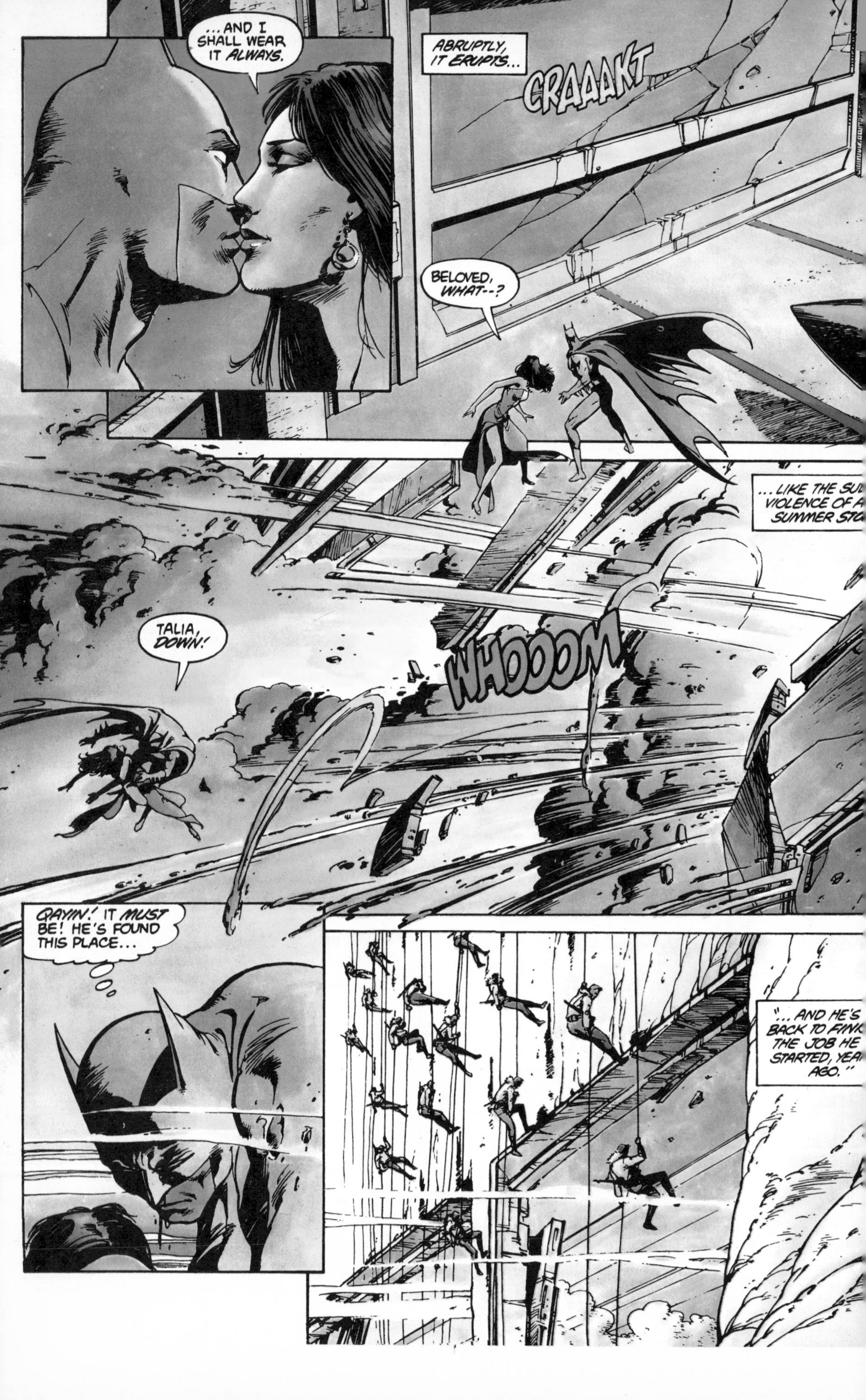
...AND I SHALL WEAR IT ALWAYS.
ABRUPTLY, IT ERUPTS...
CRAAAKT
BELOVED, WHAT--?
...LIKE THE SU
VIOLENCE OF A
SUMMER STO
TALIA, DOWN!
WHOOOM
QAYIN! IT MUST BE! HE'S FOUND THIS PLACE...
"...AND HE'S
BACK TO FINI
THE JOB HE
STARTED, YEA
AGO."

FIRST ASSAULT TEAM, GO! WE'VE CAUGHT THEM BY SURPRISE, IT'LL BE MINUTES BEFORE THEY CAN MUSTER ANY--
--ANY...
...RETALIATION?
NCH
TALIA?
WELL, BELOVED.
S FIND THEIR LEADER, AND END IT!
DAMN IT, NO! I DON'T WANT YOU OUT HERE!
BUT--

THESE ARE THE HIRELINGS OF THE MAN WHO KILLED MY MOTHER. CAN YOU NOT UNDERSTAND THAT?
MORE THAN YOU EVER WILL...
...BUT YOU'RE THE MOTHER OF MY CHILD! THAT'S MORE IMPORTANT THAN ANYTHING!
BRRRRT
NO! I WON'T HAVE YOU TAKING THAT RISK! NOT YOU--
SPANG
TANG
--AND NOT OUR BABY!
KLIK
ALL UNITS, WE HAVE INTRUDERS IN THE LANDING BAY! THEY ARE QAYIN'S MEN!
KILLED. HE WAS ALMOST KILLED.. HE MAY YET BE...

DECOYED THEM AWAY FROM TALIA, BUT THERE'S NOT MUCH EVEN I CAN DO AGAINST ODDS LIKE THESE...
...BEST BET IS TO RENDEZVOUS WITH RA'S AND HIS TROOPS...
...AND HOPE TO END THIS, HERE AND NOW!
SPLANNNG
ZINNNG
WE OCCUPY A MERE FOOTHOLD! BRING THE EXPLOSIVES...
WE SHALL NOT PENIED ACCESS HE REST OF HIS BASE!"
I THINK IT'S YOU QAYIN WANTS, RA'S.
HE DESIRES MY LIFE, YES. HE ALSO COVETS THE PIT, DETECTIVE...

... HE SHALL HAVE *NEITHER*. YOU WILL LEAD AN ASSAULT ON QAYIN AND HIS MEN FROM --
NO, RA'S. I'M *THROUGH*.
EXPLAIN YOURSELF.
TALIA'S SAFETY IS ALL THAT MATTERS TO ME, NOW...
"... AND SOON POSSIB I'M GET HER OU HERE

YES, SLAY THESE LAST FEW *GUARDS*, WHOSE LOYALTY OVERCAME THEIR *SENSE*...
BRRRRRRT

... AND AT LAST... THE LAZARUS PIT IS *MINE*.

I THINK *NOT*, QAYIN.
AL GHUL. I COMMEND YOUR COURAGE IN DARING TO *FACE* ME...

YOU ALWAYS SPOKE TOO QUICKLY, QAYIN.
YOU MAY RECALL THE STORY OF MOSES...
"...WHO WAS PERMITTED TO SEE THE PROMISED LAND...
"...BUT NEVER TO ENTER IT."
WHOOOM

KEEP FIRING! WE HAVE THEM ON THE RUN!
FALL BACK! WE HAVE LOST CONTACT WITH QAYIN!
RETURN TO HOME BASE! THIS MISSION IS OVER!
BUT WHAT OF QAYIN?
"IT WAS HIS MADNESS TH INITIATED T PLAN...
"...LET IT BE HIS EPITAPH."

NO, AL GHUL...
IT WILL NOT BE
THAT SIMPLE...
..YOU MAY TAKE
FROM ME THE
PIT...
...MY
ONLY MEANS
OF SALVATION...
...BUT IF I
AM TO DIE
FROM THE
DISEASE WITHIN
ME...
...THEN
I SWEAR
TO YOU...
WHUP WHUP WHUP
...I WILL
NOT DIE
ALONE.

DR. WELTMANN, TALIA NEEDS AN EXAMINATION.
BUT THIS MAN IS--
HE CAN WAIT.
BELOVED, THERE IS NO NEED FOR THIS, I AM--
YOU WERE ALMOST CAUGHT IN A FIREFIGHT OUT THERE, TALIA...
...I WON'T TAKE A CHANCE ON ANYTHING HAPPENING TO YOU...
"...OR TO OUR BABY."
=KRRRRK= CANAVERAL TO GOLATIA BASE, SATELLITE HAS REACHED OPTIMUM ORBIT, RECOMMEND YOU ACTIVATE. OVER.
ROGER, CANAVERAL, GOLATIA BASE COPIES...
...AND IS ACTIVATING. PREPARING TO TEST MAGNETIC FIELD GENERATOR IN FIVE SECONDS. FIVE-FOUR-THREE-TWO-ONE-

"WELL, SO FAR, SO GOOD..."

...THE MAGNETIC FIELD'S AFFECTING THE *OZONE LAYER*, ALL RIGHT. WHAT DO YOU THINK, HARRY?
READ-OUTS LOOK *GOOD*...

...LET'S TRY A LITTLE *TEST*...

"...SEE IF YOU CAN MAKE IT *RAIN*."

"THE AMERICANS HAVE ACTIVATED THE SATELLITE, GENERAL YOSSID..."
...IT SEEMS ABLE TO CONTROL THE WEATHER, AS OUR SOURCES PREDICTED.

AN AWESOME RESPONSIBIL-ITY, WEATHER CONTROL...

...LET US *RELIEVE* THEM OF IT, DR. HALLAM.

YES, MR. QAYIN. TECHNICIANS, ACTIVATE THE CIRCUITRY IMPLANT.
YES, SIR...

...NO, SIR, I DON'T KNOW *WHAT'S* CAUSING IT. THE SATELLITE'S NOT RESPONDING TO OUR COMMANDS ANYMORE, IT'S--

...SIR, IT'S GONE. VANISHED OFF THE SCREEN.
"ACTIVATE SELF-DESTRUCT."
SELF-DESTRUCT INOPERATIVE. WE'VE LOST IT, SIR.
THE SATELLITE IS OURS, MR. QAYIN.
MINE, HALLAM. LET US TRY A TEST, THEN...
"...I WOULD HAVE RAIN... NO, A STORM..."
BOO
EXCELLENT! NO NATION SHALL STAND AGAINST US!
INCREASE THE POWER OF THE STORM, HALLAM... MAKE IT A HURRICANE...
"...AFTER SENDING IT OVER THE BORDER--TO THE SOVIET UNION."
NO! THIS IS A POWERFUL WEAPON, QAYIN, BUT I DO NOT SEEK TO PROVOKE THE SOVIETS--NOT YET.
"MY ORDERS STAND, DR. HALLAM."
ARE YOU DEAF? STOP THIS IMMEDIATELY--

AVE
WN
RY
U.
P-PUT ≶GASP≶ PUT ME--
UNNNGHH
KRAKKKKK
THE HURRICANE IS HEADING INTO RUSSIA, MR. QAYIN-- HAVE YOU A SPECIFIC DESTINATION IN MIND?
"I HAVE, DR. HALLAM...
MOSCOW."
GET ME WASHINGTON.
AT ONCE, MR. GORBACHEV.

MR. PRESIDENT, A HURRICANE CAUSED BY YOUR WEATHER SATELLITE HAS ENTERED RUSSIA, AND DEVASTATED SEVERAL VILLAGES. WE--
"MR. GORBACHEV, I ASSURE YOU, THIS IS NOT OUR DOING, SOME OUTSIDE FORCE HAS TAKEN OVER OUR SATELLITE, AND--"
"PERHAPS SO, PERHAPS NOT. HOWE
IF THIS HURRICANE COMES WITHIN O
HUNDRED MILES OF MOSCOW, IT WIL
CONSIDERED AN ACT OF WAR. DO
UNDERSTAND?"
YES.
"GOOD DA
PRESIDENT;
HOPE WE W
SPEAK AGA
"MY FORCES ARE IMPAIRED, BUT STILL FUNCTIONAL..."
IT IS THE SATELLITE WHICH MUST CONCERN US NOW. OBVIOUSLY, IT WAS OVERRIDE CIRCUITRY AND AN ANTI-RADAR SCREEN WHICH QAYIN ADDED TO THE SATELLITE.
YES. HIS CO
AT BLAINE'S LA
HAVE GIVEN HI
NECESSARY
INFORM

S VERY GRAVE.
TIVE, READY
EN, WE MUST
QAYIN'S
QUARTERS
ND--
"I TOLD YOU I WAS THROUGH, RA'S."
SO YOU DID...
"...BUT I CHOSE NOT TO BELIEVE THAT YOU HAVE BECOME A COWARD."
THAT'S BENEATH YOU, RA'S. I'M NOT CONCERNED FOR MY OWN SKIN...
...I WANT OUR CHILD TO HAVE A HOME ...A FAMILY...
...EVERYTHING I NEVER HAD.
TALIA, ARE YOU ALL RIGHT? YOU HAVEN'T SPOKEN IN OVER AN HOUR.
"...WHAT DID YOU SAY, BELOVED? I DO NOT FEEL VERY--"
--VERY WELL...
TALIA!

HOW IS SHE, DOCTOR?

MERGENCY

YOU MAY SEE HER.

CAN WE GET THROUGH NOW? THIS MAN NEEDS HELP.

TALIA, IS ANYTHING WRONG? DR. WELTMANN DIDN'T SAY--

I AM WELL, BELOVED, I...

I HAVE LOST THE BABY.

"... ALL THE STRIFE OF THE RAID... ALL THE EXERTION...

"BELOVED, I AM VERY SORRY."

I KNOW YOU ARE, TALIA.

TRY TO GET SOME REST.

THE MEN ARE ALL ABOARD, MASTER.
THEN LET US DEPART, BEFORE--
"NOT SO FAST, GRIND."
I'M HERE, RA'S.
I DON'T WANT TO ANSWER ANY QUESTIONS...
...I JUST WANT TO FIND QAYIN...
..AND HOPE HE PUTS UP A FIGHT."

FINDING HIM WILL BE A TASK, DETECTIVE. A DEVICE OF MY INVENTION MAY BE ABLE TO TRACE THE SATELLITE'S TRANSMISSIONS TO THEIR SOURCE, SO--
UNNECESSARY, RA'S.
QAYIN IS THERE.
HOW CAN YOU BE SO CERTAIN?
WITH QAYIN'S BIBLICAL FIXATION...
"...WHERE ELSE WOULD HE PUT HIS BASE THAN ON MT. ARARAT, THE SPOT WHERE NOAH'S ARK FIRST TOUCHED LAND AFTER THE GREAT DELUGE?"
OF COURSE.
GOLATIA
ARARAT
U.S. ARMY BASE
"FIRST WAVE, JUMP. SECOND WAVE, PREPARE TO DEPART."
A PLANE NEARS, DR. HALLAM. MAKE KNOWN TO THEM MY POWER.
AT ONCE, MR. QAYIN.

OOOM
"... BUT IF QAYIN THINKS THAT'LL END IT, HE DOESN'T KNOW ME VERY WELL."
DAMN! THAT MAKES THE JOB THAT MUCH MORE DIFFICULT...
BE VIGILANT, ALL OF YOU! THE INVADERS MUST BE SOMEWHERE AROUND--
ZINNNG
SPWEEEE
IS ONE HAS BEARING OF A ADER! IF I AY HIM THEY--
WHAT--?

GAAAKK--!
HERE, RA'S-- YOU MAY AS WELL PUT THIS TO GOOD USE.
MY THANKS, DETECTIVE...
...THERE WA TIME WHEN WOULD NOT STOPPED H
YES.
"THE BATTLE GOES WELL, DETECTIVE. MY MEN HAVE SECURED THE PERIMETER..."
...BUT THERE STILL REMAINS THE INTERIOR, WHERE QAYIN WILL BE AT HIS MOST DANGEROUS.
GOOD...

...IT'LL MAKE WHAT I HAVE TO DO...
...THAT MUCH EASIER.
I UNDERSTAND.
THE GUARDS SEEM MOST INTENT ON KEEPING US FROM THIS CENTRAL AREA.
IT'S THEIR FUNERAL.
THE HURRICANE IS ONE HUNDRED AND TWENTY MILES OUT OF MOSCOW, MR. QAYIN. I ESTIMATE PENETRATION IN 5 MINUTES.
YOU HAVE SERVED ME WELL, HALLAM...
"I SHALL REMEMBER YOU...UNTIL THE END."
IT IS ENDED, QAYIN-- THOUGH NOT IN THE WAY YOU'D LIKE.
WELCOME. I KNEW YOU WOULD FIND ME.

THEN YOU HAVE TO KNOW IT'S OVER.
"I KNOW NO SUCH THING...
"...I REMAIN TO BE CONVINCED."
RA'S, DEACTIVATE THE RADAR SCREEN CONTROLS...
...QAYIN IS MINE.
YOU FLATTER YOURSELF, INTRUDER...
...MY INTEREST IS ONLY IN AL GHUL!
THUNK

UR ADULT LIFE IS A
ORY OF MISDIRECTED
HATRED, QAYIN...
"...IT IS NOT ME YOU WISH TO SLAY, IT IS YOURSELF..."
...BUT I WILL NOT BE A MARTYR TO YOUR HATRED.
"RA'S, THERE'S NO TIME FOR THIS! YOU TAKE OUT THE SATELLITE..."
.I'LL HANDLE QAYIN!
YOU WILL TRY.
YOUR NAME IS HALLAM, IS IT NOT? I ONCE OFFERED YOU EMPLOY IN MY ORGANIZATION.
I REFUSED THEN...
ZINNNG
...AS I REFUSE NOW.
UNFORTUNATELY, IN THIS INSTANCE...
MAY
TAKE
' FOR
NSWER.
SNAPPT
THE HURRICANE IS ONLY ONE HUNDRED AND FIFTEEN MILES OUT OF MOSCOW! ACTION IS NEEDED..

GENERAL SOMODNIK, READY MISSILE BANK A FOR FIRING...
...OR MY DREAM OF A REPLENISHED WORLD WILL BE FOR AGES LOST.
...IF YOU'RE ABLE!
THE COMPUTER IGNORES ALL MY COMMANDS. I'VE NO TIME TO FIND THE PROPER ACCESS CODE...
...BUT FOR THE PAIN YOU GAVE TO SOMEONE I LOVE-- AND TO ME.
WHUD WHUD WHUD WHUD WHUD
...PERHAPS THE INTERNAL CIRCUITRY WILL YIELD RESULTS!
AH, YES...
...THESE WIRES, PLACED IN PROXIMITY, SHOULD OVER-LOAD THE RADAR SCREEN...

MATTER. CAMPAIGN BE BACK...
"...BUT IT MUST BE DONE."
SIR, I'VE GOT THE SATELLITE BACK.
SECURE COORDINATES AND RELAY TO--
--MISSILE COMMAND, LOCKING COORDINATES...
...FIRE.
DO YOU SEE IT, QAYIN? IT'S FINISHED. ALL THE PAIN AND SUFFERING YOU CAUSED...
...ALL FOR NOTHING.

QAYIN, YOUR ORGANIZATION IS DESTROYED. IF YOU WERE TO TURN OVER YOUR KNOWLEDGE OF TERRORIST GROUPS TO THE AUTHORITIES, THEY MAY--
I AM A DEAD MAN ANYWAY, AL GHUL...
...AND SO ARE YOU.
I MAY NOT SEE THE WORLD DIE BEFORE ME, BUT AT LEAST I SHALL TAKE WITH ME THE MURDERER OF MY PARENTS!
NO.
SHAKKT
CRZZZZZZ

PERHAPS NOW HE IS AT PEACE.
RHAPS...

"... I HOPE NOT."

HOW ARE YOU FEELING, TALIA?
BETTER.
THAT'S GOOD. THAT'S GOOD.
...BUT I WOULD BE ALONE.

ALL RIGHT, I'LL COME BACK LATE--
NO, BELOVED... I WISH YOU TO LEAVE.
IF YOU'RE SURE...

BELOVED, PLEASE...
"ALL RIGHT, TALIA..."

LIVES
T SEEM
MAYBE SOMEDAY...

I'M SORRY.

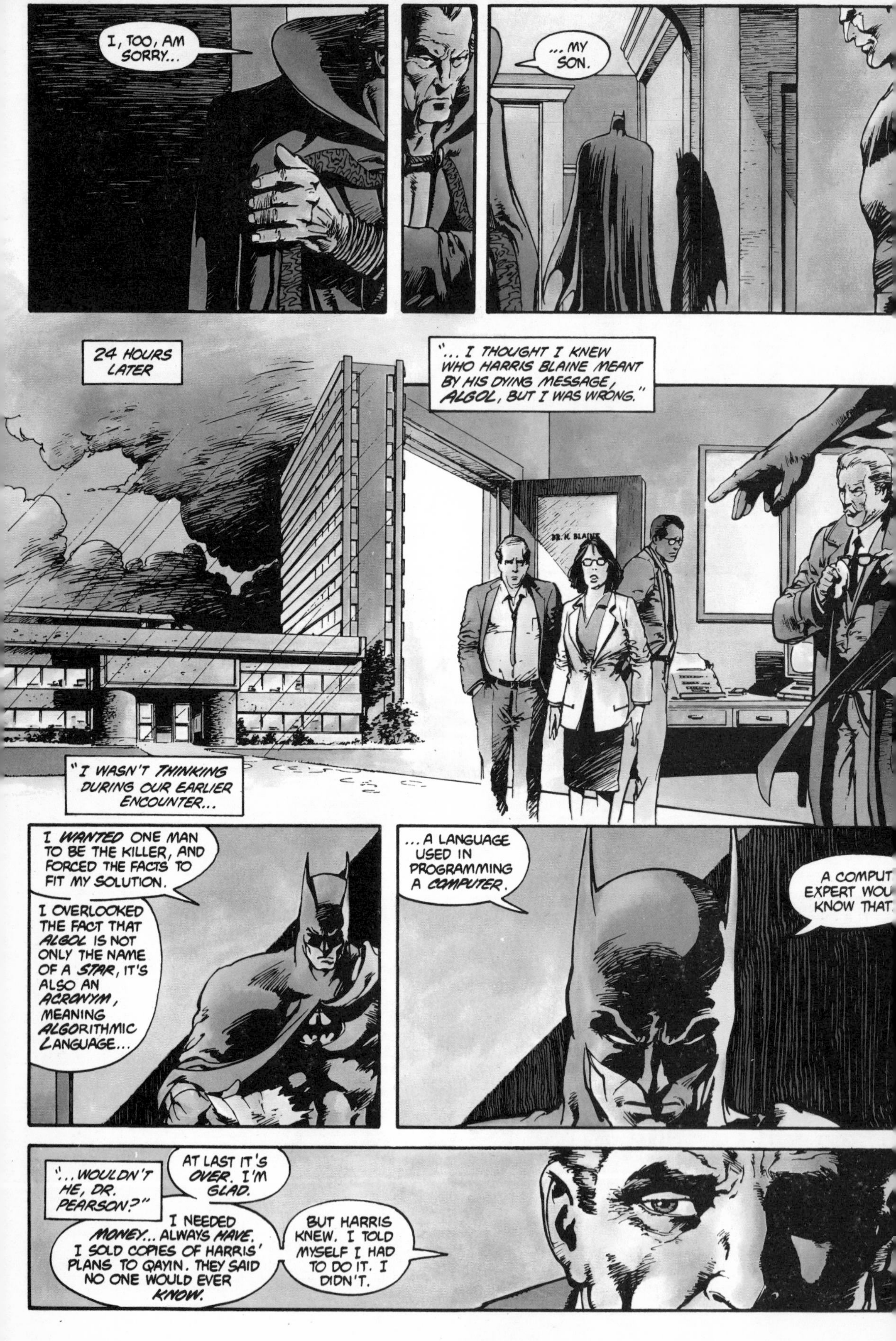

I, TOO, AM SORRY...

...MY SON.

24 HOURS LATER

"... I THOUGHT I KNEW WHO HARRIS BLAINE MEANT BY HIS DYING MESSAGE, *ALGOL*, BUT I WAS WRONG."

DR. H. BLAINE

"I WASN'T *THINKING* DURING OUR EARLIER ENCOUNTER...

I *WANTED* ONE MAN TO BE THE KILLER, AND FORCED THE FACTS TO FIT MY SOLUTION.
I OVERLOOKED THE FACT THAT *ALGOL* IS NOT ONLY THE NAME OF A *STAR*, IT'S ALSO AN *ACRONYM*, MEANING *ALGO*RITHMIC *LANGUAGE*...

...A LANGUAGE USED IN PROGRAMMING A *COMPUTER*.
A COMPUT EXPERT WOU KNOW THAT

"...WOULDN'T HE, DR. PEARSON?"
AT LAST IT'S *OVER*. I'M *GLAD*.
I NEEDED *MONEY*... ALWAYS *HAVE*. I SOLD COPIES OF HARRIS' PLANS TO QAYIN. THEY SAID NO ONE WOULD EVER *KNOW*.
BUT HARRIS KNEW. I TOLD MYSELF I HAD TO DO IT. I DIDN'T.

JOHN, YOU?
YOU...?
YOU SON OF A BITCH, I'LL--!
LET HIM LIVE WITH HIS GUILT, SON.
BUT HE HAS TO PAY, HE--
HE WILL. HE STILL HAS A CONSCIENCE...
...LETTING HIM LIVE WITH HIS GUILT IS THE BEST REVENGE.
GOODBYE, COMMISSIONER.
BATMAN, YOU LOOK LIKE YOU'VE BEEN THROUGH THE WRINGER, ARE YOU ALL RIGHT?
NO.
ANYTHING YOU WANT TO TALK ABOUT?
NO.
WELL, TAKE CARE OF YOURSELF. YOU'D BETTER GET INSIDE, IT LOOKS LIKE THE STORM IS ABOUT TO BREAK.
"COMMISSIONER...

"...IT ALREADY HAS."
NINE MONTHS LATER
"WELL, HERE WE ARE..."
BROOKSDALE ORPHANAGE
...ISN'T HE PRECIOUS? WE JUST FOUND HIM ON OUR DOORSTEP, ONE MORNING.
HE'S PERFECT.
HOW COULD ANYONE GIVE A BABY LIKE THIS UP?
I DON'T KNOW, HONEY... BUT IT'S A REAL BLESSING FOR US.
YES...
...WE'LL LOVE HIM AS THOUGH HE WERE OUR OWN...
...HE'LL BE THE HAPPIEST BABY IN THE WORLD.